IN DIFFERENTIAL

Dickenson Publishing Company, Inc.

TOPICS

EQUATIONS

ALLEN D. ZIEBUR
State University of New York at Binghamton

Belmont, California, and Encino, California

TOPICS IN DIFFERENTIAL EQUATIONS
by Allen D. Ziebur

Library of Congress Catalog Card Number: 79-131138
Printed in the United States of America

2 3 4 5 6 7 8 9 10

C O N T E N T S

**BOUNDARY VALUE PROBLEMS
AND FOURIER SERIES, 245**

P R E F A C E

This text for a one-semester introductory course in ordinary differential equations has two goals of approximately equal importance: (1) to teach some of the ideas of the modern theory of differential equations, and (2) to reinforce the student's knowledge of certain basic concepts of mathematics—particularly calculus. These goals are hardly new, of course; it is how nearly they are met that counts. We assume that the student has taken a standard three- or four-semester course in calculus that contains the introduction to linear algebra that is customary these days.

As the title of this book indicates, we have been able to include only some selected "topics" from the vast field of ordinary differential equations. Chapter 1 consists of review material, from calculus and earlier courses, that is not part of our subject itself. We start the study of differential equations with some special examples in Chapter 2 and move to the general theory of initial value problems of the first order in Chapter 3. Chapter 4 is devoted to systems of equations, principally linear systems. The theory of scalar linear differential equations of the second order is treated here, being developed as a special case of the theory of systems of two equations of the first order. The use of infinite series is the subject of Chapter 5, and in Chapter 6 we give a brief introduction to boundary value problems and Fourier series. Because we are really serious about the role of a course in differential equations in deepening a student's understanding of the mathematics he has seen before, there is a good deal of review material in this book. In addition to our introductory review chapter, there are extensive review sections on infinite series and linear algebra at the beginning of Chapters 4, 5, and 6.

Inside every fat man there is a thin man struggling to get out, and inside every textbook there are courses waiting to see the light of day. Judicious pruning of this book will reveal many such courses. For example, a "basic" course might consist of Sections 1 to 25 and 29 to 35. The review material would strengthen the student's grasp on his calculus, he could put in lots of time on the computer, and so on. At the other extreme, a "computer free" course could be constructed by taking up Sections 7 to 15, 18 to 28, and 31 to 41. This course would be somewhat more "theoretical" than the basic course, with a heavier emphasis on linear algebra. Naturally, the exact content of any given course is up to the instructor and his students, but the book was written under the assumption that about 30 sections constitute a semester's work.

Just as it is impossible to cover the whole book in one semester, it is impossible to cover most sections in one class period. Our typical section contains the explanation of one idea, some simple examples that illustrate it, a computer program for a somewhat more complicated example, and perhaps a "practical" problem. Usually, either the computer example or the practical problem will have to be skipped, or the section will require two days to complete. Furthermore, there are enough exercises, including review exercises at the end of each chapter, so that, usually, not all of them can be assigned.

A word or two about the role of the computer is probably in order. It is my conviction that the way to explain what mathematics is "really" about is via examples and exercises. Illustrative examples in the text and homework exercises are the heart of a course in mathematics. The more meaningful the exercise, the better is the lesson learned. The high-speed computer opens up a whole new world of problems that illustrate mathematical concepts. Thus, for example, a function *is* a set of ordered pairs, and a digital computer can spew out hundreds of ordered pairs in the twinkling of an eye. It follows, therefore, that a computer should be a useful device for studying functions. When a student uses a computer to go from the description of a function as the solution of an initial value problem to a set of ordered pairs of numbers, he is dealing with really fundamental ideas every step of the way. In no way do we intrude upon the field of numerical analysis; we are interested in the computer as a tool for studying theory only.

This book evolved out of a course we give at Binghamton, in which the students have access to a large time-sharing computer. No previous familiarity with the computer is assumed, and our simple computer programs are easily taught along with the rest of the material in the course. For us, the material in Chapter 1 serves both as a review of calculus and as a practice ground for the computer novice. Problem assignments are made so that the student is not *required* to spend more than an hour a week at the computer console, but most students voluntarily do considerably more than the required assignments. Our computer programs are written in FORTRAN, since that language is in common use, but it would be a trivial matter to rewrite them in some other tongue, such as BASIC, if one's computer preferred it. These programs are essentially literal translations of the standard formulas for Newton's Method, Simpson's Rule, and so on, that are taught in every calculus course. When computers come into large-scale use in mathematical instruction, it is quite possible that these "standard" formulas will be replaced by others that are more computer-oriented.

It is a pleasure to record here my gratitude for the many ways in which my publisher Richard W. Hansen has helped me over the years. The blue pencil of my longtime editor and colleague W. E. Mangas has introduced a measure of literacy that would have been lacking if I had been left to my own devices. And Professor H. A. Antosiewicz made some mathematical suggestions that profoundly affected the content of the book. All the errors, however, were committed by me alone, with no help from anyone.

A. D. Z.

Binghamton, N.Y.

CHAPTER *1*

SOME PRELIMINARY MATTERS

This introductory chapter has an attractive feature—you already know pretty much everything that is in it. We have simply collected in one place some topics from calculus and earlier courses that we will use when we begin our actual study of differential equations in Chapter 2. You can use this chapter to review forgotten details and to familiarize yourself with the particular terminology and notation that we have adopted for this book. You might also find it interesting to try out some of these previously learned ideas on the computer, if you haven't already done so. Or you can skip this chapter and plunge right into Chapter 2, referring back to these beginning sections as the need arises.

1 EQUATIONS

Anyone engaged in applying mathematics to practical problems spends a good part of his time trying to solve equations. The equations themselves are expressions of physical, economic, or other laws in mathematical terms. Thus, they are properly part of some discipline other than mathematics. But once the stage of equations has been reached, it is time to call upon mathematics to solve them. Or, if finding solutions is impossible, mathematical theory should at least give us some information about various useful properties that solutions have. In this course, we will be studying *differential* equations, but we will look at some simpler numerical equations first.

When presented with an equation, for example, the algebraic equation

$$(1\text{-}1) \qquad\qquad x^5 + x - 1 = 0,$$

the first question a mathematician asks is, "Does it have a solution?" A number r is a solution, of course, if $r^5 + r - 1 = 0$. We will then say that "$x = r$ *satisfies* Equation 1-1." In this phrase, we are interpreting the equation $x = r$, as we do in computer programing, to mean "the replacement of x by r." After he has decided that a given equation has a solution, a mathematician asks, "How many solutions are there?" "What properties do solutions have?" and so on. Notice that we have avoided the blunt question, "What is the solution?" The reason is simple. As you study various types of equations that arise in the applications of mathematics, you will see that it is seldom true that you can write down their solutions explicitly. For example, can you write down a solution of Equation 1-1?

But even though we can't write down a solution of Equation 1-1, it is easy to convince ourselves that there is one. Suppose that we write

$$(1\text{-}2) \qquad\qquad p(x) = x^5 + x - 1.$$

We see that $p(0) = -1$, a negative number, and that $p(1) = 1$, a positive number. Because Equation 1-2 defines a *continuous* function p, it follows that there is at least one point between 0 and 1 at which p takes the value 0. In other words, there is a number r between 0 and 1 such that $p(r) = 0$. In Exercise 1-3, we ask you to show that there is just one such number. Now let us see how we can find it.

A simple-to-explain but hard-to-apply method is suggested by our remarks above. Because $p(0)$ and $p(1)$ have opposite signs, we concluded that a solution r lies between 0 and 1. Now we could calculate $p(.1)$, $p(.2)$, and so on, and we would find that $p(.7)$ and $p(.8)$ have opposite signs. Therefore, $x = .7$ approximately satisfies Equation 1-1, in the sense that .7 gives us the first digit of the decimal representation of r. Then we could look at the signs of $p(.71)$, $p(.72)$, and so on, and we would find that $p(.75)$ and $p(.76)$ have opposite signs, so .75 gives us the first two digits of r. If we want to be more precise, we look at the signs of $p(.751)$, $p(.752)$, and so on.

Although this trial-and-error method sounds, and is, pretty crude, the fact is that if we use a modern computer to apply it, it will solve Equation 1-1 essentially instantaneously. And this crude method does illustrate a basic technique of solving equations. We construct a sequence, here $\{.7, .75, .754, \ldots\}$,

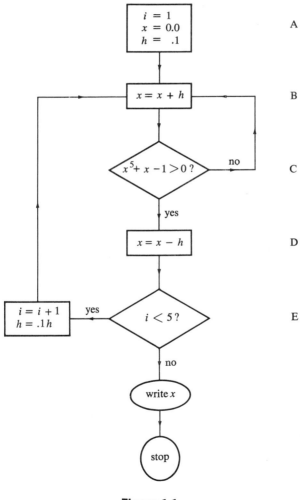

Figure 1-1

that converges to the solution. Because the limit concept is the very heart of mathematical analysis, it should not surprise you that when we go looking for a number, we usually end up by taking a limit.

Example 1-1. Make a flow chart for finding the first five decimal places of the solution *r* of Equation 1-1.

Solution. We have shown such a flow chart in Fig. 1-1. The letters A, B, . . . , E simply label points of the chart that we will refer to as we explain it. The index i tells us which decimal place we are currently working on. So we start (at point A) with $i = 1$ and set $x = 0.0$. We are going to increase x in steps of $h = .1$. Thus, since we know that $p(x) < 0$ when $x = 0.0$, we increase x by h (at point B) and then test the sign of $p(x) = x^5 + x - 1$ at point C. If $p(x)$ is not positive, we go back to point B, increase x by h, and test again. We continue this testing process until $p(x) > 0$. At this stage we have "overshot," so we subtract h from x (at point D). Numerically, we test $p(.1)$, $p(.2)$, . . . , $p(.7)$, and $p(.8)$ and find that all are negative, except $p(.8)$. So we go back to $x = .7$. We are now at point D in the flow chart. At our next step (point E), we check on the index i (which tells us which decimal place we are finding). If it is less than 5, we go on to the next decimal place (let $i = i + 1$), and we decrease our step size, making it one-tenth as long as the previous step size ($h = .1h$). So when we get back to point B, we will let $x = .7 + .01 = .71$ and again test the sign of $p(x)$. As before, we test until we "overshoot"; that is, we find that $p(.75) \leq 0$ and $p(.76) > 0$, and at point D we go back to $x = .75$. At point E we check to see if we have reached the fifth decimal place, and since we haven't, we increase the index i by 1, decrease the step size by a factor of .1, and return to point B. Eventually, the index i becomes 5, and then at point E we branch to "write" and hence print our answer and stop.

Example 1-2. ·Write a computer program to solve Equation 1-1.

Solution. We will write a Fortran program that corresponds to the flow chart in Fig. 1-1. We are using Fortran IV notation, so if you or your computer speaks a

```
        I = 1
        X = 0.0
        H = .1
   1    X = X + H
        IF(X**5 + X − 1)1,1,2
   2    X = X − H
        IF(I − 5)3,4,4
   3    H = .1*H
        I = I + 1
        GO TO 1
   4    WRITE(6,5) X
   5    FORMAT(1X, 'X = ', F7.5)
        STOP
        END
```

Figure 1-2

different language, you will have to translate our programs before you run them. When the program in Fig. 1-2 is run, it prints $x = 0.75487$.

Graphs, even rough sketches, can supply us with a great deal of information about the solutions of equations. For example, every procedure for generating a sequence $\{x_n\}$ of numbers that converges to a desired solution of a given equation requires that we start somewhere, and we can often use graphs to find the necessary starting point.

Example 1-3. Use a graph to find out something about the solutions of the equation $x - 2 \tan x = 0$.

Solution. If we write this equation as $\frac{1}{2}x = \tan x$, we see that its solutions are the X-coordinates of the points in which the curves $y = \frac{1}{2}x$ and $y = \tan x$ intersect. We have drawn these curves in Fig. 1-3, and the figure shows that two solutions of

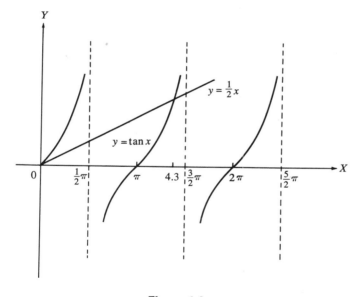

Figure 1-3

our equation are 0 and 4.3 (approximately). It is clear that there are infinitely many positive solutions and infinitely many negative solutions. If we move far to the right (or to the left) of the Y-axis, the X-coordinates of the points of intersection are approximately odd multiples of $\frac{1}{2}\pi$. Thus, for example, if $\{p_n\}$ is the sequence of *positive* solutions of our equation, then the figure suggests that

$$p_{1776} \approx \tfrac{1}{2}(2 \cdot 1776 + 1)\pi = \tfrac{3553}{2}\,\pi.$$

EXERCISE 1

1. In each of the following examples, $g(-1)$ and $g(1)$ have opposite signs. Does the equation $g(x) = 0$ have a solution in the interval $[-1, 1]$?
   (a) $g(x) = \cot x$ (c) $g(x) = x\,|x|$
   (b) $g(x) = \text{int}(x)$ (d) $g(x) = x/|x|$

2. Solve the following equations, or at least discuss the existence and number of solutions. Use graphs as appropriate.
   (a) $\sin (\sin x) = 0$ (f) $\sin x = x$
   (b) $\cos (\cos x) = 0$ (g) $\sin x = |\sin x|$
   (c) $\ln (\ln x) = 0$ (h) $\ln x^2 = 2 \ln x$
   (d) $\tan (\tan x) = 0$ (i) $\text{Sin}^{-1} x = \sin x$
   (e) $\log x = x$ (j) $\sin x = \sin |x|$

3. Show that Equation 1-1 has only one (real) solution. Does it have complex solutions? How many?

4. Suppose we arrange the non-negative solutions of the equation $\tan x = x$ in order: $0 < r_1 < r_2 \ldots .$ Can you convince yourself (perhaps by studying the points of intersection of the graphs of $y = \tan x$ and $y = x$) that $\lim\limits_{n \uparrow \infty}$
   $(r_{n+1} - r_n) = \pi$?

5. (a) Show that the equation $\sin x = 1/x$ has exactly one solution r in the interval $(10\pi, \frac{21}{2}\pi)$.
   (b) Can you show that $r - 10\pi < \frac{1}{20}$?

6. If the equation $f'(x) = 0$ has two solutions in an interval (a, b), what is the maximum possible number of solutions of the equation $f(x) = 0$ in the interval? If the equation $f''(x) = 0$ has no solutions in the interval (a, b), what is the maximum possible number of solutions of the equation $f(x) = 0$?

7. What is a simple condition, based on the derivative, that guarantees that the equation $f(x) = 0$ has at most one solution in the interval (a, b)?

8. Write a computer program, like the one in Example 1-2, that solves the equation $x^3 - 3x^2 + 4x - 3 = 0$.

9. Rewrite the program of Example 1-2, using a do loop.

10. In Example 1-3, we used a graph to convince ourselves that $x = 4.3$ approximately satisfies the equation $x - 2 \tan x = 0$. Write a computer program that gives a closer approximation.

11. Show that the terms of our sequence $\{x_n\}$ of approximations to the solution r of Equation 1-1 are given by the formula $x_n = 10^{-n} \text{int}(10^n r)$.

12. At point C in the flow chart in Fig. 1-1, we considered the two alternatives $p(x) \le 0$ or $p(x) > 0$. How would you modify the chart to consider the three possibilities $p(x) < 0$, $p(x) = 0$, or $p(x) > 0$? What are the corresponding modifications in the computer program of Fig. 1-2?

2 NEWTON'S METHOD

There are many techniques for solving numerically an equation of the form

(2-1) $$f(x) = 0.$$

One of the best is **Newton's Method,** which applies when f is a differentiable function. It is an especially appropriate method for us to study, because it is based on one of the first ideas of calculus—that a derivative of a function is the slope of a tangent line to its graph.

Newton's Method is best described in geometric language. A solution of Equation 2-1 is the X-coordinate of a point in which the graph of the equation $y = f(x)$ intersects the X-axis. Thus, the number r in Fig. 2-1 is a solution of

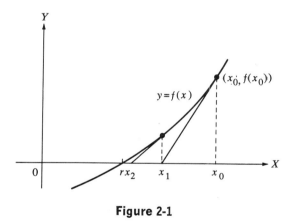

Figure 2-1

Equation 2-1. We will suppose that we don't know r, but that graphically, or by using tables, we have found a number x_0 that approximates r. We wish to improve upon this approximation. From Fig. 2-1, we see that the tangent line at $(x_0, f(x_0))$ intersects the X-axis in a point x_1 that is a closer approximation of r than x_0 is. It is easy to calculate this number x_1. We first observe that the slope of the line joining $(x_0, f(x_0))$ and $(x_1, 0)$ is

$$\frac{f(x_0) - 0}{x_0 - x_1}.$$

On the other hand, since this line is the tangent line at $(x_0, f(x_0))$, its slope is $f'(x_0)$. When we equate these two expressions for the slope of the tangent line, we get the equation

$$f'(x_0) = \frac{f(x_0) - 0}{x_0 - x_1},$$

which is easy to solve for x_1:

$$x_1 = x_0 - f(x_0)/f'(x_0).$$

This last equation gives us a rule that "transforms" an approximation x_0 into another approximation x_1. We can use the same rule to transform the approximation x_1 into a closer approximation x_2. Thus, $x_2 = x_1 - f(x_1)/f'(x_1)$. The point x_2, of course, is the point in which the tangent to the graph of f at the point $(x_1, f(x_1))$ intersects the X-axis (Fig. 2-1). We can repeat this procedure as often as we please and obtain a sequence $\{x_n\}$, each member of which (after x_1) is a closer approximation of r than the preceding member is. Therefore, *to apply Newton's Method we start with a number x_0 and obtain successive terms of the approximating sequence $\{x_n\}$ from the recursion formula*

(2-2) $$x_{n+1} = x_n - f(x_n)/f'(x_n).$$

We based our discussion of Newton's Method on Fig. 2-1, which shows a somewhat special graph. Our arguments do not apply to graphs that are too "wiggly." To be sure that Newton's Method will always yield a sequence $\{x_n\}$ such that x_2 is a closer approximation of the desired solution than x_1 is, x_3 is still closer, and so on, we should stay in an interval in which $f'(x)f''(x) \neq 0$. Then the curve is either rising or falling and is either concave up (as in Fig. 2-1) or concave down. You might experiment with a few graphs to see how the sequence $\{x_n\}$ converges toward r.

Computers are made to handle recursion formulas, and Equation 2-2 is easy to program for a machine. In Fig. 2-2, we have drawn a flow chart that

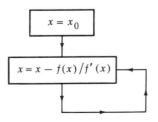

Figure 2-2

illustrates Newton's Method. Thus, we choose an initial value of x, transform it, transform this new value, and so on.

Of course, the trouble with the flow chart of Fig. 2-2 is that it is designed to generate the *entire* sequence $\{x_n\}$, all infinitely many terms of it. In any practical situation, we have got to stop the process somewhere and look at our approximation. For example, we might simply ask the computer to compute and print the number x_5. Figure 2-3 shows a flow chart and corresponding computer program for doing the job with $f(x) = x^5 + x - 1$ (Equation 1-1). When this program is run, the computer prints $x5 = 0.75488$.

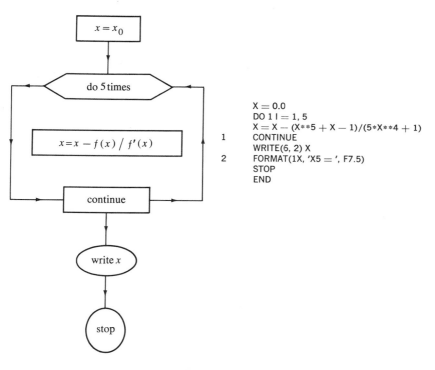

```
          X = 0.0
          DO 1 I = 1, 5
          X = X — (X**5 + X — 1)/(5*X**4 + 1)
  1       CONTINUE
          WRITE(6, 2) X
  2       FORMAT(1X, 'X5 = ', F7.5)
          STOP
          END
```

Figure 2-3

A somewhat more rational way of deciding when to stop calculating terms of a Newtonian approximating sequence is to assume that if the terms of the sequence are getting close together, then they are getting close to the solution. Thus, we might decide to stop calculating when two successive terms are within one-millionth of each other, as illustrated in Fig. 2-4. In that figure, we again use $f(x) = x^5 + x - 1$, and the program again gives us the answer $x = 0.75488$.

Throughout this course, we will present approximation methods (such as Newton's Method) without discussing in too much detail the error involved

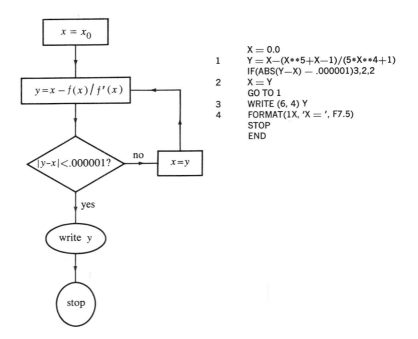

```
            X = 0.0
1           Y = X−(X**5+X−1)/(5*X**4+1)
            IF(ABS(Y−X) − .000001)3,2,2
2           X = Y
            GO TO 1
3           WRITE (6, 4) Y
4           FORMAT(1X, 'X = ', F7.5)
            STOP
            END
```

Figure 2-4

in stopping at any given point. Obviously, if we planned to use our approximations in any practical situation, we would have to find out how good they are. But we are devoting ourselves to mathematical theory, not numerical analysis, and we will leave the topic of error analysis to courses in that subject. Reference [9] in the list on p. 295 is an excellent numerical analysis text at about our level that covers many of the items we omit.

EXERCISE 2

1. Find a recursion formula for a Newtonian sequence of approximations to a solution of each of the following equations. Find x_1 and x_2 corresponding to the given initial approximation. Write a computer program to find x_6.
   (a) $x^3 - 12x^2 + 45x - 35 = 0$, $x_0 = 1$ (c) $\sin x = 1/x$, $x_0 = 3$
   (b) $x + 1 = \tan x$, $x_0 = 0$ (d) $\cos x = \sin 3x$, $x_0 = .5$

2. Use Newton's Method to solve the equation $8x^3 + 8x - 5 = 0$, taking $x_0 = .5$ as your first approximation.

3. Let us use Newton's Method to find the square root of a positive number p.
   (a) Show that Newton's Method for solving the equation $x^2 - p = 0$ leads to the recursion formula $x_{n+1} = \frac{1}{2}(x_n + p/x_n)$.

(b) Use the graph of the equation $y = x^2 - p$ to convince yourself that if x_0 is *any* positive number, then $x_{n+1} \geq \sqrt{p}$ for each $n \geq 0$.

(c) Verify the inequality in part (b) by showing that $x_{n+1}^2 - p = \frac{1}{4}(x_n - p/x_n)^2$.

(d) Can you show that $x_2 \leq x_1$, $x_3 \leq x_2$, and so on?

(e) Try this method on the computer for various choices of p.

4. Let us use Newton's Method to find Arcsin p, where $p \in (0, 1)$.

(a) What is the recursion formula for a Newtonian sequence $\{x_n\}$ of approximations to the solution of the equation Sin $x - p = 0$?

(b) Can you convince yourself graphically that if $x_0 = 0$, then $x_1 \leq x_2 \cdots \leq$ Sin$^{-1} p$?

(c) Now show that (for $n \geq 1$) $|x_{n+1} - x_n| = \left| \dfrac{p - \sin x_n}{\cos x_n} \right|$.

(d) Now show that $|x_{n+1} - x_n| \geq |p - x_n|$. (This inequality shows that in this particular case if the difference $|x_{n+1} - x_n|$ is small, the error $|p - x_n|$ is small.)

5. A limber stick 8 feet long is bent into a circular arc by tying the ends together with a piece of string 6 feet long. What is the radius of the arc?

6. Suppose that $f'(x)f''(x) > 0$ at each point of an interval I that contains a solution r of the equation $f(x) = 0$. By considering the graph of the equation $y = f(x)$, convince yourself that if x_0 is a point of I that is greater than r, then $x_0 \geq x_1 \geq x_2 \geq \cdots \geq r$. What if $x_0 < r$?

7. Modify the program in Fig. 2-3 so that it writes the numbers of the set $\{x_1, x_2, x_3, x_4, x_5\}$.

8. Use the computer to solve the equations in Exercise 2-1, stopping the sequence when two consecutive terms differ by less than $1/1,000,000$.

9. If we want to solve the equation $4x - \tan x = 0$ by Newton's Method, we consider the function f that is defined by the equation $f(x) = 4x - \tan x$. Since $f(\pi) = 4\pi(>0)$ and $\lim_{x \uparrow \frac{3}{2}\pi} f(x) = -\infty$, it is clear that there is at least one number r in the interval $(\pi, \frac{3}{2}\pi)$ such that $x = r$ satisfies the equation $f(x) = 0$. Show that there is only one. Find the recursion formula for a Newtonian sequence $\{x_n\}$ of approximations to r, and program the computer to write x_5. Since $\pi \approx 3$, and $\frac{3}{2}\pi \approx 4.7$, we will want to choose our initial value x_0 from the interval $(3, 4.7)$. Now run the program with the initial value chosen successively from the set $\{4.0, 4.1, 4.2, 4.3, 4.4, 4.5, 4.6, 4.7\}$, and explain the result.

3 FUNCTIONS

Differential equations have *functions* as their solutions, so we will now devote a section to the study of functions. Functions are used to describe quantitative relations. For example, a function might tell us *how many* inches a certain beam bends when subjected to a certain *number* of pounds of load. In applications, we view a function as a means of pairing certain quantities; for example, inches of deflection and pounds of load. Mathematically, we simply consider a function to be a set of pairs. Thus, a mathematician calls a set of pairs of real numbers a **function** if it does not contain two pairs with the same first member. The set of all the first members of the pairs that constitute a function is its **domain** and the set of second members is its **range.**

As you know, it is customary to use letters as names of functions. For example, we might have $f = \{(1, 2), (2, 4), (3, 4), (4, 6)\}$. This function is extremely simple, of course. Its domain is the set $\{1, 2, 3, 4\}$, and its range is $\{2, 4, 6\}$. Here, $f(1) = 2$, $f(2) = 4$, $f(3) = 4$, and $f(4) = 6$.

Usually, we cannot list all the pairs that comprise a function, because there are infinitely many of them. So we specify a function by giving its domain and the rule that pairs with a number in the domain a number in the range. Thus, we *describe*, rather than *list*, the pairs that make up the function. For example, we might have

(3-1) $$g = \{(x, y): x \in [-1, 1], y = \sqrt{1 - x^2}\}.$$

This function's name is g, its domain is the interval $[-1, 1]$, and with each number x of the domain is paired the number y, where $y = \sqrt{1 - x^2}$. Some of the pairs that make up g are $(0, 1)$, $(1, 0)$, $(-1, 0)$, and so on. Instead of using the rather complicated looking Equation 3-1, we normally would define the simple function g by saying that "g is the function that is defined by the equation $y = \sqrt{1 - x^2}$" or "g is the function that is defined by the equation $g(x) = \sqrt{1 - x^2}$." These equations simply give the rule or formula that pairs with x the number $g(x)$. Because it is not stated otherwise, we assume that we can replace x with any number for which the formula makes sense, and hence we infer that the domain of g is the interval $[-1, 1]$. We might also define g by the equation $g = \{(x, \sqrt{1 - x^2})\}$, a notation that indicates explicitly that g is a set of pairs.

Although we cannot list *all* the infinitely many pairs that comprise a typical function, there are, for such common functions as the trigonometric functions, logarithmic functions, and so on, tables that list many of them. At least partly because they are tabulated, we feel that we have such common functions under control. A digital computer is a splendid device for bringing other functions under the same control; that is, for making tables of values for them. It is true that a table of values does not tell us all there is to know about a given function. We can learn a lot from studying its derivatives, checking its continuity, and so on. But we should not underestimate the worth of a table, either. When we look at a function in terms of a table of values, we are getting down to fundamentals. A function *is* a set of pairs; a table lists some of them, so the table is a subset of the given function. When we have a table, we have our hands on at least part of a function.

Example 3-1. The statement "$f(x)$ is the third digit to the right of the decimal point in the decimal representation of cos x" defines a function f. For example, since cos $1 = .5403$, then $f(1) = 0$; since cos $.3 = .9553$, then $f(.3) = 5$; and so on. Make up a table of values of f at the points of the set $\{0, .1, .2, \ldots , 1.0\}$. (Of course, this function f is totally useless. We are simply trying to make the point that a computer can turn a description of a function in terms of words or formulas into a set of pairs of numbers in almost no time.)

Solution. Recall that $\text{int}(x)$ is the greatest integer in x. Thus, $\text{int}(\pi) = 3$, $\text{int}(4.5) = 4$, and so on. If we use this function, we can solve our given problem with the program shown in Fig. 3-1. We have chosen to write the heart of the program in two steps, the second and third statements. Let us, to be specific, examine what the program does with these two statements on the fifth cycle (when $x = .4$). Then the second statement reads $y = 100 * \cos(.4) - \text{int}(100 * \cos(.4))$. Since cos $.4 = .9211$, then $y = 92.11 - \text{int}(92.11) = 92.11 - 92 = .11$. Now the third

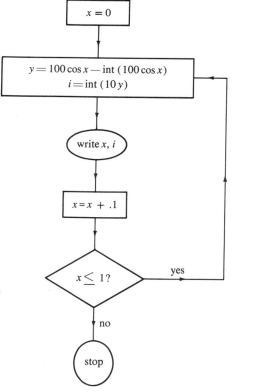

	X = 0
1	Y = 100*COS(X) — INT(100*COS(X))
	I = INT(10*Y)
	WRITE(6,2) X, I
2	FORMAT(1X, F3.1, 3X, I1)
	X = X + .1
	IF(X — 1) 1, 1, 3
3	STOP
	END

0.0	0
0.1	5
0.2	0
0.3	5
0.4	1
0.5	7
0.6	5
0.7	4
0.8	6
0.9	1
1.0	0

Figure 3-1

statement becomes $i = \text{int}(10 * .11) = \text{int}(1.1) = 1$, so $i = 1$. Figure 3-1 also shows the output of this program; that is, our calculated table of values.

Let f be a given function and consider the set $\{(y, x): (x, y) \in f\}$. In other words, we are simply reversing the order of the elements in the pairs that make up f. For the function f that we introduced in the second paragraph of this section, for example, this set is $\{(2, 1), (4, 2), (4, 3), (6, 4)\}$. This latter set is *not* a function; it has two pairs, (4, 2) and (4, 3), with the same first element. But often the set that we get by reversing the members of the pairs of f *is* a function. When it is, we call it the **inverse** of f. Then,

$$f^{-1} = \{(y, x): (x, y) \in f\}.$$

Here is an alternative wording of the definition of the inverse of a function. If for each number y in the range of a function f there is exactly one number x in the domain of f such that $y = f(x)$, then f has an inverse function f^{-1}. The domain of f^{-1} is the range of f, and the range of f^{-1} is the domain of f. The number that corresponds to a given number y in the range of f is the number x that satisfies the equation $y = f(x)$. Thus,

$$x = f^{-1}(y) \text{ if, and only if, } y = f(x).$$

To say that for each number y in the range of f the equation $y = f(x)$ has *exactly one* solution x in the domain means that two different pairs in the set

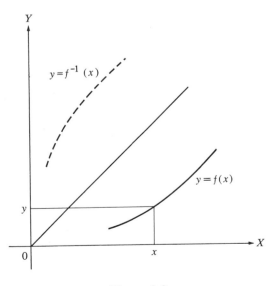

Figure 3-2

f^{-1} do not have the same first member, which is our criterion that a set of pairs of numbers should constitute a function. Figure 3-2 illustrates a typical situation graphically. Because the illustrated function f is increasing, it is clear that a given number y in its range determines exactly one number x in its domain, and hence f^{-1} exists. The graph of f^{-1} is obtained by reflecting the graph of f across the line $y = x$. Similarly, you might sketch the graph of a decreasing function and convince yourself that it has an inverse.

The trigonometric functions do not have inverses, and to get around this difficulty we construct new functions by **restricting the domains** of the trigonometric functions. For example, we define the Sine function (the capital letter S distinguishes this new function from the sine function) as the function

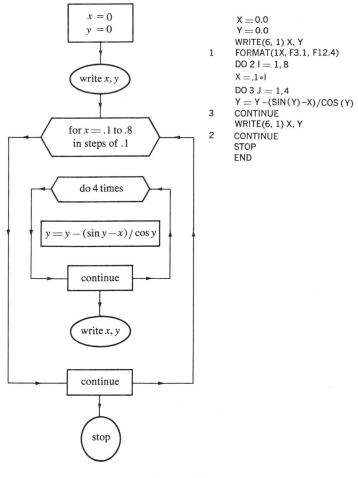

```
           X = 0.0
           Y = 0.0
           WRITE(6, 1) X, Y
    1      FORMAT(1X, F3.1, F12.4)
           DO 2 I = 1, 8
           X = .1*I
           DO 3 J = 1,4
           Y = Y -(SIN(Y)-X)/COS (Y)
    3      CONTINUE
           WRITE(6, 1) X, Y
    2      CONTINUE
           STOP
           END
```

Figure 3-3

whose domain is the interval $[-\frac{1}{2}\pi, \frac{1}{2}\pi]$, and whose rule of correspondence is expressed by the equation $y = \sin x$. In other words, Sine $= \{(x, y): -\frac{1}{2}\pi \leq x \leq \frac{1}{2}\pi, y = \sin x\}$. Therefore, its inverse, whose name is Arcsine or Sin^{-1}, is the set

$$\text{Arcsine} = \{(y, x): -\frac{1}{2}\pi \leq x \leq \frac{1}{2}\pi, y = \sin x\}.$$

Example 3-2. Make up a table of values of Arcsine at the points of the set $\{0, .1, .2, \ldots, .8\}$.

Solution. Since the equation $y = \text{Arcsin } x$ is equivalent to the equation Sin $y - x = 0$, our problem amounts to solving this last equation for y as we let $x = 0, .1, .2, \ldots, .8$. The flow chart and computer program of Fig. 3-3 show how we can use Newton's Method to solve these equations (except that we solve the first equation mentally, since it is obvious that $y = 0$ when $x = 0$). We have arbitrarily decided to use only four cycles of Newton's Method, a tactic that possesses the virtue of simplicity if not rationality.

EXERCISE 3

1. The equations $p(q) = q + 1/q$ and $q(p) = p + 1/p$ define functions p and q. What is the relation between these functions?

2. Sketch the graph of the equation $y = f(x)$ for $x \in [-1, 3]$. Is the given function continuous in this interval?
   (a) $f(x) = x - |x|$ (c) $f(x) = x - \text{int}(x)$
   (b) $f(x) = x|x|$ (d) $f(x) = x \text{ int}(x)$.

3. What is the inverse of the exponential function exp? Find the domain and range of exp^{-1}.

4. Let $f = \{(x, y): 1 \leq x \leq 3, y = 3x^2 + 1/x - \sin x\}$. What is the domain of f? Can you show that the range of f is the interval $[4 - \sin 1, \frac{82}{3} - \sin 3]$? Show that f^{-1} exists. Write a program that computes a table of values of f. Change some statements in your program for f to obtain a program that prints a table of values of f^{-1}.

5. Make a table of values of the function f that is defined by the statement "$f(x)$ is the distance between x and the nearest integer." Thus, $f(\pi) = .1416$, and so on. Sketch the graph of f. Is this function continuous? Can you find a formula for $f(x)$?

6. Sketch the graph of the equation $y = \text{Sin}^{-1}(\sin x)$ for x in the interval $[-\pi, 2\pi]$. What is y'?

7. (a) How do we define the function Tan?
   (b) The function Tan^{-1}?
   (c) Write a computer program to print a table of values of Tan^{-1}.
   (d) Show that, for a given number y, $\{x: \tan x = y\} = \{\text{Tan}^{-1} y + n\pi: n \text{ an integer}\}$.

8. Let the domain of a function f be the set $\{1, 2, 3, 4, 5, 6, 7, 8, 9\}$, and let $f(x)$ be the sum of the digits of x^2 (for example, $f(7) = 4 + 9 = 13$). Write the table of values of f; that is, explicitly write f as a set of pairs of numbers. Does f^{-1} exist? Can you write a computer program that will print the set of pairs that constitutes f?

9. From a given function f, we *derive* a new function f' by means of the definition $f'(x) = \lim\limits_{h \to 0} \dfrac{f(x + h) - f(x)}{h}$. Therefore,

(3-2)
$$f'(x) \approx \frac{f(x + .1) - f(x)}{.1}.$$

For $f(x) = \sin x$, program Approximation 3-2 for the computer, and make a table of values of f' at the points of the set $\{0.0, .1, .2, \ldots, 1.6\}$. (Why did we choose the number 1.6 here?) Since you know what f' is in this case, have your program write three columns: x, the approximation to $f'(x)$ calculated from Formula 3-2, and the true value $f'(x)$. It is more or less obvious that if we replace .1 with .05 in Approximation 3-2, we will usually get a closer approximation. It is not so obvious, but it is true nevertheless, that we also get a closer approximation by using the formula

$$f'(x) \approx \frac{f(x + .1) - f(x - .1)}{.2}.$$

Use the computer to verify this statement if $f(x) = \sin x$. Can you use Taylor's Theorem to explain why it is true?

10. Prove the following theorem: A continuous function f whose domain is an interval I has an inverse if, and only if, f is monotone (either increasing or decreasing).

4   FUNCTIONS DEFINED BY INTEGRALS

If the domain of a function f contains an interval I, we can use the fundamental process of differentiation to construct, or *derive*, a new function f' whose domain is a subset of I. Thus, with each number $x \in I$ for which the following limit exists, we pair the number $f'(x) = \lim\limits_{h \to 0} \dfrac{f(x + h) - f(x)}{h}$. This set of pairs constitutes the **derived function** f' (and $f'(x)$ is the *derivative* of $f(x)$).

We can also use the fundamental process of integration to construct a new function from f. Suppose that a is a point of the interval I and that f is integrable on *I*. Then the equation

(4-1) $$F(x) = \int_a^x f(u)\,du$$

pairs with each $x \in I$ a number $F(x)$, and so it defines a function F.

You are probably already familiar with this idea. No doubt, you have seen the logarithm function defined by the equation

$$\ln x = \int_1^x \frac{du}{u}.$$

It can be argued that one of the most logically satisfying approaches to the trigonometric functions consists of first defining the inverse functions by the equations

$$\text{Sin}^{-1} x = \int_0^x \frac{du}{\sqrt{1 - u^2}} \quad \text{and} \quad \text{Tan}^{-1} x = \int_0^x \frac{du}{1 + u^2}$$

and then inverting them to obtain the trigonometric functions. This approach avoids such technical questions as precisely what is meant by the length of a circular arc, and so on.

Example 4-1. Let int be the greatest integer function, and let the equation $I(x) = \int_0^x \text{int}(u)\,du$ define a function I. Sketch the graph of I in the interval $[0, 3]$.

Solution. In the coordinate system on the left-hand side of Fig. 4-1 we have drawn the graph of the function int in the interval $[0, 3]$. For a given number x in this

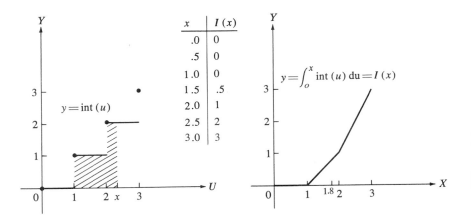

x	$I(x)$
.0	0
.5	0
1.0	0
1.5	.5
2.0	1
2.5	2
3.0	3

Figure 4-1

interval, the number $I(x)$ is the area of the region that is "between" the graph of int and the interval $[0, x]$, the shaded region in the figure. We constructed our table of values of I by computing a few of these areas. If you plot enough such points, you can probably convince yourself that the graph of I on the right-hand side of Fig. 4-1 is correct. You might also try to convince yourself graphically that $I(x)$ is given by the formula $I(x) = \text{int}(x)x - \frac{1}{2}\text{int}(x)\,\text{int}(x+1)$. (This formula looks more fearsome than it is.)

Functions defined by integrals are especially easy to differentiate, as shown by the following basic theorem, one of the fundamental theorems of calculus.

THEOREM 4-1

At each point x at which the function f is continuous, the function F defined by Equation 4-1 is differentiable, and

(4-2) $$F'(x) = f(x).$$

You will find a formal proof of this theorem in your calculus book, but we can get a good idea of what it says by referring to Fig. 4-1. For the functions illustrated in that figure, Equation 4-2 becomes $I'(x) = \text{int}(x)$. This equation tells us, for example, that the slope of the graph of I is supposed to be $I'(1.8) = \text{int}(1.8) = 1$ when $x = 1.8$. When we inspect the figure, we see that this statement is correct. You can verify the equation $I'(x) = \text{int}(x)$ in the same way for various other points of the interval $[0, 3]$. Notice that Theorem 4-1 only promises that Equation 4-2 holds at points of continuity of f. We see that it fails at points of discontinuity in our example.

Let us use the notation D_x for the "differential operator" indicating differentiation with respect to x. Thus, we will write $D_x g(x) = g'(x)$, or $D_x y = y'$. In particular, $D_x x^3 = 3x^2$, $D_x \sin x = \cos x$, and so on. The symbol d/dx is often used instead of D_x; we use D_x because it is simpler to write. In this notation, Theorem 4-1 can be summed up by the equation

(4-3) $$D_x \int_a^x f(u)\,du = f(x).$$

Recall the Chain Rule: *If* $v = g(x)$, *then* $D_x F(v) = D_v F(v)D_x v$. In this equation we will now replace $F(v)$ by $\int_a^v f(u)\,du$ and observe from Equation 4-3 that $D_v \int_a^v f(u)\,du = f(v)$. Thus, we obtain the important equation

(4-4) $$D_x \int_a^v f(u)\,du = f(v)D_x v.$$

Example 4-2. If $F(x) = \int_{-2}^{x^2} \sqrt{16 - u^4}\,du$, find $F'(1)$.

Solution. We set $v = x^2$, and find from Equation 4-4 that $F'(x) = D_x \int_{-2}^{x^2} \sqrt{16 - u^4}\, du$
$= \sqrt{16 - x^8}\, D_x x^2 = 2x \sqrt{16 - x^8}$. Therefore, $F'(1) = 2\sqrt{15}$. Can you show that the domain of F is the interval $[-\sqrt{2}, \sqrt{2}]$, and that F attains its minimum value when $x = 0$?

Example 4-3. Suppose that $p(u) = Au^2 + Bu + C$ is a quadratic polynomial. Show that

(4-5) $$\int_a^{a+2h} p(u)\, du = \frac{h}{3}[p(a) + 4p(a + h) + p(a + 2h)]$$

for any two numbers a and h.

Solution. Probably as easy a way as any to verify this equation (which will be important to us in the next section) is simply to write everything out in terms of A, B, and C and thus show that the two sides are equal. We will proceed somewhat differently, however, to give you a little practice in calculus. Let us denote the left-hand side of Equation 4-5 by $L(h)$ and the right-hand side by $R(h)$. These quantities are, it is easy to see, polynomials in h of degree 3. Hence (why?), we can verify that they are identically equal by showing that

(4-6) $L(0) = R(0)$, $L'(0) = R'(0)$, $L''(0) = R''(0)$, and $L'''(0) = R'''(0)$.

Notice that $L(0) = 0$ and that $R(0) = 0$, so the first of Equations 4-6 is correct. Now we use Equation 4-4 (with x replaced by h, and $v = a + 2h$) to see that $L'(h) = D_h \int_a^{a+2h} p(u)\, du = p(a + 2h)D_h(a + 2h) = 2p(a + 2h)$. Furthermore, $R'(h) = \frac{1}{3}[p(a) + 4p(a + h) + p(a + 2h)] + \frac{h}{3}[4p'(a + h) + 2p'(a + 2h)]$, and so $L'(0) = 2p(a) = R'(0)$. We leave the verification of the remaining two of Equations 4-6 to you.

EXERCISE 4

1. What are the domains of the functions defined by the following equations? What are the ranges?

   (a) $\ln x = \int_1^x \dfrac{du}{u}$

   (b) $\operatorname{Arcsin} x = \int_0^x \dfrac{du}{\sqrt{1 - u^2}}$

   (c) $G(x) = \int_0^x \tan u\, du$

   (d) $h(x) = \int_0^{\mathrm{int}(x)} \mathrm{int}(u)\, du$

2. What, if anything, is the difference between $D_x f(2x)$ and $f'(2x)$?

3. Find a simpler formula for $F(x)$ if $F(x) = \int_0^x \dfrac{u}{|u|}\, du$.

4. The equation $F(x) = \int_{-3}^{x} \sqrt{9 - u^2}\, du$ defines a function F. Use the area interpretation of the integral to determine the domain and the range of F.

5. Suppose that $g(x) = \int_{0}^{x} \text{Arctan } u\, du$. Use the area interpretation of the integral to find $g(1)$.

6. For x in the interval $[0, 3]$, let $r(x)$ be the distance between x and the nearest prime number. Sketch the graphs of r, r', and R, where $R(x) = \int_{0}^{x} r(u)\, du$. How is the concavity of the graph of R expressed in the graph of r'?

7. Find $D_x y$ in the following cases.

(a) $y = \int_{3}^{x} (5^u + u^5)\, du$
        (c) $y = \int_{2}^{x^2} \exp(u^2)\, du$

(b) $y = \int_{x}^{3} (1 + u^2)^{-1}\, du$
        (d) $y = \int_{3x+2}^{x^2} \sin u^2\, du$

8. For what numbers in its domain does the function F that is defined by the equation $F(x) = \int_{0}^{x} (2^u + 2^{1-u} - 3)\, du$ take maximum values? Minimum values?

9. If f' is integrable on an interval I, and a is a point of I, show that for each $x \in I$, $D_x \int_{a}^{x} f(u)\, du = \int_{a}^{x} D_u f(u)\, du + f(a)$.

10. In Exercise 3-6 we asked you to sketch the graph of the equation $y = \text{Sin}^{-1}$ $(\sin x)$ for $x \in [-\pi, 2\pi]$. Sketch the graph of the equation $y = \int_{0}^{x} \text{Sin}^{-1}$ $(\sin u)\, du$ for x in the same interval. Show that this equation defines a periodic function. Can you show that this function is an *even* function; that is, that its graph is symmetric with respect to the Y-axis?

11. Suppose that f is continuous in an interval I, and that $f(x) \neq 0$ for each $x \in I$. Let a be a point of I, and set $F(x) = \int_{a}^{x} f(u)\, du$.
(a) Show that F^{-1} exists.
(b) Show that $D_x F^{-1}(x) = 1/f(F^{-1}(x))$.
(c) Illustrate these remarks by setting $f(x) = 1/x$ and $a = 1$.

5   DIRECT INTEGRATION

In the last section, we discussed functions defined by integrals. Thus, if f is a function that is integrable on an interval I, and a is a point of I, then the equation

(5-1)
$$F(x) = \int_{a}^{x} f(u)\, du$$

defines a function F whose domain contains I. To find values of F, we must know how to evaluate integrals.

In your calculus course, you used one of the fundamental theorems of calculus to evaluate the integral in Equation 5-1. You found an antiderivative $g(u)$ of $f(u)$, and then you knew that $F(x) = g(u) \big|_a^x = g(x) - g(a)$. We may call this method of evaluating integrals "indirect integration," because we do not tackle the integral directly, only via antiderivatives. Your "methods" of finding antiderivatives in calculus were inspection and, when that failed, the use of tables. Ingenious substitutions and various devices, such as integration by parts, often prepared the way for applying one of these methods. But you must have noticed that these techniques only apply to very special integrands. Thus, they work if $f(u) = ue^{u^2}$, but fail if $f(u) = e^{u^2}$; they work if $f(u) = \sin u \ln \cos u$, but fail if $f(u) = \ln \cos u$, and so on. The only virtue of most of the integrands you encountered in calculus was that they could be found in a table of integrals (or, better, a table of antiderivatives).

In our work in differential equations, we will always suppose that f is continuous, and hence that Equation 5-1 certainly defines a function, whether the integrand is listed in a table of integrals or not. So we have to devise ways of evaluating integrals directly, without resorting to antiderivatives. Such direct evaluation of integrals will not be too difficult for us. After all, an integral is a number, and we have at our disposal a very powerful device for finding numbers, a digital computer. So let us address ourselves to the following question: Suppose that f is continuous in the interval $[a, b]$; how do we find the number $\int_a^b f(x)dx$?

The simplest way to approximate the number $\int_a^b f(x)dx$ is based on the very definition of the integral. Suppose that we pick a positive integer n and divide the interval $[a, b]$ into n equal subintervals, each $h = (b - a)/n$ units

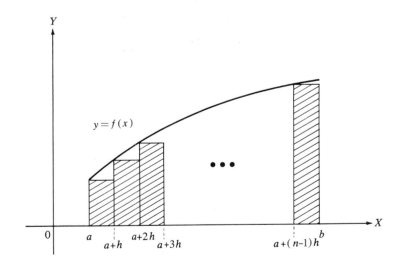

Figure 5-1

long. The points of subdivision are therefore a, $a + h$, $a + 2h$, . . . , $a + nh = b$. Then, if n is large,

(5-2)
$$\int_a^b f(x)dx \approx h \sum_{i=0}^{n-1} f(a + ih).$$

To be precise, the number $\int_a^b f(x)dx$ is the limit, as $n \uparrow \infty$, of the sum on the right-hand side of this expression. Graphically (if $f(x) \geq 0$), this sum is the area of the shaded region in Fig. 5-1, while the number $\int_a^b f(x)dx$ is the area of the region "between" the graph of f and the interval $[a, b]$. Because the integral is approximated by a sum of areas of rectangles, this method of direct integration is called the **Rectangle Rule.**

Example 5-1. Approximate π by evaluating the integral $\int_0^1 \dfrac{4}{1 + x^2} dx$ by means of the Rectangule Rule with $n = 4$.

Solution. We know that

$$\int_0^1 \frac{4}{1 + x^2} dx = 4 \text{ Tan}^{-1}x \Big|_0^1 = 4 \text{ Tan}^{-1} 1 = 4 \cdot \tfrac{1}{4}\pi = \pi,$$

so the value of the given integral *is* π. Since $n = 4$, $a = 0$, and $b = 1$, then $h = (1 - 0)/4 = \tfrac{1}{4}$, so Approximation 5-2 becomes

$$\pi \approx \frac{1}{4} \sum_{i=0}^{3} \frac{4}{1 + (\tfrac{1}{4}i)^2} = \sum_{i=0}^{3} \frac{16}{16 + i^2} = 1 + \frac{16}{17} + \frac{16}{20} + \frac{16}{25} = \frac{2874}{850} = 3.38.$$

Why is this number too large?

The Rectangle Rule is easy to describe, and it is also easy to program for a computer. But, as we saw in Example 5-1, it isn't very accurate. For greater accuracy, we turn to *Simpson's Parabolic Rule*. To calculate the number $\int_a^b f(x)dx$ by this rule, we choose a positive integer n and divide the interval $[a, b]$ into $2n$ equal subintervals, each $h = (b - a)/2n$ units long. Let us denote the points of subdivision by $x_0 = a$, $x_1 = a + h$, $x_2 = a + 2h$, and so on, and write $y_0, y_1, y_2, \ldots$ for the corresponding functional values $f(x_0), f(x_1), f(x_2), \ldots$. It is simply a matter of algebra to find numbers A, B, and C such that the graph of the equation $y = Ax^2 + Bx + C$ contains the points (x_0, y_0), (x_1, y_1), and (x_2, y_2). Since this graph is a parabola, we say that we have "passed a parabola through the points." Through the points (x_2, y_2), (x_3, y_3), and (x_4, y_4) we pass another parabola whose equation is $y = Dx^2 + Ex + F$, and so on, for each successive group of three points, as in Fig. 5-2. (It will turn out that we won't need to know the numbers A, B, C, and D, E, F, and so on. But if we had wanted to, we could have used the formula given in Exercise 5-3 to find them.)

Together, these parabolic arcs form the graph of a function that we will call p, and because the graph of p approximates the graph of f, it seems reason-

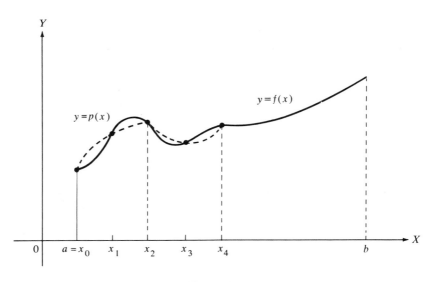

Figure 5-2

able to suppose that the integrals $\int_a^b f(x)dx$ and $\int_a^b p(x)dx$ are also approximately equal. We evaluate our approximating integral by writing it as a sum, covering two subintervals at a time:

$$(5\text{-}3) \qquad \int_a^b p(x)dx = \int_{x_0}^{x_2} p(x)dx + \int_{x_2}^{x_4} p(x)dx + \cdots + \int_{x_{2n-2}}^{x_{2n}} p(x)dx$$

$$= \sum_{i=0}^{n-1} \int_{x_{2i}}^{x_{2i+2}} p(x)dx.$$

Now we will evaluate the "typical" integral $\int_{x_{2i}}^{x_{2i+2}} p(x)dx$ appearing in this sum. Since $p(x)$ is a quadratic polynomial, we can use Equation 4-5, with x_{2i} playing the role of a. The distance between two successive division points is h, so $x_{2i} + h = x_{2i+1}$ and $x_{2i} + 2h = x_{2i+2}$. Therefore, according to Equation 4-5,

$$(5\text{-}4) \qquad \int_{x_{2i}}^{x_{2i+2}} p(x)dx = \frac{h}{3}[p(x_{2i}) + 4p(x_{2i+1}) + p(x_{2i+2})].$$

The values of f and p coincide at the points of subdivision of $[a, b]$; that is, $p(x_{2i}) = y_{2i}$, and so on, and when we make this replacement in Equation 5-4 and substitute in Equation 5-3, we obtain the equation

(5-5)
$$\int_a^b p(x)dx = \frac{h}{3} \sum_{i=0}^{n-1} (y_{2i} + 4y_{2i+1} + y_{2i+2}).$$

We want to rearrange this last sum; perhaps the easiest way to do it is to write it out (but see Exercise 5-9 for another approach):

(5-6)
$$\sum_{i=0}^{n-1} (y_{2i} + 4y_{2i+1} + y_{2i+2}) = (y_0 + 4y_1 + y_2) + (y_2 + 4y_3 + y_4)$$
$$+ (y_4 + 4y_5 + y_6) + \cdots + (y_{2n-2} + 4y_{2n-1} + y_{2n})$$
$$= y_0 + 4y_1 + 2y_2 + 4y_3 + 2y_4 + 4y_5$$
$$+ \cdots + 2y_{2n-2} + 4y_{2n-1} + y_{2n}$$
$$= y_0 + 4y_1 + y_{2n} + \sum_{i=1}^{n-1} (2y_{2i} + 4y_{2i+1}).$$

We assume that if n is large, $\int_a^b p(x)dx$ will approximate $\int_a^b f(x)dx$, and so from Equations 5-5 and 5-6 we obtain the approximation formula

$$\int_a^b f(x)dx \approx \frac{h}{3} \left[y_0 + 4y_1 + y_{2n} + \sum_{i=1}^{n-1} (2y_{2i} + 4y_{2i+1}) \right].$$

Finally, notice that $y_0 = f(a), y_1 = f(a + h), y_{2n} = f(b), y_{2i} = f(x_{2i}) = f(a + 2ih)$, and $y_{2i+1} = f(x_{2i+1}) = f(a + (2i + 1)h)$, and we have **Simpson's Parabolic Rule:**

(5-7)
$$\int_a^b f(x)dx \approx \frac{h}{3} \left[f(a) + 4f(a + h) + f(b) \right.$$
$$\left. + \sum_{i=1}^{n-1} (2f(a + 2ih) + 4f(a + (2i + 1)h)) \right].$$

Simpson's Rule fits nicely onto a digital computer. In Fig. 5-3, we have shown a general flow chart and a corresponding specific computer program that evaluates the integral $\int_0^1 \frac{4}{1 + x^2} dx$. We have chosen $n = 5$, and since $a = 0$

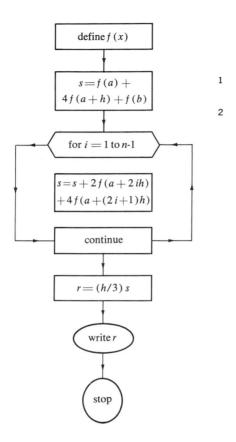

```
F(X) = 4/(1 + X*X)
S = F(0.0) + 4*F(.1) + F(1.0)
DO 1 I = 1, 4
S = S + 2*F(.2*I) + 4*F(.2*I+.1)
1   CONTINUE
R = (.1/3)*S
WRITE(6,2) R
2   FORMAT(1X, 'PI = ', F6.4)
STOP
END
```

Figure 5-3

and $b = 1$, it follows that $h = (1 - 0)/10 = .1$. If you run this program, you will find that it gives the correct value (to four decimal places) $pi = 3.1416$.

As our example indicates, Simpson's Rule is quite accurate. The following theorem is fairly easy to prove, as you can find out by consulting Reference [7, p. 487]. It shows us, in particular, that we get a considerable increase in accuracy by a relatively small decrease in h.

THEOREM 5-1

If M is a number such that for each $x \in [a, b]$, $|f^{(4)}(x)| \leq M$, and if Simpson's Rule for a given integer n yields r as the approximate value of

$\int_a^b f(x)dx$, then

$$\left| \int_a^b f(x)dx - r \right| \le \frac{b-a}{180} Mh^4,$$

where $h = (b-a)/2n$.

Thus, if $f(x) = 4/(1+x^2)$, then $f^{(4)}(x) = 96(1 - 10x^2 + 5x^4)(1+x^2)^{-5}$. It is not difficult to show that for $x \in [0, 1]$, $|f^{(4)}(x)| \le 96$, so Theorem 5-1 tells us that our computed value of $\int_0^1 \frac{4}{1+x^2} dx$ is off by no more than $\frac{96}{180} \times .0001 \approx .00005$.

You may object to our referring to the Rectangle Rule and Simpson's Rule as "direct" methods of integration, feeling that "approximation" methods would be a better term. Of course, they *are* approximation methods, and we will often refer to them as such. The point we want to make, however, when we refer to them as direct methods, is that by using them we can find, to any degree of accuracy we want, integrals of any continuous function. This point is sometimes lost sight of in elementary calculus.

EXERCISE 5

1. Use the Rectangle Rule and Simpson's Rule (with a fairly small choice of n) to evaluate the following integrals. Compare your results with the "exact" answer when you can.

   (a) $\int_0^2 (1+x^3)dx$ (c) $\int_0^{.4} \sin x\, dx$

   (b) $\int_2^{10} (1+x)^{-1}dx$ (d) $\int_0^{.4} \frac{\sin x}{x} dx$

2. Write a computer program that uses the Rectangle Rule with $n = 10$ to calculate $\int_0^1 \frac{4}{1+x^2} dx$. Run it, and compare the result with the answer we got from the program for Simpson's Rule in Fig. 5-3.

3. Show that the equation of the parabola that contains the points (x_0, y_0), (x_1, y_1), and (x_2, y_2) is

$$y = \frac{y_0(x-x_1)(x-x_2)}{(x_0-x_1)(x_0-x_2)} + \frac{y_1(x-x_0)(x-x_2)}{(x_1-x_0)(x_1-x_2)} + \frac{y_2(x-x_0)(x-x_1)}{(x_2-x_0)(x_2-x_1)}.$$

4. From its derivation, it is obvious that Simpson's Parabolic Rule gives the exact value of $\int_a^b f(x)dx$ if $f(x)$ is a quadratic polynomial. Use Theorem 5-1 to show that Simpson's Rule also yields the exact value of the integral if $f(x)$ is a cubic polynomial.

5. (a) Would you want to approximate π by evaluating the integral $\int_0^1 \dfrac{2dx}{\sqrt{1-x^2}}$

   by Simpson's Rule?

   (b) Use the computer and Simpson's Rule to approximate π by evaluating

   the integral $\int_0^{.5} \dfrac{6dx}{\sqrt{1-x^2}}$.

6. (a) Show that the program in Fig. 5-4 is an "all-purpose" Simpson's Parabolic
   Rule program, in which only the first four lines have to be completed
   for any given problem.

   (b) Write a similar all-purpose program for the Rectangle Rule.

7. If we wrote $f(x) = 4 * \text{sqrt}(1 - x * x)$, $a = 0$, $b = 1$, and $n = 5$ in the program of Fig. 5-4, what do you think it would print?

```
         F(X) =
         A =
         B =
         N =
         H = (B−A)/(2*N)
         S = F(A) + 4*F(A+H) + F(B)
         K = N − 1
         DO 1 I = 1, K
         S = S + 2*F(A+2*I*H) + 4*F(A+(2*I+1)*H)
   1     CONTINUE
         R = (H/3)*S
         WRITE(6, 2) R
   2     FORMAT(1X, 'INTEGRAL = ', F12.4)
         STOP
         END
```

Figure 5-4

8. (a) Same as Exercise 5-2, but use the Trapezoidal Rule instead of the
   Rectangle Rule.

   (b) Same as Exercise 5-2, but use the Tangent Rule instead of the Rectangle
   Rule.

   (If you have forgotten the Trapezoidal or Tangent Rules, see your
   calculus book.)

9. Notice that

$$\sum_{i=0}^{n-1}(y_{2i} + 4y_{2i+1} + y_{2i+2}) = y_0 + 4y_1 + \sum_{i=1}^{n-1}(y_{2i} + 4y_{2i+1}) + \sum_{i=0}^{n-2}y_{2i+2} + y_{2n}.$$

Now notice that $\displaystyle\sum_{i=0}^{n-2} y_{2i+2} = \sum_{i=1}^{n-1} y_{2i}$, and hence derive Equation 5-6.

10. If $\{x_n\}$ is a Newtonian sequence of approximations of the solution of the

equation $1 - \int_1^x \dfrac{du}{u} = 0$, show that $x_{n+1} = x_n\left(2 - \int_1^{x_n} \dfrac{du}{u}\right)$. Start with

$x_0 = 1$ and calculate a few terms, using numerical integration as necessary. What is the exact answer?

6 COMPUTING TABLES OF VALUES OF FUNCTIONS DEFINED BY INTEGRALS

By definition, a function is a set of pairs, and now we are going to see how a formula involving an integral sign can be made to yield a set of pairs of numbers. In other words, we are going to take up the question of printing tables of values of functions defined by integrals. So suppose that f is continuous in an interval I, that a is a point of I, and define F by the equation

$$F(x) = \int_a^x f(u)du.$$

How should we go about programing the computer to write a table of values of F at the points of the set $\{0, 1, 2, 3, 4, 5\}$ (which we will assume to be a subset of I)?

Figure 6-1 shows a schematic flow chart for doing the job. As it stands,

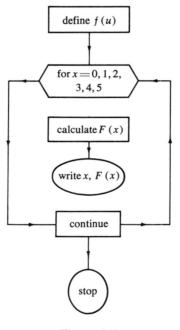

Figure 6-1

this flow chart isn't very specific; it merely tells us to choose x from the given set, calculate $F(x)$, and then print the resulting pair $(x, F(x))$. It does not tell us *how* to calculate $F(x)$. We can easily remedy this deficiency, however. All we have to do is replace the box labeled "calculate $F(x)$" with a flow chart for evaluating $\int_a^x f(u)\,du$ by one of our direct integration procedures—for example, the Rectangle Rule or Simpson's Rule.

This remedy is easy to apply, but it is inefficient. If we apply it, we will have to evaluate the six integrals

$$\int_a^0 f(u)\,du, \ \int_a^1 f(u)\,du, \ \int_a^2 f(u)\,du, \ \int_a^3 f(u)\,du, \ \int_a^4 f(u)\,du, \ \text{and} \ \int_a^5 f(u)\,du.$$

But there is no point, for example, in integrating all the way from a to 5, when we have just finished integrating from a to 4. In order to take advantage of previously calculated integrals, we use the relation

$$\int_a^x f(u)\,du = \int_a^{x-1} f(u)\,du + \int_{x-1}^x f(u)\,du;$$

that is,

(6-1) $$F(x) = F(x - 1) + \int_{x-1}^x f(u)\,du.$$

We calculate $F(0)$ separately, and then Equation 6-1 enables us to compute $F(1), F(2), \ldots, F(5)$ successively by integrating over intervals that are one unit long. Although we may have to use numerical integration to find $F(0)$, in most of our examples we can do it mentally.

A flow chart embodying Equation 6-1 for finding the desired values of F is shown in Fig. 6-2 (the letters A, B, C, and so on, are for later reference). To make this flow chart more specific, we can replace the box labeled "calculate $\int_{x-1}^x f(u)\,du$" with a flow chart for evaluating this integral by Simpson's Rule.

Example 6-1. If $F(x) = \int_0^x \sqrt{1 + u^3}\,du$, write a computer program that computes the values of F at the points of the set $\{0, 1, 2, 3, 4, 5\}$.

Solution. We must translate the flow chart of Fig. 6-2 into a computer program. In the program shown in Fig. 6-3, we let y stand for $F(x)$ and r stand for $\int_{x-1}^x f(u)\,du$. Here, $F(0)$ is obviously 0, so the first value of y is 0. We evaluate the integral $\int_{x-1}^x f(u)\,du$ by means of Simpson's Rule, with $n = 5$; that is, we set $a = x - 1$ and $b = x$, and $h = .1$ in Formula 5-7:

(6-2) $$\int_{x-1}^x f(u)\,du \approx (.1/3)\Big[f(x - 1) + 4f(x - .9) + f(x)$$

$$+ \sum_{j=1}^{4} (2f(x - 1 + .2j) + 4f(x - .9 + .2j))\Big].$$

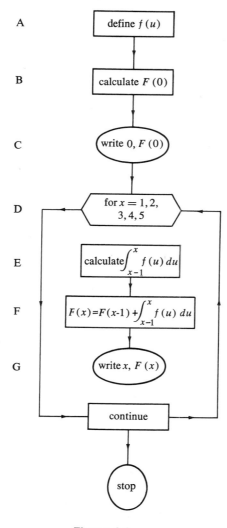

A   define $f(u)$

B   calculate $F(0)$

C   write $0, F(0)$

D   for $x = 1, 2, 3, 4, 5$

E   calculate $\displaystyle\int_{x-1}^{x} f(u)\,du$

F $F(x) = F(x-1) + \displaystyle\int_{x-1}^{x} f(u)\,du$

G   write $x, F(x)$

continue

stop

Figure 6-2

The letters A, B, C, D, E, F, and G label corresponding parts of the flow chart and the computer program. The output of this program also is listed in Fig. 6-3.

Example 6-2.   Write a computer program for printing a table of logarithms.

Solution. Since $\ln x = \int_{1}^{x} \dfrac{du}{u}$, we can use the ideas set forth in this section to calculate the table of values of ln at the points of the set $\{1.0, 1.1, 1.2, \ldots , 10.0\}$. Here, $f(u)$ is simply $1/u$, so we need not bother to define it with a special state-

```
A            F(U) = SQRT(1 + U**3)
B            Y = 0
             X = 0
C            WRITE(6, 1) X, Y
     1       FORMAT(1X, F3.1, F10.3)
D            DO 2 I = 1, 5
             X = I
             S = F(X−1) + 4*F(X−.9) + F(X)
             DO 3 J = 1, 4
E            S = S + 2*F(X−1+.2*J) + 4*F(X−.9+.2*J)
     3       CONTINUE
             R = (.1/3)*S
F            Y = Y + R
G            WRITE(6, 1) X, Y
     2       CONTINUE
             STOP
             END

     0.0     0.0
     1.0     1.111
     2.0     3.241
     3.0     7.341
     4.0     13.983
     5.0     23.596
```

Figure 6-3

ment. Also, since we are proceeding in steps of .1, there is no need to use many terms in Simpson's Rule. We can get quite satisfactory results with the approximation

$$(6\text{-}3) \quad \int_{x-.1}^{x} \frac{du}{u} \approx \frac{.025}{3}\left(\frac{1}{x-.1} + \frac{4}{x-.075} + \frac{2}{x-.05} + \frac{4}{x-.025} + \frac{1}{x}\right).$$

The program in Fig. 6-4 will therefore supply us with a table of logarithms. (Again, the letters *B*, *C*, and so on, refer to corresponding letters on the flow chart of Fig. 6-2.)

```
B            Y = 0
             X = 1.0
C            WRITE(6, 1) X, Y
     1       FORMAT(1X, F4.1, F10.4)
D            DO 2 I = 11, 100
             X = .1*I
E&F          Y = Y + (.025/3)*(1/(X−.1) + 4/(X−.075)
     1        + 2/(X−.05) + 4/(X−.025) + 1/X)
G            WRITE(6, 1) X, Y
     2       CONTINUE
             STOP
             END
```

Figure 6-4

EXERCISE 6

1. (a) Verify Approximation Formula 6-2.
   (b) Verify Approximation Formula 6-3.

2. Run the program in Fig. 6-4 on the computer and compare the printout with a log table.

3. Modify the program in Fig. 6-4 so that it prints three columns: x, our approximation of ln x, and the correct value of ln x.

4. Modify the program in Fig. 6-4 so that it uses the Rectangle Rule, rather than Simpson's Rule, to evaluate $\int_{x-.1}^{x} \frac{du}{u}$. Use the same number of subdivisions of the interval $[x - .1, x]$. Run the resulting program and see how the output compares with the results you got when you used Simpson's Rule.

5. Use the computer to print a table of values of Arcsine at the points of the set $\{.0, .1, .2, \ldots, .8\}$ and compare the results with the table calculated from the program of Example 3-2.

6. Use the computer to print a table of values of Arctan and compare the results with the table you calculated in Exercise 3-7.

7. Suppose, in the program in Fig. 6-4, that we replace the statement write (6, 1) x, y with the *two* statements $z = \exp(y)$ and write(6, 1) x, z. What *should* the program print now? What *does* it print?

8. Modify the program of Fig. 6-4 so that it gives you a table of *common* logarithms (logarithms to the base 10).

9. Modify the program of Fig. 6-4 so that it gives you a table of values of the function that is defined by the equation $y = \int_{1}^{x^2} \frac{du}{u}$.

10. Use the computer to write a table of values at the points of the set $\{1.0, 1.1, 1.2, \ldots, 3.0\}$ of the function defined by the equation $y = \int_{1}^{x} \text{int}(u) du$.

REVIEW EXERCISE, CHAPTER 1

Use the following exercises to test yourself on the material in this chapter.

1. (a) Explain why the set $f = \{(x, y): x^2 + y^2 = 1, y > 0\}$ is a function.
   (b) Sketch the graph of f.
   (c) What is the domain and what is the range of f?
   (d) Does f have an inverse?
   (e) Restrict the domain of f to obtain a function that has an inverse.

2. Suppose that f is a continuous function and that $f(a)f(b) < 0$. Then we know that there is a number $r \in (a, b)$ such that $f(r) = 0$. As a way to approximate r, we might find the point in which the segment that joins the points $(a, f(a))$ and $(b, f(b))$ intersects the X-axis. Show that this procedure gives us

$$r \approx \frac{af(b) - bf(a)}{f(b) - f(a)}.$$

3. Let $f(x) = x^3 + ax^2 + bx + c$. Find a relation among the numbers a, b, and c that guarantees that f^{-1} exists.

4. Find a particular choice of f, a, b, and n for which the Rectangle Rule gives a closer approximation of $\int_a^b f(x)\,dx$ than Simpson's Rule does.

5. Figure I-1 shows the graphs of the equations $v = g(u)$ and $v = h(u)$.
   (a) Explain why $f = \{(x, y): g(y) = h(x)\}$ is a function.
   (b) Determine graphically the domain and range of f.
   (c) Does f have an inverse?

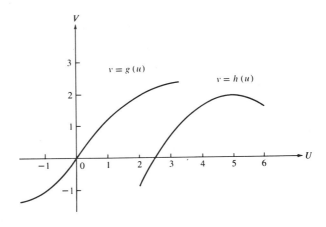

Figure I-1

6. A function f is **periodic** with period p if $f(x + p) = f(x)$ for every x. Suppose that f is periodic with period p and let $F(x) = \int_a^x f(u)\,du$. Show that F is periodic with period p if, and only if, $\int_0^p f(u)\,du = 0$.

7. Does Simpson's Rule give exact values of integrals of linear functions?

8. Suppose that f is a function such that $xf(x) \geq 0$ for each x, and let $F(x) = \int_0^x f(u)\,du$. Show that $F(x) \geq 0$ for each x.

9. Prove the following theorem. If M is a number such that for each $x \in [a, b]$, $|f'(x)| \leq M$, and if the Rectangle Rule for a given integer n yields r as the approximate value of $\int_a^b f(x)\,dx$, then $\left| \int_a^b f(x)\,dx - r \right| \leq M(b - a)^2/2n$.

10. In Exercise 3-10, we pointed out that a function that is continuous in an interval I has an inverse if, and only if, it is monotone, either increasing or decreasing. Show that if f is increasing, then f^{-1} is increasing, while if f is decreasing, then f^{-1} is decreasing. Use these facts to explain why there is no continuous function f that satisfies the functional equation $f^{-1}(x) = 1/f(x)$.

CHAPTER 2

SOME INITIAL VALUE PROBLEMS

Now we will take up the subject of differential equations itself. Leaving an exposition of the general theory to Chapter 3, we devote this chapter to some specific examples. The more one studies differential equations, the more he becomes aware of subtleties and fine points. If you can keep examples like the ones we will look at now clearly in mind, you are not so likely to get lost in peripheral matters. Bear in mind that differential equations are *equations* and their solutions are *functions*. In this chapter we will consider some types of differential equations whose solutions can be expressed in terms of functions that are defined by integrals. Furthermore, many differential equations have their genesis in "practical" problems of physics, economics, and so on, and we will look at several such examples, too.

7 THE SIMPLEST INITIAL VALUE PROBLEM

The equation

$$(7\text{-}1) \qquad\qquad y' = 3x^2$$

is an extremely simple example of a *differential equation*. We say it is simple because we can solve it at a glance. You can easily check that $y = x^3$ satisfies Equation 7-1, that $y = x^3 + 9$ satisfies the equation, and so on. As we study more complicated differential equations, we will find that most of them *cannot* be solved at a glance, but that they do, in general, share with Equation 7-1 the property of having more than one solution. For this reason, we don't study differential equations, but rather *initial value problems*, problems that consist of a differential equation plus an *initial condition*. For example, we might ask for the solution of Equation 7-1 that satisfies the initial condition $y = 3$ when $x = 2$. You can easily see that $y = x^3 - 5$ satisfies this problem. Can you show that nothing else does?

The initial value problem we have just discussed has the following form. We are given a function f that is continuous at each point of some interval I, a point $x_0 \in I$, and a number y_0. We seek a function w such that $y = w(x)$ satisfies the **initial value problem**

$$(7\text{-}2) \qquad \begin{aligned} y' &= f(x) \\ y &= y_0 \text{ when } x = x_0. \end{aligned}$$

In other words, we want $w'(x) = f(x)$ for each $x \in I$, and $w(x_0) = y_0$. In the example we discussed in the preceding paragraph, $f(x) = 3x^2$, $y_0 = 3$, $x_0 = 2$, and $w(x) = x^3 - 5$.

When we meet an initial value problem, we ask two basic questions:

(1) Does the problem have a solution? (Existence question).

(2) If so, is there only one solution? (Uniqueness question).

Question 1 is certainly a natural one to ask. If a problem has no solution, we will not want to waste much time on it. Question 2 is not quite so natural. Why should we worry if a problem has more than one solution? The more there are, the easier it should be to find one. We are interested in problems that have only one solution because most initial value problems are mathematical models of certain "real" experiments in physics, economics, and the like. (We will see examples as we go along.) These real experiments have, presumably, exactly one outcome, the one determined by the laws of physics, economics, or whatever. So if our mathematical model has more than one solution, we conclude that it does not represent the real situation we are studying, and we must either modify it or discard it.

It is easy to show that each of our questions has an affirmative answer for Initial Value Problem 7-2. Let us take up the uniqueness question first. Suppose that $y = w(x)$ and $y = v(x)$ both satisfy Problem 7-2. We will show that $w(x) = v(x)$ for each $x \in I$, or, what is the same thing, that if $g(x) = w(x) - v(x)$, then $g(x) = 0$ for each $x \in I$. To this end, let x be a point of I. Then, according to the Theorem of the Mean, there is a number t between x_0 and x such that $g(x) - g(x_0) = g'(t)(x - x_0)$. Now $g'(t) = w'(t) - v'(t)$, and since w and v are solutions of the differential equation of Problem 7-2, $w'(t) = v'(t) = f(t)$. Hence, $g'(t) = 0$, and so $g(x) = g(x_0)$. But $g(x_0) = w(x_0) - v(x_0) = y_0 - y_0 = 0$, and we see that $g(x) = 0$, as was to be shown.

We prove the existence of the solution of Problem 7-2 in the most convincing possible way; we exhibit it.

THEOREM 7-1

If f is continuous at each point of an interval I that contains the point x_0, then

(7-3)
$$y = y_0 + \int_{x_0}^{x} f(u)\,du$$

satisfies Problem 7-2 on I.

Proof. The proof is simply a matter of verification; we will show that $D_x y = f(x)$ and that $y = y_0$ when $x = x_0$. Thus, we first apply Equation 4-3 to see that

$$D_x \left(y_0 + \int_{x_0}^{x} f(u)\,du \right) = 0 + D_x \int_{x_0}^{x} f(u)\,du = f(x),$$

and so the differential equation is satisfied. Now we replace x with x_0, and the expression $y_0 + \int_{x_0}^{x} f(u)\,du$ reduces to y_0. Therefore, the initial condition is satisfied, too, and our verification is complete.

Example 7-1.   At each point (x, y) of a certain graph, the slope is $\sec^2 x$. Furthermore, the graph contains the point $(\frac{1}{4}\pi, 3)$. Find the equation of the graph.

Solution. Since the slope of the graph is y', we see that y must satisfy the differential equation $y' = \sec^2 x$. In addition, we are told that $y = 3$ when $x = \frac{1}{4}\pi$. Therefore, we are to solve the initial value problem

$$y' = \sec^2 x \text{ and } y = 3 \text{ when } x = \tfrac{1}{4}\pi.$$

According to Theorem 7-1, the solution of this problem is given by the equation

$$y = 3 + \int_{\frac{1}{4}\pi}^{x} \sec^2 u\,du = 3 + \tan u \Big|_{\frac{1}{4}\pi}^{x}$$

$$= 3 + \tan x - 1 = 2 + \tan x.$$

We cannot emphasize too strongly that Equation 7-3 gives the solution of Problem 7-2, no matter what (continuous) function f appears. We may have to evaluate the integral by numerical methods, but that is a simple matter for a computer. A solution of a differential equation is a function, and a function is a set of pairs. Hence, if we can find the right set of pairs, we can solve our initial value problem.

Example 7-2. Find the values of the solution of the initial value problem

$$y' = \sqrt{1 + x^3} \text{ and } y = 2 \text{ when } x = 0$$

at the points of the set $\{0, 1, 2, 3, 4, 5\}$.

Solution. According to Theorem 7-1, the solution of our problem is defined by the equation

$$y = 2 + \int_{0}^{x} \sqrt{1 + u^3}\,du.$$

Unlike our previous example, we cannot find $\int \sqrt{1 + u^3}\,du$ in a table of integrals, but that does not mean that we cannot evaluate the integral that appears in our expression for y. In fact, in Example 6-1 we did just that. To obtain the desired table of values of the solution of our present initial value problem, we need only add 2 to each number in the right-hand column of the table in Fig. 6-3. We leave it to you to make the necessary modifications of the computer program of that example to come up with a program that solves the problem given here.

The physical sciences are a prime source of initial value problems. In fact, it is often said that differential equations constitute the language of physics. Expressing physical laws in this language is really the job of a physicist, not a mathematician. How well the physicist does his job is determined when the equations are solved and the solutions are checked against observed behavior. If the solution predicts what actually happens, then we assume that the initial value problem really is a mathematical model of the physical situation. Otherwise, we know it is not. No one should study differential equations without examining some of these applications. They give the subject life. Let us look at one of the very first applications.

Recall that if a body is displaced s meters from some initial position t seconds after some initial instant, then the numbers $s' = v$ and $s'' = v' = a$

represent its velocity and acceleration. It is a physical fact that the acceleration of an unsupported body in a vacuum near the surface of the earth is approximately -9.8 meters per second per second, so its displacement s satisfies the differential equation $s'' = -9.8$.

Here, we are measuring distance on a number scale that is perpendicular to the surface of the earth, as shown in Fig. 7-1. The minus sign results from the

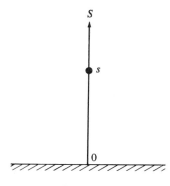

Figure 7-1

fact that the scale is pointed upward and gravity acts downward. We have chosen the origin of our number scale to be on the surface of the earth so that the displacement s is the number of meters the body is above the surface.

If our body has a velocity of v_0 meters per second when $t = 0$ and is s_0 meters above the surface of the earth at that instant, then we have two initial conditions to adjoin to our differential equation to produce the initial value problem

(7-4)
$$s'' = -9.8$$
$$s = s_0 \text{ and } s' = v_0 \text{ when } t = 0.$$

(Because the highest derivative of s that appears in our differential equation is the second, the differential equation is said to be of the *second order*. As this problem illustrates, when we deal with a differential equation of the second order, we need *two* initial conditions to determine the solution. We will discuss this point in more detail later.)

If we replace s' with v, we can break Problem 7-4 into two problems:

(7-5)
$$v' = -9.8$$
$$v = v_0 \text{ when } t = 0$$

and

(7-6)
$$s' = v$$
$$s = s_0 \text{ when } t = 0.$$

Both these problems have the form of Problem 7-2, so we can solve them successively by means of Theorem 7-1. Thus, Problem 7-5 is satisfied by

$$v = v_0 + \int_0^t (-9.8)du = v_0 - 9.8t.$$

Now we substitute this expression for v in Problem 7-6, and we obtain the problem

$$s' = v_0 - 9.8t$$
$$s = s_0 \text{ when } t = 0.$$

We solve this problem (and hence the original Problem 7-4) by means of Theorem 7-1:

(7-7)
$$s = s_0 + \int_0^t (v_0 - 9.8u)du = s_0 + v_0t - 4.9t^2.$$

You undoubtedly recognize this equation from physics.

> **Example 7-3.** You are in a hotel window 30 meters up with a paper bag full of water. A man is walking toward the spot directly under your window at the rate of 3 meters per second. If you throw the bag straight down when he is 6 meters from the spot, how fast should you throw it to hit him?
>
> *Solution.* We may use Equation 7-7 to find the initial velocity v_0. We are told that the initial height is $s_0 = 30$. Furthermore, since the target will be in position when $t = 2$, we want $s = 0$ at that time (humanely, we aim the bag at the victim's feet). Therefore, Equation 7-7 becomes
>
> $$0 = 30 + 2v_0 - 4.9 \cdot 2^2.$$
>
> From this equation we find that $v_0 = -5.2$. We must throw the bag downward with a speed of 5.2 meters per second.

EXERCISE 7

1. Solve the following initial value problems (without using the computer).
   (a) $y' = \sin 2x$
       $y = \frac{1}{2}\pi$ when $x = \frac{1}{4}\pi$
   (b) $y' = 3/x$
       $y = 3$ when $x = e$
   (c) $y' = 2|x|$
       $y = 5$ when $x = 0$
   (d) $y' = x + |x|$
       $y = 0$ when $x = 0$
   (e) $y' = \exp(1/x)/x^2$
       $y = 0$ when $x = 1$
   (f) $y' = \sin^2 x \cos^2 x$
       $y = 0$ when $x = \pi$

2. Find the equation of the curve with the given slope m and containing the given point.
   (a) $m = x \sin x^2$, $(\sqrt{\pi}, 2)$
   (b) $m = e^{2x}$, $(\ln 2, 5)$
   (c) $m = \ln x$, $(1, 2)$
   (d) $m = \ln |x|$, $(-1, 2)$

3. A certain curve contains the points $(0, 4)$ and $(1, 8)$, and its slope at each point is proportional to the X-coordinate of the point. What is its equation?

4. Sketch the graph of the solution of the initial value problem $y' = \text{Cos}^{-1}(\cos x)$ and $y = 2$ when $x = 0$, in the interval $[-\pi, 2\pi]$.

5. If the man in Example 7-3 were 9 meters from the aiming point when you threw the bag, what would the correct initial velocity be?

6. At lift-off, a certain small rocket weighs 1500 kilograms, of which 1000 kilograms are fuel. The fuel burns at the rate of 10 kilograms per second, producing a thrust of 20,000 newtons. Show that at the end of t seconds the rocket is acted on by an upward force of 20,000 netwons and a downward force of $9.8(1500 - 10t)$ newtons. What is the resultant of these forces? According to Newton's Second Law of Motion, this force equals the product of the mass, $1500 - 10t$, and the acceleration, v', of the rocket. Thus, we have the initial value problem

$$v' = -\frac{98t + 5300}{10t - 1500} \text{ and } v = 0 \text{ when } t = 0.$$

What is the velocity of the rocket at burn-out? How high is it then? How high does it finally go?

7. Write and run computer programs to find the values of the solutions of the following initial value problems at the points of the set $\{0, .1, .2, \ldots, 1.0\}$.
   (a) $y' = \sqrt{1 + x^3}$
       $y = -4$ when $x = 0$
   (b) $y' = x + |x|$
       $y = 0$ when $x = 0$
   (c) $y' = e^{-x^2}$
       $y = 1$ when $x = 0$
   (d) $y' = \tan x^2$
       $y = 2$ when $x = 0$

8. Suppose that $f(x) \leq g(x)$ at each point x of an interval $[x_0, x_1]$. Let u and v be the solutions of the initial value problems $y' = f(x)$ and $y = y_0$ when $x = x_0$ and $y' = g(x)$ and $y = y_0$ when $x = x_0$, respectively. Is it true that $u(x) \leq v(x)$ for each $x \in [x_0, x_1]$? What if the form of our basic interval were $[x_1, x_0]$?

8   INITIAL VALUE PROBLEMS WHOSE DIFFERENTIAL EQUATIONS ARE LINEAR

The general initial value problem of the first order has the form

$$y' = f(x, y) \text{ and } y = y_0 \text{ when } x = x_0,$$

where f is a function whose domain is some set in the XY-plane that contains the given initial point (x_0, y_0). How easy it is to solve such a problem depends on how complicated $f(x, y)$ is. In the last section, we saw how to solve the problem if $f(x, y)$ is independent of y (that is, $f(x, y) = f(x)$), and now we will study a slightly more general case that is still easy to handle.

We say that $f(x, y)$ is *linear in y* if $f(x, y) = p(x)y + r(x)$. Then our initial value problem has a **linear differential equation:**

(8-1)
$$y' = p(x)y + r(x)$$
$$y = y_0 \text{ when } x = x_0.$$

Here, we assume that p and r are continuous functions in an interval I that contains x_0, and that y_0 is a given number. We seek a function w such that $w(x_0) = y_0$ and, for each $x \in I$, $w'(x) = p(x)w(x) + r(x)$.

For example, the initial value problem

(8-2) $$y' = (\tan x)y - 2 \sin x \text{ and } y = 1 \text{ when } x = 0$$

has a linear differential equation. We can take as our basic interval I the set $(-\frac{1}{2}\pi, \frac{1}{2}\pi)$, and the coefficient functions p and r are defined by the equations $p(x) = \tan x$ and $r(x) = -2 \sin x$. The initial point is $(x_0, y_0) = (0, 1)$. Simply by replacing y with $\cos x$, we verify that our problem has a solution w which is defined by the equation $w(x) = \cos x$ for each $x \in I$.

Of course, it is one thing to *verify* that a given function is a solution of an initial value problem and quite another thing to *find* the solution when it isn't given, so the real goal of this section is to develop a method for solving linear problems. A mathematician always likes to reduce a new problem to one that he has solved before, and that is what we will do with Problem 8-1. By making a suitable substitution, we will reduce it to Problem 7-2.

We let

(8-3) $$P(x) = \int_{x_0}^{x} p(v)\,dv,$$

and multiply both sides of our linear differential equation by $e^{-P(x)}$, writing the resulting equation as

$$e^{-P(x)}y' - p(x)e^{-P(x)}y = e^{-P(x)}r(x).$$

This equation, in turn, can be written as

(8-4) $$D_x(e^{-P(x)}y) = e^{-P(x)}r(x).$$

For,

$$D_x(e^{-P(x)}y) = e^{-P(x)}D_xy + (D_xe^{-P(x)})y \qquad \text{(Product rule of differentiation)}$$

$$= e^{-P(x)}y' - (D_xP(x))e^{-P(x)}y \quad (D_xe^u = e^uD_xu)$$

$$= e^{-P(x)}y' - p(x)e^{-P(x)}y \qquad \text{(From Equation 8-3, } D_xP(x) = p(x)\text{).}$$

Equation 8-4 suggests the substitution

(8-5) $$z = e^{-P(x)}y,$$

which reduces our original linear differential equation to the equivalent equation $z' = e^{-P(x)}r(x)$. Furthermore, since $P(x_0) = \int_{x_0}^{x_0} p(v)dv = 0$, and since $y = y_0$ when $x = x_0$, it follows that $z = e^0y_0 = y_0$ when $x = x_0$. Therefore, the substitution indicated in Equation 8-5 reduces Initial Value Problem 8-1 to the form

$$z' = e^{-P(x)}r(x) \text{ and } z = y_0 \text{ when } x = x_0.$$

Now we are back to an initial value problem that we have seen before (Problem 7-2), and so we know that it is satisfied by

$$z = y_0 + \int_{x_0}^{x} e^{-P(u)}r(u)du.$$

When we use Equation 8-5 to replace z in terms of y, we see that we have proved the following theorem.

THEOREM 8-1

Initial Value Problem 8-1 is satisfied by

(8-6) $$y = e^{P(x)}y_0 + e^{P(x)}\int_{x_0}^{x} e^{-P(u)}r(u)du,$$

where $P(x) = \int_{x_0}^{x} p(v)dv.$

It is probably a bad idea to try to memorize this complicated formula. Just recall that multiplying the given differential equation by $e^{-P(x)}$ reduces our linear problem to the one we studied in Section 7.

Example 8-1. Solve Initial Value Problem 8-2.

Solution. Here, we set $P(x) = \int_0^x \tan v \, dv = \ln \sec v \Big|_0^x = \ln \sec x$. Therefore, we are to multiply the given differential equation by $e^{-P(x)} = e^{-\ln \sec x} = e^{\ln \cos x} = \cos x$, which reduces our problem to

$$y' \cos x - y \sin x = -2 \sin x \cos x \text{ and } y = 1 \text{ when } x = 0,$$

or

$$D_x(y \cos x) = -2 \sin x \cos x \text{ and } y = 1 \text{ when } x = 0.$$

Now we set $z = y \cos x$ to obtain the initial value problem

$$z' = -2 \sin x \cos x \text{ and } z = 1 \text{ when } x = 0.$$

Hence,

$$z = 1 - \int_0^x 2 \sin u \cos u \, du = 1 - \sin^2 u \Big|_0^x = 1 - \sin^2 x = \cos^2 x.$$

Because $z = y \cos x$, we are thus led to the equation $y = \cos x$ that gives the solution of Problem 8-2.

Example 8-2. Solve the initial value problem

$$xy' = 2y + e^x \text{ and } y = 3 \text{ when } x = 1.$$

Solution. In "standard form" (see Problem 8-1) our linear differential equation is

$$y' = (2/x)y + e^x/x,$$

and so $P(x) = \int_1^x \dfrac{2}{v} dv = 2 \ln x = \ln x^2$. Therefore, $e^{-P(x)} = e^{-\ln x^2} = x^{-2}$, and when we multiply the differential equation by this factor and rearrange terms, we get the equation

$$x^{-2}y' - 2x^{-3}y = x^{-3}e^x;$$

that is,

$$D_x(x^{-2}y) = x^{-3}e^x.$$

Thus (making the substitution $z = x^{-2}y$ mentally),

$$x^{-2}y = 3 + \int_1^x u^{-3}e^u du,$$

or

$$y = \left(3 + \int_1^x u^{-3}e^u du\right) x^2.$$

By slightly modifying a program we developed in Section 6, we can get the computer to print the values of the function that is defined by this equation at the points of the set $\{1, 2, 3, 4, 5\}$. In the program in Fig. 8-1, $t = \int_1^x u^{-3}e^u du$, and we have essentially copied the program of Example 6-1 to calculate it. In the present

```
        F(U) = EXP(U)/U**3
        T = 0
        X = 1
        Y = 3
        WRITE(6, 1) X, Y
1       FORMAT(1X, F3.1, F10.4)
        DO 2 I = 2, 5
        X = I
        S = F(X—1) + 4*F(X—.9) + F(X)
        DO 3 J = 1, 4
        S = S + 2*F(X—1+.2*J) + 4*F(X—.9+.2*J)
3       CONTINUE
        R = (.1/3)*S
        T = T + R
        Y = (3 + T)*X*X
        WRITE(6, 1) X, Y
2       CONTINUE
        STOP
        END
```

Figure 8-1

problem, however, $y = (3 + t)x^2$, so we have to add a statement to perform this computation.

A large number of "practical" experiments can be modeled by initial value problems in which the differential equation is linear. In fact, because we have a simple technique for solving them, we often use such problems as models even when we know that they only approximately describe reality. The following example is somewhat typical.

Example 8-3. A parachutist steps out of a balloon at a height of 2000 meters. One second later he is falling at the rate of 7 meters per second. How fast is he falling when he hits the ground?

Solution. When we studied the falling body in the last section, we neglected the effects of air resistance. If our jumper didn't believe in air resistance, he wouldn't use a parachute, so we have to introduce a new term into our differential equation. Let us suppose that the force due to air resistance is proportional to velocity. This assumption is at least somewhat reasonable, in that it provides for increasing resistance with increasing speed (and no resistance with no speed). Since force is proportional to acceleration, we see that the effect of air resistance is to add to the acceleration v' of the parachutist a term that is proportional to velocity. Because air resistance acts in the direction opposite to the motion of the chutist, we write this term as $-rv$, where r is a constant of proportionality that we do not yet know. When we add this term to the acceleration due to gravity, we obtain the initial value problem

(8-7)
$$v' = -9.8 - rv$$
$$v = 0 \text{ when } t = 0.$$

(Our jumper just "steps" out of the balloon, so his initial velocity is 0.)

To solve Initial Value Problem 8-7, we multiply the linear differential equation by e^{rt} and write the resulting equation as

$$D_t(e^{rt}v) = -9.8e^{rt}.$$

It follows that

$$e^{rt}v = -9.8 \int_0^t e^{ru}du = -\frac{9.8}{r}e^{ru}\Big|_0^t = -\frac{9.8}{r}(e^{rt} - 1),$$

and so

(8-8)
$$v = -\frac{9.8}{r}(1 - e^{-rt}).$$

(We get a negative velocity because the parachutist is falling, whereas the positive direction is upward.) Since $v = s'$, the initial value problem for s becomes

$$s' = -\frac{9.8}{r}(1 - e^{-rt})$$

$$s = 2000 \text{ when } t = 0.$$

Thus, according to Theorem 7-1,

(8-9) $$s = 2000 - \frac{9.8}{r}\int_0^t (1 - e^{-ru})du = 2000 - \frac{9.8}{r}t - \frac{9.8}{r^2}e^{-rt} + \frac{9.8}{r^2}.$$

To finish our problem, we could proceed as follows. We are told that $v = -7$ when $t = 1$. Therefore, Equation 8-8 yields the equation $7 = \frac{9.8}{r}(1 - e^{-r})$. We could solve this equation for r, using Newton's Method (and the computer, of course). We leave it to you to show that $r = .7$. Knowing r, we can use Equation 8-9 to find out *when* our parachutist lands; that is, we find the value of t for which $s = 0$. Thus, we must solve the equation

$$2000 - \frac{9.8}{.7}t - \frac{9.8}{.49}e^{-.7t} + \frac{9.8}{.49} = 0$$

for t. Finally, we insert this value of t (and $r = .7$) in Equation 8-8, and we find the answer to the original question.

We can, however, avoid a great deal of this work. A drop of 2000 meters (over a mile) is a big one, and it will take quite awhile. Hence, the time of fall t is lengthy, and so $e^{-rt} = e^{-.7t}$ is small. If we neglect this term in Equation 8-8, we see that the velocity of our chutist is $-9.8/r$ meters per second. Since $r = .7$, it follows that he hits the ground at about 14 meters per second. Does this figure suggest that our man should have used a bigger parachute?

We haven't been too careful about specifying the basic interval I in which we are working. Usually, it is obvious from the context, and we don't have to think about it. Sometimes, we do.

Example 8-4.   Solve the initial value problem

$$y' = \frac{1}{x}y + 5x^5 \text{ and } y = 3 \text{ when } x = -1.$$

Solution. Our basic interval I must contain the point $x_0 = -1$, and the largest interval that contains this point and in which the equation $p(x) = 1/x$ defines a continuous function is the interval $(-\infty, 0)$. So we infer that $I = (-\infty, 0)$. In this problem,

$$P(x) = \int_{-1}^{x} \frac{1}{v}\,dv = \ln{(-v)} \Big|_{-1}^{x} = \ln{(-x)}.$$

Therefore, we multiply the given differential equation by $e^{-\ln{(-x)}} = -1/x$ and obtain the equation

$$-(1/x)y' + (1/x^2)y = -5x^4,$$

which we write as

$$D_x[-(1/x)y] = -5x^4.$$

Thus, because $-(1/x)y = 3$ when $x = -1$,

$$-(1/x)y = 3 - \int_{-1}^{x} 5u^4\,du = 3 - u^5 \Big|_{-1}^{x} = 3 - x^5 - 1 = 2 - x^5.$$

Finally, therefore, we see that

$$y = x^6 - 2x$$

satisfies the given initial value problem.

EXERCISE 8

1. Solve the following initial value problems.

   (a) $y' = -2y + 3$
       $y = 1$ when $x = 0$

   (b) $y' = 2y - 3$
       $y = 0$ when $x = 1$

   (c) $y' = y - e^x$
       $y = 1$ when $x = 0$

   (d) $y' = 5y + e^{6x}$
       $y = -2$ when $x = 0$

   (e) $y' = (\tan x)y$
       $y = 3$ when $x = -\pi$

   (f) $y' = (\cot x)y - \sin x$
       $y = 2$ when $x = \frac{1}{2}\pi$

   (g) $y' = 2|x|y$
       $y = 6$ when $x = 0$

   (h) $y' = 2(x + |x|)y + 4xe^{x^2 + x|x|}$
       $y = 6$ when $x = 0$

2. Let $r(x)$ be the distance between x and the nearest prime number, and let w be the solution of the initial value problem

$$y' = 3y/x + x^3 r(x) \text{ and } y = 3 \text{ when } x = 1.$$

   Find $w(4)$.

3. Show that $y = y_0 \exp\left(\int_{x_0}^x p(v)\,dv\right) + \int_{x_0}^x \exp\left(\int_u^x p(v)\,dv\right) r(u)\,du$ satisfies Initial Value Problem 8-1.

4. Write a computer program to print the values of the solution of the initial value problem

$$y' = -(1/x)y + \sqrt{1 + x^3}/x \text{ and } y = 3 \text{ when } x = 1$$

   at the points of the set $\{1, 2, 3, 4, 5\}$.

5. Write a computer program to print the values of the solution of the initial value problem

$$y' = -2y + e^{-2x}\sqrt{1 + x^3} \text{ and } y = 3 \text{ when } x = 0$$

   at the points of the set $\{0, 1, 2, 3, 4\}$.

6. Write a computer program to print a small table of values of the solution of the initial value problem $y' = (\tan x)y + (\sec x) \exp(-x^2)$ and $y = 3$ when $x = 0$.

7. Show that the substitution $u = y^{1-n}$ reduces the **Bernoulli Differential Equation** $y' = p(x)y + r(x)y^n$ to a linear differential equation, and solve the following initial value problems.

   (a) $y' = 3y + e^x y^2$
       $y = 2$ when $x = 0$

   (b) $y' = (3/x)y + 12x^3/y$
       $y = 3$ when $x = 1$

8. In many situations, the rate of growth is proportional to the present population. Thus, if there are y individuals t time units after measurement starts, then there is a constant of proportionality r such that $D_t y = ry$. So we can think of such linear equations as "growth" equations. For example, if one invests \$1000 at 5% interest compounded instantaneously, we have the following initial value problem for the number y of dollars in our account t years after we open it:

$$y' = .05y \text{ and } y = 1000 \text{ when } t = 0.$$

How much is in the account after 10 years? In how many years would our account double? What interest, compounded instantaneously, is necessary so that an investment will double in 15 years? Suppose an embezzler works at our bank and steals $100 a year from our account (which is drawing 5% interest). Explain why our initial value problem is now

$$y' = .05y - 100 \text{ and } y = 1000 \text{ when } t = 0.$$

When will the account be empty?

9. The Dean of Women fills a 5-gallon container with fruit punch (no alcohol) for the freshman party. It is consumed at the rate of 2 quarts per minute, and the evil senior who is keeping the container full is pouring in 100 proof whiskey (50% alcohol). How long does it take the punch to get to be 20% alcohol? If $A(t)$ is the number of quarts of alcohol in the punch t minutes after the party starts, what is $\lim_{t \uparrow \infty} A(t)$? (Answer this question two ways: (a) Find a formula for $A(t)$ and take the limit, and (b) use common sense.)

9   INITIAL VALUE PROBLEMS WITH SEPARABLE DIFFERENTIAL EQUATIONS

We have studied the initial value problem

$$y' = f(x, y) \text{ and } y = y_0 \text{ when } x = x_0$$

when $f(x, y)$ has one of the forms $f(x)$ or $p(x)y + r(x)$. We can also solve our problem if $f(x, y) = f(x)/g(y)$. In this case, we say that $f(x, y)$ is **separated** into the quotient $f(x)/g(y)$. Thus, suppose that f is a continuous function in an interval that contains x_0, and that g is a continuous function in an interval that contains y_0, and suppose that $g(y) \neq 0$ for each y in this latter interval. Then consider the initial value problem

(9-1)
$$y' = f(x)/g(y)$$
$$y = y_0 \text{ when } x = x_0.$$

As with the linear problem that we investigated in the last section, the trick in solving this initial value problem is to find a substitution that reduces it to the simple case we discussed in Section 7. Here, we let

$$z = \int_{y_0}^{y} g(u)\,du.$$

Equation 4-4 now tells us that $z' = g(y)y'$, and therefore our separable differential equation $y' = f(x)/g(y)$ reduces to $z' = f(x)$. Furthermore, since $y = y_0$ when $x = x_0$, we see that $z = 0$ when $x = x_0$, and hence Problem 9-1 becomes

$$z' = f(x) \text{ and } z = 0 \text{ when } x = x_0.$$

Now we are back to a problem we treated in Section 7. We know that it is satisfied by $z = \int_{x_0}^{x} f(v)dv$, and when we equate our two expressions for z, we find that we have proved the following theorem.

THEOREM 9-1

To determine the solution of Initial Value Problem 9-1, solve the equation

(9-2) $$\int_{y_0}^{y} g(u)du = \int_{x_0}^{x} f(v)dv$$

for y.

Example 9-1.   Solve the initial value problem

$$y' = e^{x+y} \text{ and } y = 3 \text{ when } x = 0.$$

Solution. Here, $f(x, y) = e^x/e^{-y}$, so we can take $f(x) = e^x$ and $g(y) = e^{-y}$. Thus, Theorem 9-1 tells us that we are to solve the equation

$$\int_{3}^{y} e^{-u}du = \int_{0}^{x} e^v dv$$

for y. Upon integrating, we obtain the equation

$$-e^{-u}\Big|_{3}^{y} = e^v\Big|_{0}^{x},$$

or $-e^{-y} + e^{-3} = e^x - 1$. We solve this equation for y and find that $y = -\ln(e^{-3} + 1 - e^x)$.

Because it is simpler, we have been writing $D_x y$ for the derivative of y with respect to x, rather than dy/dx. But you recall from calculus that the differential notation is a great aid to the memory. In it, the Chain Rule and the rule for differentiating an inverse are expressed as

$$\frac{dy}{dx} = \frac{dy}{du}\frac{du}{dx} \quad \text{and} \quad \frac{dx}{dy} = 1 \Big/ \frac{dy}{dx}.$$

Thus, the differential notation makes certain basic theorems of calculus look like trivial algebraic identities. Similarly, it is easy to use formal manipulations with differentials to help us remember the content of Theorem 9-1. We can write our separable differential equation as

$$\frac{dy}{dx} = \frac{f(x)}{g(y)}.$$

This equation suggests that $g(y)dy = f(x)dx$, which in turn suggests Equation 9-2.

Example 9-2. Solve the initial value problem $y' = \sqrt{\dfrac{1 - y^2}{1 - x^2}}$ and $y = 0$ when $x = \frac{1}{2}$.

Solution. We may write our differential equation as

$$\frac{dy}{dx} = \sqrt{\frac{1 - y^2}{1 - x^2}} = \frac{\sqrt{1 - y^2}}{\sqrt{1 - x^2}},$$

which suggests that

$$\frac{dy}{\sqrt{1 - y^2}} = \frac{dx}{\sqrt{1 - x^2}}.$$

Now we refer to our initial conditions to obtain the limits on the integrals in the equation

$$\int_0^y \frac{du}{\sqrt{1 - u^2}} = \int_{\frac{1}{2}}^x \frac{dv}{\sqrt{1 - v^2}},$$

which we are to solve for y. This equation is simply

$$\text{Sin}^{-1} u \Big|_0^y = \text{Sin}^{-1} v \Big|_{\frac{1}{2}}^x \quad \text{or} \quad \text{Sin}^{-1} y = \text{Sin}^{-1} x - \tfrac{1}{6}\pi.$$

Hence, $y = \text{Sin}\,(\text{Sin}^{-1} x - \tfrac{1}{6}\pi) = \tfrac{1}{2}(\sqrt{3}\,x - \sqrt{1 - x^2})$.

Example 9-3. Solve the initial value problem

$$y' = (1 + y^2)\,\sqrt{1 + x^3} \text{ and } y = 0 \text{ when } x = 0.$$

Solution. According to Theorem 9-1, we are to solve the equation

(9-3)
$$\int_0^y \frac{du}{1+u^2} = \int_0^x \sqrt{1+v^3}\, dv$$

for *y*. Since $\int_0^y \frac{du}{1+u^2} = \text{Tan}^{-1} y$, we therefore obtain

(9-4)
$$y = \text{Tan}\left(\int_0^x \sqrt{1+v^3}\, dv\right).$$

If we want a table of values of the function defined by this equation at the points of the set $\{0.0, 0.1, 0.2, \ldots, 1.0\}$, we can compute it readily by means of the program in Fig. 9-1. Notice that we computed the integral $\int_{x-1}^x f(v)dv$ by using Simpson's Rule with $n = 2$, actually writing out all the terms of the sum in Approximation 5-7. Figure 9-1 also lists the output of this program.

```
    F(V) = SQRT(1 + V**3)              0.0   0.0
    Z = 0                             0.1   0.1003
    X = 0                             0.2   0.2029
    Y = 0                             0.3   0.3104
    WRITE(6, 1) X, Y                  0.4   0.4625
  1 FORMAT(1X, F3.1, F10.4)           0.5   0.5563
    DO 2 I = 1, 10                    0.6   0.7075
    X = .1*I                          0.7   0.8926
    Z = Z + (.025/3)*(F(X—.1) + 4*F(X—.075)    0.8   1.1337
  1  + 2*F(X—.05) + 4*F(X—.025) + F(X))        0.9   1.4753
    Y = SIN (Z)/COS(Z)                1.0   2.0217
    WRITE(6, 1) X, Y
  2 CONTINUE
    STOP
    END
```

Figure 9-1

The left-hand side of Equation 9-3 is $\text{Tan}^{-1} y$, so it is easy to solve the equation for *y* and thus obtain Equation 9-4. But if *g* is a fairly complicated function, it may be hard to solve Equation 9-2. It is an interesting, but not too simple, exercise (Exercise 9-12, for example) to use a combination of Newton's Method and numerical integration to solve this equation. It is probably easier to attack the original Initial Value Problem 9-1 directly with numerical methods that we will discuss later.

Now we will look at an "applied" problem.

Example 9-4. A projectile is fired straight up from the surface of the earth. How fast do we need to shoot it so that it never comes back down?

Solution. To obtain the differential equation that describes this problem, we equate two expressions for the acceleration of the projectile. First, we use the Chain Rule to write the acceleration $D_t v$ as $D_t v = D_s v D_t s = v D_s v$. Our second expression for the acceleration comes from Newton's Inverse Square Law of Gravitation. This law states that the acceleration of the projectile is inversely proportional to the square of its distance from the center of the earth. Thus, $a = k/s^2$. We know that the acceleration is -9.8 meters per second per second, or $-9.8/1000$ kilometers per second per second, when $s = 6380$ (the radius of the earth in kilometers). Therefore, $-9.8/1000 = k/6380^2$, from which it follows that k is about $-400,000$. Our two expressions for acceleration are vD_sv and $-400,000s^{-2}$, so our differential equation is $D_sv = -400,000/s^2v$. To this equation we adjoin the initial condition $v = v_0$ when $s = 6380$, and we obtain the initial value problem

$$D_sv = -400,000/s^2v \text{ and } v = v_0 \text{ when } s = 6380.$$

Here, in the notation of Problem 9-1, we can take $g(v) = v$ and $f(s) = -400,000s^{-2}$. Therefore, according to Theorem 9-1, we find the solution of our initial value problem by solving the equation

$$\int_{v_0}^{v} t\,dt = -400,000 \int_{6380}^{s} u^{-2}du$$

for v. After we integrate and simplify, this equation reduces to

$$v^2 = \frac{800,000}{s} + v_0^2 - \frac{800,000}{6380}.$$

We have expressed the square of our projectile's velocity in terms of its distance s from the center of the earth and its initial velocity v_0. If the projectile is to escape from the earth, its velocity can never become 0 (if it ever stops, it will fall back). Therefore, no matter how large s becomes, we must have $v^2 > 0$, so we must choose v_0 so that $v_0^2 - \dfrac{800,000}{6380} \geq 0$. The smallest possible such number is $v_0 = \sqrt{\dfrac{800,000}{6380}} \approx 11$. Thus, we must fire our projectile with a speed of at least 11 kilometers per second, or it will fall back to earth.

EXERCISE 9

1. Solve the following initial value problems.
   (a) $y' = (1 + y^2)/(1 + x^2)$
   　　$y = 2$ when $x = 0$
   (b) $y' = (1 + y)/(1 + x)$
   　　$y = 2$ when $x = 0$
   (c) $y' = |x/y|$
   　　$y = 2$ when $x = 0$
   (d) $y' = |y/x|$
   　　$y = 2$ when $x = 1$
   (e) $y' = \cos x \csc y$
   　　$y = \frac{1}{2}\pi$ when $x = 0$
   (f) $y' = 2x \cos^2 y$
   　　$y = \pi$ when $x = 0$

2. Find the formula for $f(x)$ if $f'(x) = \exp(x + f(x))$ and $f(\ln 3) = \ln \frac{1}{2}$.

3. At each point (x, y) of an arc connecting the points $(-1, 2)$ and $(4, 7)$ the slope is directly proportional to x and inversely proportional to y. What is the equation of the arc?

4. Solve the initial value problem $y' = 3x^2 \sec y$ and $y = \pi$ when $x = 0$.

5. Suppose that f and g are the functions that appear in Initial Value Problem 9-1. Let $G(y) = \int_{y_0}^y g(u)\,du$. Which of our assumptions allows us to assert that G^{-1} exists? Show that $y = G^{-1}\left(\int_{x_0}^x f(v)\,dv\right)$ satisfies Problem 9-1.

6. Make a sketch illustrating Example 9-4. Where is the origin of the number scale? What are the units on the number scale?

7. Let $r(x)$ be the distance between x and the nearest prime number. Find $w(4)$ if w is the solution of the initial value problem $y' = r(x)/y$ and $y = 2$ when $x = 0$. (Hint: Sketch the graph of the equation $z = r(v)$ for v in the interval $[0, 4]$, and perform your integration graphically.)

8. If w is the solution of the inital value problem $y' = x/r(y)$ and $y = 9$ when $x = 0$ (where r is the function defined in the previous exercise), show that $w(2) = 11$. Find $w(1)$. Explain why w is an *even* function; that is, $w(-x) = w(x)$. (Hint: Sketch the graph of the equation $z = r(u)$ in a neighborhood of $u = 9$ and interpret integrals graphically.)

9. Suppose that we start with a colony of 1000 bacteria on an agar plate, and that t minutes later there are y organisms. It seems reasonable to assume that the "birth rate" of the bacteria is proportional to the number present, so there is a number r such that our colony tends to increase at the rate of ry bacteria per minute. On the other hand, members of the colony are constantly dying, and the death rate increases rapidly with the number of bacteria present (overcrowding). Let us suppose that the death rate is proportional to the square of the population. Hence, there is a number s such that bacteria are dying at the rate of sy^2 per minute. Thus, the net increase in population is expressed by the differential equation $y' = ry - sy^2$. Show that $y = 1000r/(1000s + |r - 1000s|e^{-rt})$. How would you go about finding r and s experimentally? What is the limiting population of our agar plate?

10. Write a computer program for printing the values of the solution of the initial value problem $y' = e^{-y}\sqrt{1 + x^3}$ and $y = 2$ when $x = 0$ at the points of the set $\{0, 1, 2, 3, 4, 5\}$.

11. Write a computer program for printing the values of the solution of the initial value problem $y' = \sqrt{1 + x^3}/(5y^4 + 1)$ and $y = 2$ when $x = 0$ at the points of the set $\{0, 1, 2, 3, 4, 5\}$. (This exercise is harder than the preceding one; you may want to use Newton's Method to solve Equation 9-2 for y.)

12. Since $y = \operatorname{Tan} x$ satisfies the initial value problem $y' = 1 + y^2$ and $y = 0$ when $x = 0$, the theory we developed in this section tells us that values of the Tangent function can be obtained by solving the equation

$$\int_0^y \frac{du}{1 + u^2} = x$$

for y. The program in Fig. 9-2 solves this equation, for x in the set $\{0, .1, .2, \ldots, .8\}$, using Newton's Method and evaluating integrals by Simpson's Rule. You might analyze it to see how it works. How could you modify it to obtain a program that prints values of the Sine function?

```
            G(U) = 1/(1 + U*U)
            X = 0
            Y = 0
            Z = 0
            WRITE(6, 1) X, Y
    1       FORMAT(1X, F3.1, F10.4)
            DO 2 I = 1, 8
            DO 3 J = 1, 3
            S = G(Z) + 4*G(.25*Y+.75*Z) + 2*G(.5*Y+.5*Z)+
    1       4*G(.75*Y+.25*Z) + G(Y)
            R = −.1 + ((Y−Z)/12)*S
            Y = Y − R/G(Y)
    3       CONTINUE
            Z = Y
            X = X + .1
            WRITE(6, 1) X, Y
    2       CONTINUE
            STOP
            END
```

Figure 9-2

10   SOLVING PROBLEMS OF THE SECOND ORDER BY FIRST ORDER METHODS. THE EQUATION OF THE PENDULUM

An initial value problem involving a differential equation of the second order has the general form

(10-1)
$$y'' = f(x, y, y')$$
$$y = y_0, \; y' = y_1 \text{ when } x = x_0,$$

where f is a function whose domain is a region in three-dimensional space that contains the point (x_0, y_0, y_1). For example,

(10-2)
$$y'' = -2xy'$$
$$y = 1, \; y' = 2 \text{ when } x = 0$$

is an initial value problem of the second order. In this example, $f(u, v, w) = -2uw$, $y_0 = 1$, $y_1 = 2$, and $x_0 = 0$.

Since we know how to handle only a few special cases of first order problems, it is obvious that we are far from ready for the most general problem of the second order. Only if $f(x, y, y')$ has a particularly simple form can we hope to solve Problem 10-1. However, as we saw in the case of the falling body in Section 7, there are important problems of the second order that are easy to reduce to first order problems.

Problem 10-2 is an example of the simplest such case. In that problem, y does not explicitly appear in $f(x, y, y')$; that is, the problem takes the form

$$y'' = f(x, y')$$

(10-3)

$$y = y_0, y' = y_1 \text{ when } x = x_0.$$

To solve this problem, we set $z = y'$, thus replacing *one* problem of the second order with *two* problems of the first order,

$$z' = f(x, z)$$

$$z = y_1 \text{ when } x = x_0$$

and

$$y' = z$$

$$y = y_0 \text{ when } x = x_0,$$

which we solve successively.

Example 10-1.   Solve Initial Value Problem 10-2.

Solution. We use the substitution $y' = z$ to decompose our given problem of the second order into two problems of the first order:

$$z' = -2xz \text{ and } z = 2 \text{ when } x = 0$$

and

$$y' = z \text{ and } y = 1 \text{ when } x = 0.$$

The first of these new problems is linear, so we multiply the differential equation by e^{x^2} and thus reduce the problem to

$$D_x(e^{x^2}z) = 0 \text{ and } z = 2 \text{ when } x = 0.$$

Hence, $e^{x^2}z = 2$; that is, $z = 2e^{-x^2}$. Now that we know z, the first order problem for y can be written as

$$y' = 2e^{-x^2} \text{ and } y = 1 \text{ when } x = 0,$$

so, finally,

$$y = 1 + \int_0^x 2e^{-u^2}du.$$

We leave it to you and the computer to print a table of values of the function that is defined by this equation.

The second special case of Problem 10-1 that we want to consider in this section has the form

(10-4)
$$y'' = f(y, y')$$
$$y = y_0, y' = y_1 \text{ when } x = x_0.$$

Here, x does not appear explicitly in $f(x, y, y')$. For example, if a is a given number, we might have the problem

(10-5)
$$y'' + a^2 y = 0$$
$$y = 0, y' = a \text{ when } x = 0.$$

In this example, $f(y, y') = -a^2 y$, $y_0 = 0$, and $y_1 = a$.

As in our previous special case of Problem 10-1, the key to solving Problem 10-4 is the substitution $z = y'$. It follows, of course, that $y'' = D_x z$, but now we use the Chain Rule to write $D_x z = D_y z \, D_x y$. Since $D_x y = z$, we have $D_x z = z \, D_y z$ (we used this same trick in Example 9-4). Hence, the differential equation in Problem 10-4 becomes $z \, D_y z = f(y, z)$, and so that problem is reduced to the two problems of the first order

(10-6)
$$D_y z = f(y, z)/z$$
$$z = y_1 \text{ when } y = y_0$$

and

(10-7)
$$D_x y = z$$
$$y = y_0 \text{ when } x = x_0.$$

Now we find the solution w of Problem 10-6 and replace z with $w(y)$ in Problem 10-7. We thus obtain the separable problem $D_x y = w(y)$ and $y = y_0$ when $x = x_0$, and the methods of the previous section apply. So everything really hinges on our ability to solve the first order Problem 10-6.

Example 10-2.   Solve Initial Value Problem 10-5, assuming that a is a given number.

Solution. Here, Problem 10-6 becomes

$$D_y z = -a^2 y/z \text{ and } z = a \text{ when } y = 0,$$

a first order problem with a separable differential equation. Therefore, Theorem 9-1 applies; we solve our problem by solving the equation

$$\int_a^z u\,du = -a^2 \int_0^y v\,dv$$

for z. But this equation is simply $\frac{1}{2}z^2 - \frac{1}{2}a^2 = -\frac{1}{2}a^2y^2$. Since $z = a$ when $y = 0$, we have $z = a\sqrt{1 - y^2}$, and Problem 10-7 becomes

$$D_x y = a\sqrt{1 - y^2} \text{ and } y = 0 \text{ when } x = 0.$$

Again Theorem 9-1 applies; we solve this problem by solving the equation

$$\int_0^y \frac{du}{\sqrt{1 - u^2}} = a \int_0^x dv$$

for y. Since this last equation is simply $\text{Sin}^{-1} y = ax$, we finally see that

$$y = \sin ax$$

satisfies Problem 10-5.

   We close this section by considering a physical problem that leads to an initial value problem of the type we have been discussing. This example is such a good one that we will be referring to it again in Section 25 and in Section 28. Specifically, we will derive the initial value problem whose solution describes the motion of a pendulum.

   Figure 10-1 shows a pendulum that consists of a bob having a mass of m kilograms attached to a pivot point O by a "weightless" arm r meters long. We will suppose that t seconds after we start measuring time, the arm makes an angle of θ radians with the vertical, as shown. The differential equation of motion will simply be Newton's Second Law, force = mass × acceleration.

   Since the number $r\theta$ measures arclength, the number $D_t^2(r\theta) = r\theta''$ is the (tangential) acceleration of the bob. We will assume that the only forces acting are the force of gravity and a force due to air resistance that is proportional to the velocity of the bob. The gravitational force is mg newtons acting downward, and its component in the direction of motion is therefore $-mg \sin \theta$ (see Fig. 10-1). Since the (tangential) velocity of the bob is $D_t(r\theta) = r\theta'$, the assumption that air resistance is proportional to velocity amounts to saying that there is a number k such that the force of air resistance is $-rk\theta'$ newtons. The resultant (tangential) force acting on the bob is therefore $-rk\theta' - mg \sin \theta$, and so the equation force = mass × acceleration becomes $-rk\theta' - mg \sin \theta = mr\theta''$. Thus, the initial value problem that describes the motion of the pendulum is

(10-8)
$$\theta'' + \frac{k}{m} \theta' + \frac{g}{r} \sin \theta = 0$$

$$\theta = \theta_0, \ \theta' = \theta_1 \text{ when } t = 0,$$

where θ_0 (in radians) is the initial angular displacement, and θ_1 (in radians per

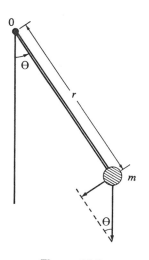

Figure 10-1

second) is the initial angular velocity of the pendulum. In the units we are using, the gravitation constant g is approximately 9.8.

Problem 10-8 has the form of Problem 10-4, so our theory tells us that we can try to solve it by replacing it with two problems of the first order. Here, θ plays the role of y, and $f(\theta, \theta') = -\dfrac{k}{m} \theta' - \dfrac{g}{r} \sin \theta$. Therefore, our two initial value problems of the first order are

(10-9) $D_\theta z = -\dfrac{k}{m} - \dfrac{g}{r} \dfrac{\sin \theta}{z}$ and $z = \theta_1$ when $\theta = \theta_0$

and

(10-10) $D_t \theta = z$ and $\theta = \theta_0$ when $t = 0$.

The first of these problems does not yield to any of the techniques we now know, so we either have to develop new solution methods (numerical methods, for instance) or make further simplifying assumptions. For example, if we assume that $k = 0$ (no air resistance), the differential equation in Problem 10-9 becomes separable. Another trick we will introduce later is to assume that our oscillations have a small amplitude, so that $\sin \theta \approx \theta$. Then we replace $\sin \theta$ with θ in Problem 10-9, or directly in Problem 10-8, and thus obtain a differential equation we can handle. As we will see, the simple pendulum is the source of many interesting problems in differential equations.

EXERCISE 10

1. Solve the following initial value problems.
   (a) $y'' + 2y' = 8x$
       $y = 2, y' = 0$ when $x = 0$
   (b) $y'' = 4yy'$
       $y = 1, y' = -6$ when $x = 0$
   (c) $y'' = 1 + y'^2$
       $y = 2, y' = 0$ when $x = \pi$
   (d) $y'' - y'^2 = 0$
       $y = 2, y' = -3$ when $x = 0$

2. Solve the following initial value problems.
   (a) $D_x^2 y = (D_x y)^2$
       $y = 0, D_x y = 2$ when $x = 0$
   (b) $D_x^2 y = D_x y^2$
       $y = 2, D_x y = 8$ when $x = 0$

3. Find a function f such that $f(0) = p$ and $f'(0) = q$, where p and q are arbitrary numbers (with $p \neq 0$) and such that

$$\begin{vmatrix} f(x) & f'(x) \\ f'(x) & f''(x) \end{vmatrix} = 0.$$

4. In Example 10-1, we found an equation that defines the solution of Problem 10-2 in terms of an integral. Write a computer program for printing a table of values of this solution.

5. The initial value problem $y'' - y' = 3$ and $y = 1, y' = 0$ when $x = 0$, has the form of Problem 10-3 and also of Problem 10-4. Which method of solution is easier?

6. In Example 10-2, we found that $y = \sin ax$ satisfies the initial value problem $y'' + a^2 y = 0$ and $y = 0, y' = a$ when $x = 0$. Show that $y = (b/a) \sin ax$ satisfies the initial value problem we get by changing the initial condition $y' = a$ to $y' = b$, where b is an arbitrary given number. Solve the initial value problem $y'' + 9y = 0$ and $y = 0, y' = 5$ when $x = 0$.

7. In Example 10-2, we found that $y = \sin ax$ is one solution of the differential equation $y'' + a^2 y = 0$. Solve the initial value problem $y'' + a^2 y = 0$ and $y = 0, y' = a$ when $x = -\pi/2a$ and hence find that $y = \cos ax$ is another solution of this differential equation.

8. Solve the initial value problem that consists of the differential equation $y'' - y = 0$ and the following initial conditions.
   (a) $y = 1, y' = 1$ when $x = 0$
   (b) $y = 1, y' = -1$ when $x = 0$

9. Suppose that the pendulum we discussed in this section is ticking away in a vacuum, so that $k = 0$. Furthermore, suppose that $\theta_0 = 0$ and θ_1 is a small positive number; that is, we start the pendulum in the "bob down" position and give it a little shove to the right. Show that the angular displacement θ satisfies the initial value problem

$$\theta' = \sqrt{\theta_1^2 + \frac{2g}{r}(\cos \theta - 1)} \text{ and } \theta = 0 \text{ when } t = 0,$$

and tell how you would go about solving this problem. What is the amplitude of the oscillation? Can you figure out a method for finding the period of this pendulum? How could we use the computer to help us?

REVIEW EXERCISE, CHAPTER 2

Use the following exercises to test yourself on the material in this chapter.

1. What is the linear differential equation of the first order that is satisfied by $y = e^x$ and $y = \sin x$?

2. Show that if u and v are solutions of the "homogeneous" linear differential equation $y' = p(x)y$, then $y = u(x) + v(x)$ also satisfies this equation, but that $y = u(x)v(x)$ satisfies the linear differential equation $y' = 2p(x)y$.

3. Find *two* solutions u and v of the initial value problem

$$y'^2 - 4x^2y^2 = 0 \text{ and } y = 1 \text{ when } x = 0.$$

4. A certain arc contains the point $(0, 0)$, and at each point its slope is the average of its X- and Y-coordinates. What is its equation?

5. (a) Show that the initial value problem $y'' = f(x)$ and $y = y_0$, $y' = y_1$ when $x = x_0$ is satisfied by $y = y_0 + y_1(x - x_0) + \int_{x_0}^{x} (x - u)f(u)du$.
   (b) Use the computer to make a table of values of the solution of the problem $y'' = \sqrt{1 + x^3}$ and $y = 3$, $y' = 4$ when $x = 0$ at the points of the set $\{0.0, .1, .2, \ldots, 1.0\}$.

6. (a) Use the substitution $z = y/x$ and solve the initial value problem

$$y' = (x^2 + y^2)/2xy \text{ and } y = 2 \text{ when } x = 1.$$

   (b) Change the initial conditions to $y = \frac{1}{2}$ when $x = 1$, and solve the problem.

7. (a) Solve the initial value problem $y' = \exp(y^2 - x^2)$ and $y = 2$ when $x = 2$.
   (b) Can you show that if w is the solution of the initial value problem $y' = \exp(y^2 - x^2)$ and $y = 4$ when $x = 2$, then $w(x) > x$ for each x? $\left(\text{Hint: Show that } \int_{x}^{w(x)} e^{-u^2}du = \int_{2}^{4} e^{-u^2}du.\right)$

8. Solve the initial value problem $y' = |y| + 1$ and $y = 0$ when $x = 0$.

9. By making the substitution $z = x + y$, show how to solve the initial value problem $y' = f(x + y)$ and $y = y_0$ when $x = x_0$.

10. (a) Explain why the point $(0, 2)$ is a local minimum point of the solution curve of the initial value problem $y' = \sin(xy)$ and $y = 2$ when $x = 0$.
    (b) If w is the solution of the problem of part (a), what is $w''(0)$?

CHAPTER 3

INITIAL VALUE PROBLEMS

OF THE FIRST ORDER

Now that we are familiar with a few particular initial value problems, we can start looking at initial value problems of the first order in general. A good deal of this chapter is on the theoretical side, but its message can be put quite simply. Any "reasonable" initial value problem *has* a solution, it has only one solution, and one can program a computer to rattle off tables of values of this solution. Furthermore, it is possible to read from an initial value problem (without explicitly solving it) many properties of its solution. For example, we may be able to infer that the solution is an increasing or a decreasing function, that its graph is concave upward or downward, that it is an even or an odd function, and so on. As we will

63

see later, much of what we learn here about initial value problems of the first order also applies to initial value problems of higher order.

11   DIFFERENTIAL EQUATIONS

Our initial value problems consist of a **differential equation**

(11-1) $$y' = f(x, y)$$

plus an **initial condition**

(11-2) $$y = y_0 \text{ when } x = x_0.$$

Differential Equation 11-1 is a differential equation of the *first order*, because it contains only the first derivative of y. Later, we will discuss differential equations of the second, and higher, orders. In this section, we are going to look briefly at Equation 11-1 alone, without an accompanying initial condition.

We suppose that the given function f is defined in some domain D of the XY-plane. By a **solution** of Equation 11-1, we mean, of course, a differentiable function w such that $y = w(x)$ satisfies the equation. Thus, the domain of w should be an interval I such that for each $x \in I$, the point $(x, w(x))$ belongs to D, and $w'(x) = f(x, w(x))$. Figure 11-1 shows the graph of a solution; we will call such a graph a **solution curve.**

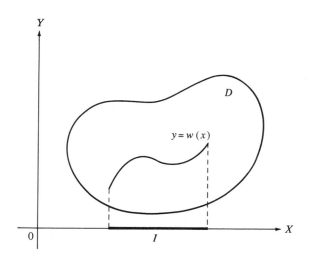

Figure 11-1

Example 11-1. What do we mean when we say that the equation $w(x) = \sqrt{4 - x^2}$ determines a solution w of the differential equation $y' = -x/y$?

Solution. Technically, our statement of the differential equation is incomplete. Clearly, $f(x, y) = -x/y$, but a complete statement would also include the specification of the domain D in which we are working. We naturally assume that D consists only of points for which the formula $f(x, y) = -x/y$ makes sense. Therefore, since we must refrain from dividing by 0, our domain D cannot contain points of the X-axis. Deleting the X-axis divides the XY-plane into two connected sets, the upper and lower half-planes. Since our solution function w does not take negative values, we can eliminate the lower half-plane from consideration and assume that D is the upper half-plane; that is, that $D = \{(x, y): y > 0\}$.

According to the usual conventions, the equation $w(x) = \sqrt{4 - x^2}$ defines a function whose domain is the closed interval $[-2, 2]$. But it is not true that each point of the graph of this function belongs to D (the points $(-2, 0)$ and $(2, 0)$ do not). So we might take as the domain of the solution w the open interval $I = (-2, 2)$. With this choice of domain, the graph of w *is* a subset of D (see Fig. 11-2),

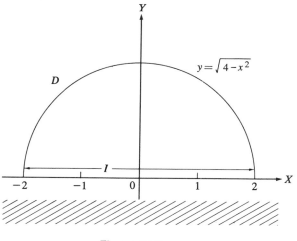

Figure 11-2

and it is a matter of simple calculation to show that for each $x \in I$, $w'(x) = D_x \sqrt{4 - x^2} = -x/\sqrt{4 - x^2} = -x/w(x)$.

Other choices of D and I are possible. For example, we could choose the same D and take I to be the interval $[-1, 1]$, and we would have a well-defined solution of a well-defined differential equation. In this case, our solution curve would be a subset of the solution curve we discussed in the last paragraph. It is more natural (and usually more useful) to take D and I to be as large as possible. It would be ridiculous, in this first course, to discuss such fine points every time we talk about a differential equation. Nevertheless, they are part of every problem in differential equations, whether we say so explicitly or not.

Now we will interpret Equation 11-1 geometrically. To say that f is defined in D means that to each point $(x, y) \in D$ a number $f(x, y)$ is assigned. Thus, the equation $f(x, y) = -x/y$ assigns to the point $(1, 3)$ the number $-\frac{1}{3}$. In Equation 11-1, we have equated the numbers $f(x, y)$ and y'. Since y' is a slope, we are therefore to think of the number $f(x, y)$ that is assigned to the point (x, y) as representing a slope. So let us, at each point (x, y) of D, consider a short segment with a slope of $f(x, y)$, as shown in Fig. 11-3. Equation 11-1

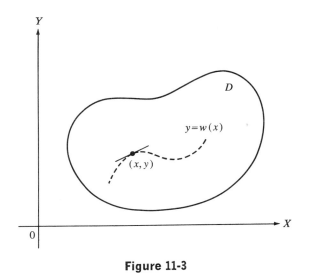

Figure 11-3

simply says that at the point (x, y) the graph of a solution is tangent to this segment. Thus, if we plot a number of these *direction segments*, we will have a number of tangents to solution curves, from which we can infer something about the solutions of the differential equation.

Example 11-2. By plotting a number of direction segments, discuss the behavior of solutions of the differential equation $y' = x + y$.

Solution. Figure 11-4 shows some short direction segments, the segment at a point (x, y) having the slope $x + y$. We have sketched in a few of the solution curves that the figure suggests. Notice that some of the direction segments "line up" and form the line $y = -x - 1$, which tells us that $y = -x - 1$ satisfies our differential equation. You can check and see that, in fact, it does.

The preceding discussion suggests that a typical differential equation has a whole "family" of solution curves, every point of D belonging to a member of the family. When we discuss "existence" and "uniqueness" in Sections 12

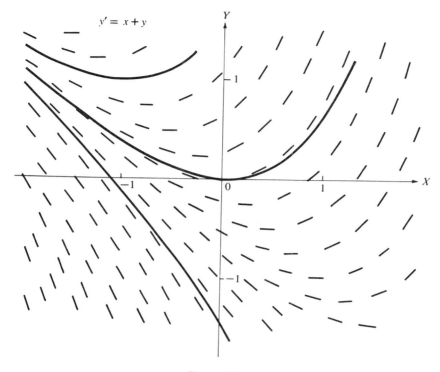

Figure 11-4

and 14, we will see that this statement is correct (if f is a reasonably well-behaved function, anyway). So let us talk about families of curves for a moment. We say, for example, that the equation $x^2 + y^2 = c$ *represents* the family of circles whose center is the origin. That is, we obtain the members of this family by replacing c with various positive numbers. Similarly, the equation $y = cx$ represents the family of lines that contain the origin, and so on.

More generally, let G be a function whose domain is a set of points in the XY-plane (for example, $G(x, y) = x^2 + y^2$). Then for each number c in the range of G, the graph of the equation

(11-3) $G(x, y) = c$

will, at least in the "usual" cases that we consider, be a curve in the plane. We will say that Equation 11-3 **represents** the family of curves that we obtain in this way.

Example 11-3. Discuss the family of curves that is represented by the equation

$$\frac{x^2 + y^2}{2x} = c.$$

Solution. This example illustrates a number of points, one of which is that Equation 11-3 is not always the neatest representation of a given family. It would be preferable, for example, to write the equation of our present family as $x^2 + y^2 = 2cx$. In the form of Equation 11-3, we run into trouble when $x = 0$. We will not get sidetracked into such discussions, however, but will try to keep our eyes focused on the main issue.

We can write the equation $x^2 + y^2 = 2cx$ as

$$(x - c)^2 + y^2 = c^2,$$

and in this form we see that we are dealing with circles of radius $|c|$ and center $(c, 0)$. Figure 11-5 shows some members of this family.

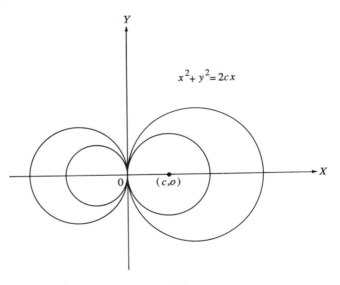

Figure 11-5

Two questions about families of curves arise in connection with differential equations:

(1) Given a differential equation, what is its family of solution curves?
(2) Given a family of curves, what differential equation is satisfied by its members?

Question (2) is easy to answer, and Question (1) is difficult, so we will start with Question (2).

Suppose that w is a differentiable function whose graph in some interval I belongs to the family of curves represented by Equation 11-3; that is,

$$G(x, w(x)) = c \text{ for each } x \in I.$$

We differentiate both sides of this equation with respect to x, and thus $D_x G(x, w(x)) = D_x c = 0$. According to the Chain Rule, $D_x G(x, w(x)) = G_1(x, w(x)) + G_2(x, w(x))w'(x)$, where G_1 and G_2 are the first derived functions of G $\left(\text{that is, } G_1(x, y) = \dfrac{\partial G(x, y)}{\partial x} \text{ and } G_2(x, y) = \dfrac{\partial G(x, y)}{\partial y}\right)$. Therefore, assuming that G_2 does not take the value 0 for points of the graph of w, the equation $D_x G(x, w(x)) = 0$ can be written as $w'(x) = -G_1(x, w(x))/G_2(x, w(x))$. In other words, w is a solution of the differential equation

(11-4)
$$y' = -\frac{G_1(x, y)}{G_2(x, y)}.$$

We say that Equation 11-4 is *the differential equation of the family* represented by Equation 11-3.

Example 11-4. What is the differential equation of the family of Example 11-3?

Solution. Here, $G(x, y) = (x^2 + y^2)/2x$, and so

$$G_1(x, y) = \frac{\partial}{\partial x}[(x^2 + y^2)/2x] = (x^2 - y^2)/2x^2$$

and

$$G_2(x, y) = \frac{\partial}{\partial y}[(x^2 + y^2)/2x] = y/x.$$

Therefore, according to Equation 11-4, the differential equation of the family of circles illustrated in Fig. 11-5 is

$$y' = -(x^2 - y^2)/2xy.$$

Notice that this equation does yield an "infinite slope" when $y = 0$, as Fig. 11-5 suggests that it should.

Our rule for finding the differential Equation 11-4 of the family represented by Equation 11-3 can be phrased as follows: *Differentiate both sides of Equation 11-3 with respect to x, and solve for y'.* Sometimes we can work this rule backwards, and hence solve a given differential equation. It used to be that students spent considerable time and effort learning to use this technique to answer our Question (1). It takes a lot of practice to become good at it, and at best it is a method of dubious general utility.

Example 11-5. Find the family of curves whose differential equation is $y' = -y/x$.

Solution. If we write this equation as $xy' + y = 0$, we see that the left-hand side is $D_x(xy)$, because $D_x(xy) = xD_xy + (D_xx)y$. So our given differential equation is equivalent to $D_x(xy) = D_xc$, from which we infer that the equation $xy = c$ represents the family of solution curves of the differential equation.

We are not going to spend much time on either Question (1) or Question (2). It is easier, both from a theoretical and from a practical point of view, to discuss individual solutions of a differential equation rather than whole families of solutions. Therefore, we will spend practically all of our time on *initial value problems*, where we use an initial condition to select in advance one particular solution of the given differential equation. Such problems are the ones that arise in practice, anyway. In applications, we want just *one* solution of the differential equation, not all possible ones.

Nevertheless, one is well on his way to solving an initial value problem if he *can* answer Question (1); that is, if he can find the family of solutions of its differential equation. For it is usually quite easy to find the particular member of the solution family that satisfies the given initial condition. This method for solving initial value problems—finding a family of solutions and then selecting the desired individual member—was the standard one in past years. It is especially suitable for very simple differential equations, but it is totally unsuitable for use with a digital computer.

Example 11-6. Solve the initial value problem

$$y' = -(x^2 - y^2)/2xy \text{ and } y = 5 \text{ when } x = 2.$$

Solution. From Example 11-4, we see that the family of solution curves of our differential equation is represented by the equation $x^2 + y^2 = 2cx$. To find the member of this family that contains the given initial point $(2, 5)$, we must pick c so that the coordinates $(2, 5)$ satisfy the equation $x^2 + y^2 = 2cx$. Hence, we simply replace x with 2, y with 5, and solve for c:

$$4 + 25 = 4c,$$

$$c = \tfrac{29}{4}.$$

The equation of the desired solution is therefore $x^2 + y^2 = \tfrac{29}{2}x$, and so $y = \sqrt{\tfrac{29}{2}x - x^2}$ satisfies the given initial value problem.

Now we will touch briefly on one more interesting feature of families of curves. The family of curves that meets each member of a given family at right angles is called the family of **orthogonal trajectories** of the original family.

In Fig. 11-6, for example, we have sketched the family of equilateral hyperbolas that is represented by the equation

(11-5)
$$x^2 - y^2 = c$$

as solid curves and its family of orthogonal trajectories as dashed curves. Physically, a given family might represent equipotential curves, and then the orthogonal trajectories would be lines of flow. There is no need for us to go into the general theory of orthogonal trajectories, for an example will tell us everything we need to know about them.

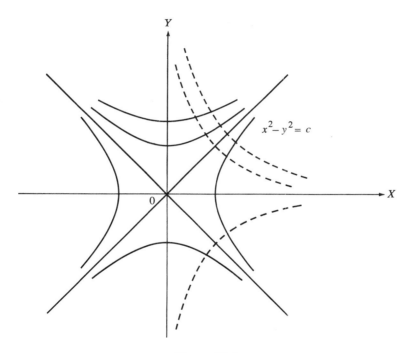

Figure 11-6

Example 11-7. Find the equation that represents the orthogonal trajectories of the family of hyperbolas represented by Equation 11-5.

Solution. We first find the differential equation of the family of hyperbolas by differentiating both sides of Equation 11-5 and solving for y':

$$2x - 2yy' = 0,$$

(11-6)
$$y' = x/y.$$

The orthogonal trajectories are perpendicular to the hyperbolas, so their slopes are the negative reciprocals of the slopes of the hyperbolas. In symbols, this statement (and Equation 11-6) states that the orthogonal trajectory that contains (x, y) has at that point a slope of $-1/(x/y) = -y/x$. Hence, the differential equation of the orthogonal trajectories is

$$y' = -y/x.$$

In Example 11-5, we found that the family of solution curves of this differential equation is represented by the equation

$$xy = c,$$

which is, therefore, the equation we are seeking. In terms of Fig. 11-6, does this answer look reasonable?

This section on differential equations, families of curves, and so on, has been quite brief. In fact, perhaps it is so brief as to be misleading. All of this material, in particular, the logic by which one "goes backward" from Equation 11-4 to Equation 11-3, can be put on a perfectly sound mathematical basis, but it requires both care and time to do so. For a fuller treatment, you are referred to almost any other book on elementary differential equations. Reference [1] has an especially good discussion. As an indication of its true place in the theory of differential equations, however, you will find that it is not even mentioned in advanced books on the subject, such as the standard text [6].

EXERCISE 11

1. The equation $w(x) = mx + b$ defines a *linear function* w. Find a linear solution of the differential equation $y' = 3x + 4y$. How many linear solutions does this equation have? (Hint: What does it mean when we say that $y = mx + b$ satisfies the differential equation?)

2. Sketch a collection of direction segments for each of the following differential equations.
   (a) $y' = y^{1/3}$ (c) $y' = y/x$
   (b) $y' = x^{1/3}$ (d) $y' = y + |y|$

3. In what ways, if any, do the families of curves represented by the following equations differ?
   (a) $xy = c$ (c) $\ln xy = c$
   (b) $e^{xy} = c$ (d) $\sin(xy) = c$

4. Find the differential equations of the following families of curves.
   (a) $y = cx$ (c) $e^{x^2}y = c$
   (b) $x^2 + y^2 = c$ (d) $\int_2^y \sqrt{1 + u^3}\, du + \int_0^x e^{-v^2} dv = c.$

5. For an arbitrary initial point (x_0, y_0), find the solution curve of the differential equation $y' = -x/y$ that contains (x_0, y_0). Use this result to find an equation

that represents the family of solution curves of this differential equation. What are the orthogonal trajectories of this family? Draw some graphs that illustrate this problem.

6. For an arbitrary initial point (x_0, y_0), find the solution curve of the differential equation $y' = x + y$ that contains the point (x_0, y_0). Use this result to find an equation that represents the family of solution curves of this differential equation. What is the differential equation of the orthogonal trajectories of this family? Can you solve it?

7. Show that the differential equation of the orthogonal trajectories of the family of curves represented by the equation $G(x, y) = c$ is $y' = G_2(x, y)/G_1(x, y)$.

8. What is the differential equation of the family of orthogonal trajectories of the family of orthogonal trajectories of the family of curves represented by the equation $G(x, y) = c$?

9. In Example 11-5, we found the family of solution curves of the differential equation in the initial value problem $y' = -y/x$ and $y = 3$ when $x = 2$. Use this information to solve the problem.

10. Notice that the solution curve of the following initial value problem must lie in the first and third quadrants (which will enable you to take care of the absolute value signs), and then solve it: $y' = |x| + |y|$ and $y = 0$ when $x = 0$.

11. Describe geometrically the family of curves that is represented by the equation $\dfrac{x^2}{4} + y^2 = c$. What is the differential equation of this family? What is the differential equation of the family of orthogonal trajectories? Show that if we multiply both sides of this (linear) differential equation by $\exp\left(-\int_1^x \dfrac{4}{v}\,dv\right)$, it becomes $D_x(x^{-4}y) = 0$. What, therefore, is an equation that represents the orthogonal trajectories of our given family?

12. Sketch some members of the family represented by the equation $y^2 - \cos x = c$. Find the differential equation of the family of orthogonal trajectories. Show that if both sides of this (linear) differential equation are multiplied by $\exp\left(\int_{\frac{1}{2}\pi}^x \dfrac{2}{\sin v}\,dv\right)$, it becomes $D_x[(\csc x - \cot x)^2 y] = 0$. Hence, find an equation that represents the family of orthogonal trajectories.

12   INITIAL VALUE PROBLEMS OF THE FIRST ORDER. EXISTENCE OF SOLUTIONS

An **initial value problem** of the first order consists of a differential equation of the first order *plus* an initial condition. Thus, suppose that D is a plane domain (as shown in Fig. 12-1) that contains a point (x_0, y_0), and

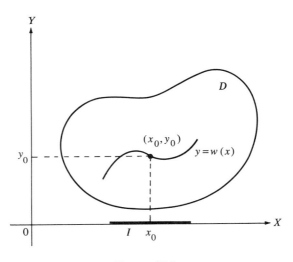

Figure 12-1

let f be a function whose domain is D. We will study the initial value problem

(12-1)
$$y' = f(x, y)$$
$$y = y_0 \text{ when } x = x_0.$$

A solution of Problem 12-1 is a solution w of the differential equation $y' = f(x, y)$, one whose domain is an interval I that contains x_0 and for which $w(x_0) = y_0$. In other words, $y = w(x)$ satisfies the differential equation *and* the initial condition. Notice that the problem of finding a solution w includes the problem of finding its domain, since the domain is an essential part of a function.

Naturally, the first question we ask is, "Does a given initial value problem *have* a solution?" The answer is yes, if f is a reasonable function. In particular, if f is continuous in D, Problem 12-1 has a solution. This answer is easy to state but rather tedious to prove. Therefore, we will only outline the ideas of a proof. To specify the solution function w, we must find an interval I to serve as its domain and supply a rule that assigns to each point $x \in I$ a number $w(x)$. We stated earlier that important numbers in mathematical analysis are limits, so now we will set up a sequence $\{w_n(x)\}$ of numbers, of which $w(x)$ is a limit.

Logically, we should first choose our basic interval I, but it will be easier to explain how we find it *after* we have constructed our approximating sequence. So let us simply assume that we are working in an interval $I = [a, b]$, where a and b are numbers to be determined later. Our construction is based on some ideas that we introduced in the last section. With (x_0, y_0) as the left endpoint, draw a short direction segment of slope $f(x_0, y_0)$. Now use the other endpoint

(x_1, y_1) of this segment as the left endpoint of a new direction segment with a slope of $f(x_1, y_1)$. The right endpoint (x_2, y_2) of this direction segment is now to serve as the left endpoint of a new direction segment with slope $f(x_2, y_2)$, and so on. This process produces the polygonal path shown in Fig. 12-2, and we could do the same thing to get a polygonal path to the left of the initial point (x_0, y_0). The hope, of course, is that by taking shorter and shorter direction segments, the resulting polygonal paths will converge to a solution curve.

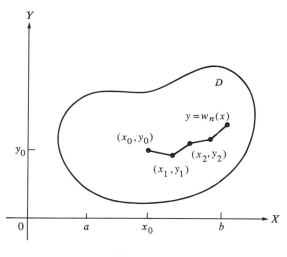

Figure 12-2

Let us formalize this procedure. As illustrated in Fig. 12-2, we will set up our sequence $\{w_n\}$ of approximating functions only in the interval $[x_0, b]$; it will be obvious how to extend the construction to the left in the interval $[a, x_0]$. So suppose that n is a positive integer. Let $h = (b - x_0)/n$, and divide the interval $[x_0, b]$ into n subintervals, each h units long, by means of the points $x_1 = x_0 + h, \; x_2 = x_0 + 2h, \; \ldots, \; x_n = x_0 + nh = b$. With each of these X-coordinates, we want to associate a Y-coordinate so as to obtain a sequence of points $\{(x_k, y_k)\}$ such that if we join successive points we have a set of direction segments. Therefore, we choose these Y-coordinates so that for each index k, the slope of the segment joining the successive points (x_k, y_k) and (x_{k+1}, y_{k+1}) is $f(x_k, y_k)$. In symbols, this last statement is the equation

$$\frac{y_{k+1} - y_k}{x_{k+1} - x_k} = f(x_k, y_k).$$

Since $x_{k+1} - x_k = h$, we therefore see that the members of the sequence $\{(x_k, y_k)\}$

are determined by the recursion formulas

(12-2)
$$x_{k+1} = x_k + h$$
$$y_{k+1} = y_k + hf(x_k, y_k), \qquad k = 0, 1, 2, \ldots, n - 1.$$

The "broken line curves" that join successive points are called **Euler-Cauchy** polygonal approximations. For each positive integer n, we define w_n as the function whose graph is the nth polygonal approximation (Fig. 12-2). It was our hope that the sequence $\{w_n\}$ would converge to a function w that is a solution of Initial Value Problem 12-1, but it need not work out quite that way. If f is merely assumed to be continuous, we can only prove (see Reference [**6**, p. 6]) that there is a *subsequence* of $\{w_n\}$ that converges to a solution w. However, this proof establishes the *existence* of a solution, so we have the following existence theorem.

THEOREM 12-1

If f is continuous in D, then Initial Value Problem 12-1 has a solution.

Actually, in any practical case, the entire sequence $\{w_n\}$, not just a subsequence, does converge to a solution. In Section 14, we will discuss the uniqueness of the solution of Problem 12-1. It can be shown that if Problem 12-1 has just one solution, then the sequence $\{w_n\}$ of Euler-Cauchy polygonal approximations converges to it.

Example 12-1. Let b be any number, and show how the values at b of the Euler-Cauchy approximations converge to $w(b)$, where w is the solution of the initial value problem $y' = y$ and $y = 1$ when $x = 0$.

Solution. In this example, we have $x_0 = 0$, $y_0 = 1$, and $f(x, y) = y$. We are asked to show that $\lim_{n \uparrow \infty} w_n(b) = w(b)$. For each index n, the point $(b, w_n(b))$ is the last vertex of the Euler-Cauchy polygon that is based on the interval from 0 to b. In other words, $w_n(b) = y_n$, and so we are to calculate $\lim_{n \uparrow \infty} y_n$.

Because $f(x_k, y_k) = y_k$ here, the second of Equations 12-2 reduces to

$$y_{k+1} = y_k + hy_k = (1 + h)y_k,$$

where $h = (b - 0)/n = b/n$. Therefore,

$$y_1 = (1 + h)y_0 = (1 + h) \cdot 1 = 1 + h,$$
$$y_2 = (1 + h)y_1 = (1 + h)^2,$$

and so on. Clearly, then,

$$y_n = (1 + h)^n = \left(1 + \frac{b}{n}\right)^n,$$

and so

$$\lim_{n \uparrow \infty} y_n = \lim_{n \uparrow \infty} \left(1 + \frac{b}{n}\right)^n = e^b.$$

(You will find this last limit evaluated in your calculus book, if you have forgotten it.) We now notice that this limit *is* the solution value $w(b)$, because $y = e^x$ satisfies our given linear initial value problem.

In Example 12-1, we studied a case in which $f(x, y)$ was independent of x. Things are even simpler if $f(x, y)$ is independent of y.

Example 12-2.   Let f be a function that is continuous in the interval $[a, b]$ and discuss the convergence of the Euler-Cauchy approximations to $w(b)$, where w is the solution of the initial value problem

$$y' = f(x) \text{ and } y = 0 \text{ when } x = a.$$

Solution. From Theorem 7-1, we know that the solution w of this initial value problem is defined by the equation $w(x) = 0 + \int_a^x f(t)dt$. Hence,

$$w(b) = \int_a^b f(t)dt.$$

Now let us verify that the Euler-Cauchy method yields this same result.
   We first choose an integer n and divide the interval $[a, b]$ into n parts, each $h = (b - a)/n$ units long. Then we compute our X-values, $x_1 = a + h$, $x_2 = a + 2h$, and so on. Next we calculate

$$y_1 = y_0 + hf(x_0) = hf(x_0),$$
$$y_2 = y_1 + hf(x_1) = hf(x_0) + hf(x_1),$$
$$y_3 = y_2 + hf(x_2) = hf(x_0) + hf(x_1) + hf(x_2),$$

and so on. It is clear that

$$y_n = hf(x_0) + hf(x_1) + \cdots + hf(x_n).$$

The right-hand side of this equation is simply the right-hand side of the Rectangle Rule Formula 5-2 for approximating the integral $\int_a^b f(x)dx$, and so we see that $\lim_{n \uparrow \infty} y_n = \int_a^b f(x)dx = w(b)$, as we expected.

What this example shows is that the Euler-Cauchy approximation method is a generalization to differential equations of the Rectangle Rule of numerical integration.

Now we come back to the question of the domain of the solution that we construct as a limit of Euler-Cauchy polygons. In how large an interval $[a, b]$ can we assert that a subsequence of $\{w_n\}$ converges to a solution w? About all we can say in answer to this question is that there is convergence if the interval $[a, b]$ is "short enough." Roughly speaking, we have got to insure that there is a closed and bounded subset of D that contains all of our polygonal approximations, and we can insure that there is as follows.

Since f is continuous in D, there is a neighborhood of the point (x_0, y_0) in which f is bounded; that is, there is a number M such that $|f(x, y)| \leq M$ for each point (x, y) in the neighborhood. Now we construct a rectangle whose center is the point (x_0, y_0), which lies entirely in D and in which $|f(x, y)|$ is bounded by M, whose base is an interval $I = [a, b]$ of the X-axis, and whose altitude is $M(b - a)$ units long (Fig. 12-3). We may have to take a and b quite

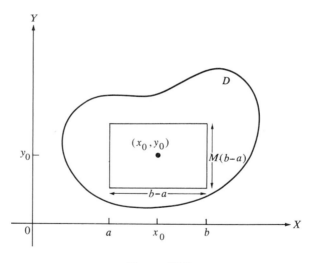

Figure 12-3

close to x_0 to fit this rectangle into D, but we can surely do it, and in this way we obtain the basic interval $[a, b]$ which forms the domain of the functions in the approximating sequence $\{w_n\}$. It is easy to show (and we leave it to you in Exercise 12-6) that, since $|f(x, y)| \leq M$ for each point of the rectangle we have just constructed, each polygonal approximation also lies in this rectangle, from which it follows that our solution curve does. What we show when we prove Theorem 12-1 is that Problem 12-1 has a solution "in the small"; that is, there is a neighborhood of the initial point (x_0, y_0) in which a solution curve exists. The question of how large we can take this neighborhood to be is obviously important, is quite difficult to answer, and is one that we will say a little more about later.

Finally, it is frequently useful to write Initial Value Problem 12-1 as the equivalent **integral equation**

$$(12\text{-}3) \qquad\qquad w(x) = y_0 + \int_{x_0}^{x} f(t, w(t))dt.$$

What we mean by the equivalence of our initial value problem and our integral equation is explained in the following theorem.

THEOREM 12-2

Suppose that f is continuous. Then a continuous function w is a solution of Equation 12-3 in an interval I if, and only if, it is a solution of Problem 12-1 in I.

Proof. If $y = w(x)$ satisfies Problem 12-1, then $w'(t) = f(t, w(t))$ for each $t \in I$, and $w(x_0) = y_0$. Thus, if x is any point of I, then

$$\int_{x_0}^{x} w'(t)dt = \int_{x_0}^{x} f(t, w(t))dt.$$

Since $\int_{x_0}^{x} w'(t)dt = w(x) - w(x_0) = w(x) - y_0$, Equation 12-3 holds. Conversely, if Equation 12-3 holds, then surely $w(x_0) = y_0$. Also,

$$w'(x) = D_x \int_{x_0}^{x} f(t, w(t))dt = f(x, w(x)),$$

so $y = w(x)$ satisfies the differential equation $y' = f(x, y)$, and our proof is complete.

Theorem 12-2 suggests that the way to solve an integral equation like Equation 12-3 is to differentiate it and then use the techniques of differential equations.

Example 12-3. Find the equation of the curve formed by a chain hanging from two pegs.

Solution. Figure 12-4 shows our chain, with the pegs at points P and Q. We have located the coordinate axes so that $(0, 0)$ is the low point of the chain. The chain forms the graph of an equation $y = f(x)$; our goal is to find the formula for $f(x)$. So we pick a point x and look at the segment $S(x)$ that we have illustrated.

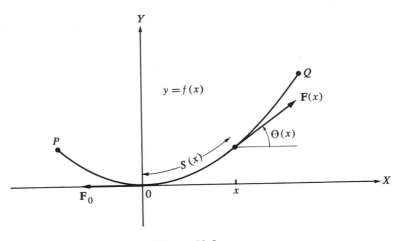

Figure 12-4

Two forces, F_0 and $F(x)$ (acting tangentially, since the chain is flexible), hold $S(x)$ in equilibrium. The horizontal component, $|F(x)| \cos \theta(x)$, of $F(x)$ balances the horizontal force of magnitude $|F_0|$, and the vertical component, $|F(x)| \sin \theta(x)$, balances the weight of the segment. Here, $\theta(x)$ is the angle of inclination of the tangential force vector $F(x)$ with the positive X-axis. So, if we write $h = |F_0|$ for short, we have

$$(12\text{-}4) \qquad\qquad |F(x)| \cos \theta(x) = h$$

as the equation expressing the balance of horizontal forces. The weight of $S(x)$ is the product of its weight per unit length, which we will assume is w newtons per meter, and its length. We know (see your calculus book if you have to) that $S(x)$ is

$$\int_0^x \sqrt{1 + f'(t)^2}\, dt$$

meters long, so when we multiply these numbers and equate the result to the vertical component of $F(x)$, we obtain the equation expressing the balance of vertical forces:

$$(12\text{-}5) \qquad\qquad |F(x)| \sin \theta(x) = w \int_0^x \sqrt{1 + f'(t)^2}\, dt.$$

Now we divide Equation 12-5 by Equation 12-4, and we obtain the equation

$$\tan \theta(x) = \frac{w}{h} \int_0^x \sqrt{1 + f'(t)^2}\ dt.$$

But $\tan \theta(x)$ is the slope of our curve; that is, $\tan \theta(x) = f'(x)$, and therefore

(12-6) $$f'(x) = \frac{w}{h} \int_0^x \sqrt{1 + f'(t)^2}\, dt.$$

In other words, f' is a solution of the integral equation $u(x) = \int_0^x F(t, u(t))dt$, where $F(x, z) = \frac{w}{h} \sqrt{1 + z^2}$. Thus, according to Theorem 12-2, $z = f'(x)$ satisfies the initial value problem

(12-7) $$z' = \frac{w}{h} \sqrt{1 + z^2} \text{ and } z = 0 \text{ when } x = 0.$$

It is easy to solve the separable Problem 12-7; we find that $z = \sinh \dfrac{w}{h} x$ satisfies it. Since $z = f'(x)$, and we have chosen our coordinate system so that $f(0) = 0$, it follows immediately that $f(x) = \dfrac{h}{w}\left(\cosh \dfrac{w}{h} x - 1\right)$. Thus, if we substitute p for $\dfrac{w}{h}$, we see that

(12-8) $$y = \frac{1}{p}(\cosh px - 1)$$

is the equation of the hanging chain. This curve is called a **catenary**. To find the specific form of a given chain, we of course have to replace p with an appropriate number. In Exercise 12-5, we give you some hints on how to do that.

EXERCISE 12

1. Solve the following integral equations.

   (a) $w(x) = 2 + \int_1^x \left(3t - \dfrac{w(t)}{t}\right) dt$ (c) $w(x) = 3 + \int_\pi^x \sqrt{1 - w(t)^2}\, dt$

   (b) $w(x) = 1 + \int_\pi^x \dfrac{\cos t}{3w(t)^2}\, dt$ (d) $w(x) = -\pi + \int_{\ln 2}^x e^t \cos^2 w(t) dt$

2. Let w_2 be the second Euler-Cauchy approximation to the solution of the initial value problem $y' = x + y$ and $y = 0$ when $x = 0$ in the interval $[0, 1]$.
   (a) What is $w_2(\frac{3}{4})$?
   (b) Sketch the graph of the equation $y = w_2(x)$.
   (c) If w is the solution of the initial value problem, show that $w(x) \geq w_2(x)$ for each $x \in [0, 1]$.
   (d) Can you convince yourself that for each $x \in [0, 1]$, $w_5(x) \geq w_3(x)$?

3. Consider the initial value problem $y' = y + 1$ and $y = 2$ when $x = 0$, and let b be a given number and n be a positive integer. Show that the Y-coordinate of the point (b, y_n) of the Euler-Cauchy polygonal approximation w_n is $y_n = 3(1 + b/n)^n - 1$. What is $\lim_{n \uparrow \infty} y_n$? Check this result by solving the given problem.

4. Let b be any number, and show how the values of the Euler-Cauchy approximations converge to $w(b)$, where w is the solution of the initial value problem $y' = 2y$ and $y = 3$ when $x = 0$.

5. Let us find the equation of a chain that is 50 centimeters long and is hanging from two pegs at the same height above the ground and 33 centimeters apart.

    (a) Go through our derivation of the equation of the hanging chain and use Equation 12-6 to show that the length of $S(x)$ is $\dfrac{1}{p} f'(x) = \dfrac{1}{p} \sinh px$ centimeters.

    (b) Now use the obvious symmetry of our present situation to convince yourself that $S(16.5)$ is half the chain and hence that p is the solution of the equation $\sinh 16.5p = 25p$.

    (c) We could use the computer to solve this equation for p, but a table of values of sinh says that $\sinh 1.65 = 2.5$. So use this last equation to find p, and then write the equation of this particular hanging chain.

6. Show that the graph of each Euler-Cauchy approximation w_n lies in the rectangle illustrated in Fig. 12-3.

7. Show that if $\{w_n\}$ is the sequence of Euler-Cauchy approximations for the initial value problem $y' = f(x, y)$ and $y = y_0$ when $x = 0$ in the interval $[0, 1]$, then

$$w_n(x) = y_0 + \int_0^x f\left(\frac{\text{int } (nt)}{n}, w_n\left(\frac{\text{int } (nt)}{n}\right)\right) dt.$$

8. Figure 12-5 shows the roadway of a suspension bridge; $y = f(x)$ is the equation of the cables that hold it up. The difference between this situation and the hanging chain is that here weight is evenly distributed *horizontally*, not along the cable. (That is, we assume that we can neglect the weight of the cable compared to the weight of the roadway.) Hence, Equation 12-5 becomes simply $|\mathbf{F}(x)| \sin \theta(x) = wx$, where we assume that the roadway weighs w newtons per meter.

    (a) Show that $f'(x) = \dfrac{w}{h} x$ and $f(0) = 0$.

    (b) Solve the initial value problem of part (a).

    (c) Suppose that our roadway is 100 meters long and weighs 10,000 newtons per meter. Suppose, further, that our cables are only strong enough to withstand a force of 1,000,000 newtons. How high do we make the towers of the bridge?

9. Show that $y = x^3$ satisfies the initial value problem $y' = 3xy^{1/3}$ and $y = 0$ when $x = 0$. Now apply the Euler-Cauchy technique to this initial value problem (on an arbitrary interval $[0, b]$), and see what solution you get.

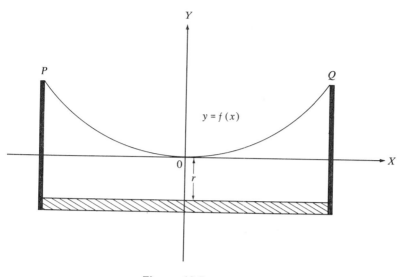

Figure 12-5

10. Another well-known way to construct a sequence $\{w_n\}$ of functions whose limit is the solution of Problem 12-1 is **Picard's Method** of successive approximations. We start with a more or less arbitrary initial function w_0 (for example, we might choose $w_0(x) = y_0$) and calculate the remaining members of the sequence by means of the recursion formula

$$w_{n+1}(x) = y_0 + \int_{x_0}^{x} f(t, w_n(t))dt, \qquad n = 0, 1, 2, \ldots .$$

It can be shown that if f satisfies the hypotheses of Theorem 14-1, then $\{w_n\}$ converges to a solution w. Thus, for the initial value problem of Example 12-1 we would have $w_0(x) = 1$ and

$$w_{n+1}(x) = 1 + \int_{0}^{x} w_n(t)dt.$$

Find $w_1(x)$, $w_2(x)$, and $w_3(x)$. Can you guess the formula for $w_n(x)$? What is $\lim_{n \uparrow \infty} w_n(x)$?

13 EULER-CAUCHY APPROXIMATIONS

We introduced the Euler-Cauchy polygons to show that the initial value problem

(13-1) $y' = f(x, y)$ and $y = y_0$ when $x = x_0$

has a solution if *f* is continuous. Furthermore, since in practical cases the polygons converge to a solution curve, we can use them as approximations to a solution. In other words, the Euler-Cauchy technique is an approximation method as well as the basis for an existence proof. In this section, we will consider it as an approximation method.

Not only are Euler-Cauchy polygons easy to visualize from a theoretical point of view (by thinking of direction segments, and so on), but it is easy to program a computer to calculate their vertices.

Example 13-1.   Find the vertices of the Euler-Cauchy polygonal approximation w_{20} to the solution of the initial value problem

$$y' = 1 + y^2 \text{ and } y = 0 \text{ when } x = 0$$

in the interval $[0, 1]$.

Solution. Since $f(x, y) = 1 + y^2$ in this example, and $h = \frac{1}{20} = .05$, Recursion Formulas 12-2 become $x_{k+1} = x_k + .05$ and $y_{k+1} = y_k + .05(1 + y_k^2)$. Our initial condition tells us that we start with the vertex $(x_0, y_0) = (0, 0)$, and we can calculate the other vertices we seek $\{(x_1, y_1), (x_2, y_2), \ldots, (x_{20}, y_{20})\}$ by means of the flow chart and corresponding computer program of Fig. 13-1.

Although the Euler-Cauchy method is easy to understand and to program for a computer, it is not as accurate as other approximation methods, and most numerical analysts would use a different technique (perhaps one of the ones we will introduce in Sections 16 and 17) if they were faced with the problem of solving a particular differential equation.

Example 13-2.   See how accurate the results we obtained in Example 13-1 are.

Solution. Let us modify the program of Fig. 13-1 to print *three* columns, the two it printed before, plus a column of values of the solution *w* at the points of the set $\{x_0, x_1, \ldots, x_{20}\}$. You can use the techniques covered in Section 9 to find that $y = \text{Tan } x$ satisfies our given (separable) problem. So we write the program shown in Fig. 13-2, in which *w* represents the value of the true solution. Figure 13-2 also shows the output of this program. As you see, the results are not especially accurate, but they might be adequate for some purposes.

Of course, we really want to use approximation methods to solve initial value problems that we *cannot* solve otherwise.

Example 13-3.   Find approximations to the values of the solution of the initial value problem

(13-2) $y' = x^2 + y^2 \text{ and } y = 0 \text{ when } x = 0$

at the points of the set $\{0, .1, .2, .3, .4, .5\}$.

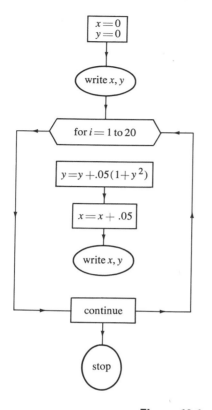

```
          X = 0
          Y = 0
          WRITE(6, 1) X, Y
1         FORMAT(1X, F4.2, F10.4)
          DO 2 I = 1, 20
          Y = Y + .05*(1 + Y*Y)
          X = X + .05
          WRITE(6, 1) X, Y
2         CONTINUE
          STOP
          END
```

Figure 13-1

```
          X = 0
          Y = 0
          W = 0
          WRITE(6, 1) X, Y, W
1         FORMAT(1X, F4.2, 2F10.4)
          DO 2 I = 1, 20
          Y = Y + .05*(1 + Y*Y)
          X = X + .05
          W = SIN(X)/COS(X)
          WRITE(6, 1) X, Y, W
2         CONTINUE
          STOP
          END
```

(X)	(approx.)	(true)
0.0	0.0	0.0
0.05	0.0500	0.0500
0.10	0.1001	0.1003
0.15	0.1506	0.1511
0.20	0.2018	0.2027
0.25	0.2538	0.2553
0.30	0.3070	0.3093
0.35	0.3617	0.3650
0.40	0.4183	0.4228
0.45	0.4770	0.4831
0.50	0.5384	0.5463
0.55	0.6029	0.6131
0.60	0.6711	0.6841
0.65	0.7436	0.7602
0.70	0.8212	0.8423
0.75	0.9049	0.9316
0.80	0.9959	1.0296
0.85	1.0955	1.1383
0.90	1.2055	1.2602
0.95	1.3281	1.3984
1.00	1.4663	1.5574

Figure 13-2

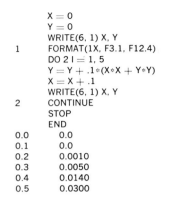

```
         X = 0
         Y = 0
         WRITE(6, 1) X, Y
1        FORMAT(1X, F3.1, F12.4)
         DO 2 I = 1, 5
         Y = Y + .1*(X*X + Y*Y)
         X = X + .1
         WRITE(6, 1) X, Y
2        CONTINUE
         STOP
         END
   0.0      0.0
   0.1      0.0
   0.2      0.0010
   0.3      0.0050
   0.4      0.0140
   0.5      0.0300
```

Figure 13-3

Solution. Here, $f(x, y) = x^2 + y^2$, and $h = .1$. The program in Fig. 13-3 is a fairly obvious modification of the program in Fig. 13-1.

Because this is not a course in numerical analysis, we have left to one side certain technical, but obviously important, questions. How accurate are our numerical methods? To what problems do they apply? What we hope to do in this book is to help you understand some of the theory of differential equations so that you can come to grips with these questions later. Here is an example that uses some of the theory we talked about in the last section.

Example 13-4. In the preceding example, we assumed that Initial Value Problem 13-2 *has* a solution in the interval [0, .5]. How do we know that this assumption is correct?

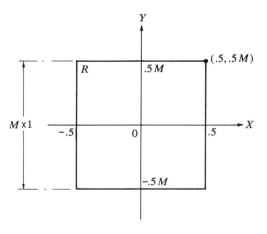

Figure 13-4

Solution. In Fig. 12-3, we surrounded our initial point (x_0, y_0) with a rectangle that is constructed so as to insure the existence of a solution in the interval that forms the base of the rectangle. We will apply this construction to our present problem. Here, $(x_0, y_0) = (0, 0)$, and we are hoping to make the interval $[-.5, .5]$ the base of the rectangle. Thus, the general situation pictured in Fig. 12-3 becomes the particular situation pictured in Fig. 13-4. Since the rectangle R is to be $M \times 1 = M$ units high, the coordinates of its upper right-hand vertex are $(.5, .5M)$, where M is an upper bound for $|f(x, y)|$. In the present problem, $f(x, y) = x^2 + y^2$, and we will assume that the domain D is the entire XY-plane. Thus, we are to finish specifying our rectangle R (which now amounts only to choosing M) in such a way that $x^2 + y^2 \leq M$ for each point $(x, y) \in R$. Because the maximum value of f in R is the number $f(.5, .5M) = .25 + .25M^2$, we must have

(13-3) $.25 + .25M^2 \leq M.$

This inequality holds, for example, if $M = 1$; that is, if R is the 1 by 1 square whose center is the origin, then $|f(x, y)| \leq 1$ for each point $(x, y) \in R$. Therefore, our theory says that Euler-Cauchy polygons with the interval $[-.5, .5]$ as domain converge to a solution curve of Problem 13-2. We could satisfy Inequality 13-3 with other choices of M. For example, $M = 2$ satisfies the inequality. But we only need to find *one* solution M to assure us that our Euler-Cauchy polygons lead to a solution in the entire interval $[-.5, .5]$.

EXERCISE 13

1. Why are the approximate values in the table in Fig. 13-2 smaller than the true values?

2. Halve the step-size in the program of Example 13-1, and see how the accuracy of the computation is improved.

3. Show that the program in Fig. 13-5 (which applies to the initial value problem of Example 13-1) prints only the pairs (x_0, y_0), (x_{10}, y_{10}), and (x_{20}, y_{20}). Halve the

```
          X = 0
          Y = 0
          WRITE(6, 1) X, Y
    1     FORMAT(1X, F4.2, F10.4)
          DO 2 I = 1, 2
          DO 3 J = 1, 10
          Y = Y + .05*(1 + Y*Y)
          X = X + .05
    3     CONTINUE
          WRITE(6, 1) X, Y
    2     CONTINUE
          STOP
          END
```

Figure 13-5

step-size in this program, and have it print the pairs (x_0, y_0), (x_{20}, y_{20}), and (x_{40}, y_{40}). This device keeps us from getting more computer output than we really want. Make a flow chart for this program.

4. Fill in the blanks so that the "all-purpose" Euler-Cauchy program of Fig. 13-6 will solve the initial value problem in Example 13-1. Use the all-purpose program to solve the initial value problem in Example 13-3. Write a similar general program (along the lines of the program in Fig. 13-5) that prints the coordinates of $m + 1$ vertices only (including the first and the last), using a step size of $h = (b - a)/mn$, where m and n are given positive integers. In Exercise 13-3, $m = 2$ and $n = 10$.

```
      F(X, Y) = _____
      X = _____
      Y = _____
      B = _____
      N = _____
      WRITE(6, 1) X, Y
  1   FORMAT(1X, F10.4, F20.4)
      H = (B − X)/N
      DO 2 I = 1, N
      Y = Y + H*F(X, Y)
      X = X + H
      WRITE(6, 1) X, Y
  2   CONTINUE
      STOP
      END
```

Figure 13-6

5. Use your program of Exercise 13-4 to solve the initial value problem of Example 9-3. Compare your output with the output listed in Fig. 9-1.

6. Write a program that computes the vertices of the Euler-Cauchy polygonal approximation w_{20} to the solution of the initial value problem of Example 13-1 in the interval $[0, 2]$. What is wrong with this idea? Run it on the computer, anyway, and plot the graph of w_{20}.

7. Does Inequality 13-3 hold if $M = 4$? Does it matter?

8. Show that the argument we used in Example 13-4 will not work if we replace the interval $[-.5, .5]$ with $[-1, 1]$. Does it therefore follow that the problem does not have a solution in the interval $[-1, 1]$?

14 UNIQUENESS.   DIFFERENTIAL INEQUALITIES

We have seen that an initial value problem

(14-1)
$$y' = f(x, y)$$
$$y = y_0 \text{ when } x = x_0,$$

where f is continuous in a domain D that contains the point (x_0, y_0), *has a solution*, so now we ask if it has *only* one. Let us start with an example that suggests why this question may be an important one to ask and that shows that the answer can be no.

Suppose we roll a stone off a cliff, as illustrated in Fig. 14-1, so that t seconds after it goes over the edge it has fallen y meters. A mathematical model of this physical experiment is, as we pointed out in Section 7, the initial value problem

(14-2) $y'' = 9.8$ and $y = 0, y' = 0$ when $t = 0$.

The solution of this problem is given by the familiar formula

(14-3) $y = 4.9t^2$.

Now we differentiate Equation 14-3,

(14-4) $y' = 9.8t$,

and also solve it for t, $t = \sqrt{y/4.9}$. When we substitute this expression for t in Equation 14-4, we see that $y' = 9.8\sqrt{y/4.9} = 4.4\sqrt{y}$. Notice that $y = 0$ when $t = 0$, so in addition to satisfying Problem 14-2, $y = 4.9t^2$ also satisfies the initial

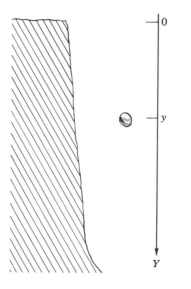

Figure 14-1

value problem

(14-5) $y' = 4.4 \sqrt{y}$ and $y = 0$ when $t = 0$.

Thus, we are tempted to say that Problem 14-5 is also a mathematical model of the physical experiment of pushing a stone over the edge of a cliff. But it isn't. For Problem 14-5 *has more than one solution*. Not only does $y = 4.9t^2$ satisfy it, but $y = 0$ does, too. This latter solution tells us that the rock doesn't fall but remains floating in space. There are still other solutions of Problem 14-5, but the fact that it has at least two is enough to convince us that, as a mathematical model of a physical experiment, the problem is worthless. Two different solutions cannot represent what really happens.

This example and Theorem 12-1 show that continuity of f is enough to guarantee the *existence* of a solution of Initial Value Problem 14-1, but continuity alone will not guarantee that the problem has a *unique* solution. In this section, we will show that uniqueness is guaranteed if we also suppose that the derived function f_2 is bounded in a neighborhood of (x_0, y_0). Notice that this condition is violated in our example of the falling stone. There, $f(t, y) = 4.4 \sqrt{y}$, and so

$$f_2(t, y) = \frac{\partial 4.4 \sqrt{y}}{\partial y} = 2.2/\sqrt{y} \text{ if } y \neq 0.$$ But our initial point is $(0, 0)$, and f_2 is not bounded in a neighborhood of that point.

The key to our uniqueness theorem is the following theorem on *differential inequalities*, a subject that is interesting in its own right. In the next section, we will use this theorem on differential inequalities as a tool for investigating the behavior of solutions of initial value problems. Roughly speaking (and assuming that f satisfies certain "reasonable" hypotheses), this theorem states that if v is a solution of the problem that is obtained by replacing the first two $=$'s in Problem 14-1 with $\leq$'s, and w is a solution of the original problem, then $v(x) \leq w(x)$ for each $x \geq x_0$. For example, if $v'(x) \leq 5v(x)$ and $v(0) \leq 3$, then for each $x \geq 0$, we have $v(x) \leq 3e^{5x}$, since $y = 3e^{5x}$ satisfies the initial value problem $y' = 5y$ and $y = 3$ when $x = 0$. The basic ideas behind the proof of this theorem are quite simple, but you may find it difficult to work your way through the complicated details. Even though you cannot keep all these details in mind, you should at least try to understand what the theorem says.

THEOREM 14-1

Suppose that f is continuous and f_2 is bounded in a plane domain D that contains the point (x_0, y_0). Let w be a solution of Initial Value Problem 14-1 in an interval $[x_0, b]$ and let v be a differentiable function such that

(i) $v(x_0) \leq y_0,$

and for each $x \in [x_0, b]$ the point $(x, v(x))$ belongs to D and

(ii) $$v'(x) \le f(x, v(x)).$$

Then $v(x) \le w(x)$ for each $x \in [x_0, b]$. The theorem remains true if the symbol $\le$ is replaced by the symbol $\ge$ throughout.

Proof. We will suppose that the conclusion is *not* true and arrive at a contradiction. So suppose there were a point $q \in (x_0, b]$ such that $v(q) > w(q)$. The functions v and w are continuous, and the graph of v starts below the graph of w; that is, $v(x_0) \le w(x_0)$. Therefore, if we trace backward along the graphs of v and w from the line $x = q$, we must come to a first point of intersection. In other words, we will reach a point p to the left of q such that $v(p) = w(p)$, and $v(x) > w(x)$ for each $x \in (p, q]$ (see Fig. 14-2). We can pick a point $r > p$ so that the "triangle" formed by

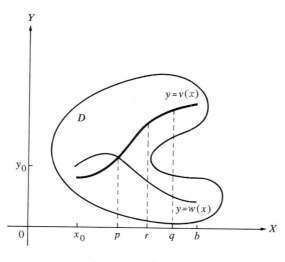

Figure 14-2

the graphs of v and w and the line $x = r$ lies entirely in D. Since $r \in (p, q]$, it must be true that

(14-6) $$v(r) > w(r),$$

and it is this inequality that we will now contradict.

    Since v and w satisfy our differential inequality and our differential equation, respectively, we have, for each $x \in [p, r]$,

(14-7) $$v'(x) - w'(x) \leq f(x, v(x)) - f(x, w(x)).$$

Recall the Theorem of the Mean of elementary calculus, which states that if (a, b) and (a, c) are two endpoints of a segment contained in D, then there is a number m between b and c such that $f(a, b) - f(a, c) = f_2(a, m)(b - c)$. When we apply this theorem to the right-hand side of Inequality 14-7, with x, $v(x)$, and $w(x)$ playing the roles of a, b, and c, we see that there is a number m between $v(x)$ and $w(x)$ such that

(14-8) $$v'(x) - w'(x) \leq f_2(x, m)[v(x) - w(x)].$$

We don't know the point (x, m) exactly, but we really don't care. For our hypotheses tell us that there is a number K such that *all* values of f_2 at points of D are less than or equal to K. Therefore, whatever the number m is, it is true that $f_2(x, m) \leq K$. Hence, since $v(x) - w(x) \geq 0$, we have

$$f_2(x, m)[v(x) - w(x)] \leq K[v(x) - w(x)],$$

and therefore Inequality 14-8 tells us that

$$D_x[v(x) - w(x)] \leq K[v(x) - w(x)] \text{ for } x \in [p, r].$$

We treat this linear differential inequality exactly as if it were an equation; that is, we multiply both sides by e^{-Kx} and write the result as

$$e^{-Kx}D_x[v(x) - w(x)] - Ke^{-Kx}[v(x) - w(x)] \leq 0 \text{ for } x \in [p, r].$$

By using the rule for differentiating a product, you can verify that this inequality could also be written as

$$D_x\{e^{-Kx}[v(x) - w(x)]\} \leq 0 \text{ for } x \in [p, r].$$

Now we integrate from p to r:

$$e^{-Kx}[v(x) - w(x)] \Big|_p^r \leq 0.$$

When we recall that we chose p as a point for which $v(p) - w(p) = 0$, we see that this inequality is simply $e^{-Kr}[v(r) - w(r)] \leq 0$. But $e^{-Kr} > 0$, so this last inequality would imply that $v(r) - w(r) \leq 0$, which contradicts Inequality 14-6.

Thus, there cannot be a point $q > x_0$ such that $v(q) > w(q)$; we must have $v(x) \leq w(x)$ for each $x \in [x_0, b]$. In Exercise 14-9, we ask you to write out the proof for the case of the reversed inequality signs. Notice that in this theorem we are always working to the right of the initial point x_0. Of course, there is an analogous theorem for an interval $[a, x_0]$ to the left of x_0, and we have stated it in Exercise 14-10.

Example 14-1. Show that if $y = v(x)$ satisfies the initial value problem

$$y' = x^2 + y^2 \text{ and } y = 0 \text{ when } x = 0,$$

then $v(x) \leq \text{Tan } x$ for each $x \in [0, 1]$.

Solution. In this example, our initial point is $(x_0, y_0) = (0, 0)$, and our basic interval of the X-axis is $[x_0, b] = [0, 1]$. We are assuming that $v'(x) = x^2 + v(x)^2$, and since $x^2 \leq 1$, it follows that $v'(x) \leq 1 + v(x)^2$. Therefore, we can take inequalities (i) and (ii) of Theorem 14-1 to be

$$\text{(i) } v(0) \leq 0 \quad \text{and} \quad \text{(ii) } v'(x) \leq 1 + v(x)^2.$$

The theorem states that for each $x \in [0, 1]$ it is true that $v(x) \leq w(x)$, where w is a solution of the initial value problem we get by replacing the $\leq$ signs by $=$ signs. In other words, $y = w(x)$ is to satisfy the initial value problem

$$y' = 1 + y^2 \text{ and } y = 0 \text{ when } x = 0.$$

We have solved this separable problem before, and we know that $w(x) = \text{Tan } x$. Therefore, $v(x) \leq \text{Tan } x$, as we were to show.

Theorem 14-1 immediately yields a uniqueness theorem. For suppose that v and w are two solutions of Problem 14-1 in an interval $[x_0, b]$. Since v satisfies conditions (i) and (ii) of our theorem, we can conclude that $v(x) \leq w(x)$. But v also satisfies conditions (i) and (ii) with the symbol $\leq$ replaced by $\geq$, and so we see that $v(x) \geq w(x)$. Thus, $v(x) = w(x)$. To prove uniqueness in an interval $[a, x_0]$ to the left of the initial point x_0, we could use the analogue of Theorem 14-1 that is valid to the left of x_0 (Exercise 14-10). We therefore have the following uniqueness theorem.

THEOREM 14-2

Suppose that f is continuous and that f_2 is bounded in a domain D that contains the point (x_0, y_0). Let v and w be solutions of Initial Value Problem 14-1 in the interval $[a, b]$ and whose graphs lie in D. Then $v(x) = w(x)$ for each $x = [a, b]$.

There are various other uniqueness criteria, but they are of interest mainly to specialists in differential equations. Theorem 14-2 assures us that any "reasonable" initial value problem has a unique solution. For the assumption that f_2 is bounded is not a very heavy restriction. It is a theorem of mathematical analysis that a function that is continuous in a closed and bounded region is automatically bounded in the region, and it follows that we can replace the hypothesis that f_2 be bounded in D by the hypothesis that f_2 be continuous in D. (We can make this replacement in both Theorems 14-1 and 14-2.) This condition is satisfied for almost any f that one is likely to meet in practice.

Example 14-2. Use Theorem 14-2 to show that the initial value problem of Example 14-1 has a unique solution.

Solution. In this initial value problem, $f(x, y) = x^2 + y^2$, so $f_2(x, y) = \dfrac{\partial}{\partial y}(x^2 + y^2) = 2y$. The domain of f is the entire XY-plane, and both f and f_2 are obviously continuous at each point. Therefore, according to our remarks that precede this example, Theorem 14-2 applies (and so does Theorem 12-1), and hence our initial value problem has a unique solution.

Example 14-3. Discuss the set of solutions of the differential equation

$$y' = y^2 - y$$

whose graphs intersect the Y-axis.

Solution. To find the solution curve that contains a given point $(0, y_0)$ of the Y-axis, we solve the initial value problem

$$(14\text{-}9) \qquad y' = y^2 - y \text{ and } y = y_0 \text{ when } x = 0.$$

Here, $f(x, y) = y^2 - y$, and hence $f_2(x, y) = 2y - 1$. Both f and f_2 are continuous, so our existence and uniqueness theorems apply. Thus, each point $(0, y_0)$ of the Y-axis belongs to exactly one solution curve, the graph of a solution that we will call w_{y_0}. For example, it is easy to verify that $w_1(x) = 1$ and that $w_0(x) = 0$, and we have sketched the graphs of these solutions in Fig. 14-3.

Let us also look at the solutions w_{-1}, $w_{.5}$, and w_2 that correspond to the initial conditions $y = -1$ when $x = 0$, $y = .5$ when $x = 0$, and $y = 2$ when $x = 0$, respectively. Notice that when x is close to 0, Y-coordinates of the graph of w_{-1} are negative, and hence $y' = y^2 - y > 0$. The curve is rising. Our uniqueness theorem says that *solution curves cannot intersect.* For if they should intersect in a point (x_1, y_1), then the initial value problem $y' = y^2 - y$ and $y = y_1$ when $x = x_1$ would have more than one solution, in violation of Theorem 14-2. So the graph of w_{-1} rises, but it cannot intersect the X-axis (the graph of w_0).

Now look at $w_{.5}$. The graph of this function starts with Y-coordinates between 0 and 1, and hence $y' = y^2 - y < 0$. The curve is falling, but it, too,

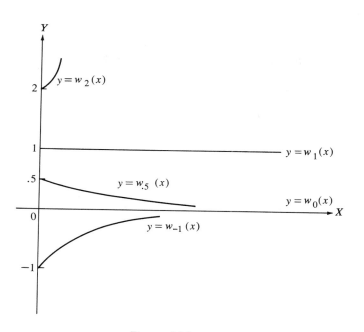

Figure 14-3

cannot intersect the X-axis. Finally, for w_2 we have $y' = y^2 - y > 0$, and so the graph of w_2 rises.

Our analysis here is very incomplete. We have not begun to tap the wealth of information about the solutions of a differential equation that is available from the equation itself. We will discuss this differential equation more fully in the exercises and in the next section. Usually, of course, we apply this type of discussion to differential equations that we cannot solve explicitly. In this simple example, though, it is easy to see that the equation $w_{y_0}(x) = y_0/[y_0 + (1 - y_0)e^x]$ defines the solution of Initial Value Problem 14-9, and you can use this equation to check our qualitative results.

EXERCISE 14

1. Do Theorems 12-1 and 14-2 guarantee the existence and uniqueness of solutions of the following initial value problems in a neighborhood of the initial point? Can we solve any of them?
   (a) $y' = \sin(xy)$
      $y = 2$ when $x = 3$
   (b) $y' = |x| + y^2$
      $y = 2$ when $x = 0$
   (c) $y' = xy|y|$
      $y = 0$ when $x = 1$
   (d) $y' = \tan \ln (x^4 \sec^2 y^2)$
      $y = 1492$ when $x = 1066$

2. If $v'(x) \le 3v(x) + 6$ and $v(0) = 4$, use Theorem 14-1 to show that $v(x) \le 6e^{3x} - 2$ for each $x \ge 0$.

3. Use Theorem 14-1 (as we did in Example 14-1) to show that if v is the solution of the initial value problem $y' = x^2 + y^2$ and $y = 2$ when $x = 1$ in an interval $[1, b]$, then for each $x \in [1, b]$, $v(x) \geq \tan x$. What does this inequality tell us about b?

4. The following questions refer to solutions of the differential equation of Example 14-3.
   (a) Can w_3 have a maximum or a minimum point in the interval $(0, \infty)$?
   (b) What are the formulas for $w_{-1}(x)$, $w_{.5}(x)$, and $w_2(x)$?
   (c) Use the formula for $w_{.5}(x)$ to show that (as Fig. 14-3 seems to indicate)
   $$\lim_{x \uparrow \infty} w_{.5}(x) = 0.$$

5. Let u be the solution of the initial value problem $y' = y^2 - y - y^4 e^{xy}$ and $y = .5$ when $x = 0$.
   (a) Show that $u(x) \leq w_{.5}(x)$ for each $x \geq 0$ (where $w_{.5}$ is defined in Example 14-3).
   (b) How do you know that $u(x) \geq 0$ for each x?
   (c) What is $\lim_{x \uparrow \infty} u(x)$? (Hint: See Exercise 14-4(c).)

6. (a) Sketch (in the TY-plane) the graph of the function that is defined by the equations
   $$y = 0 \text{ for } 0 \leq t \leq 1,$$
   $$= 4.9(t - 1)^2 \text{ for } t \geq 1.$$

   (b) Show that this function is a solution of Initial Value Problem 14-5.
   (c) How would this function "describe" the behavior of the stone we rolled over the cliff?

7. Sketch the graphs of the functions u and v that are defined by the equations $u(x) = 0$ and $v(x) = 8(|x| + x)^{3/2}$. Show that both functions are solutions of the initial value problem $y' = 12y^{1/3}$ and $y = 0$ when $x = 0$. What solution are we led to by the Euler-Cauchy polygonal approximations? (One interesting feature of this initial value problem is that solutions are "unique to the left" of the initial point $(0, 0)$, but not to the right.)

8. A manufacturer of rat poison claims that if you feed his product to a group of y (≤ 10) rats, their number will decrease at the rate of $\sqrt{100 - y^2}$ rodents per week. Thus, if you have 10 rats in the house when you start putting out the poison, the population at any later time is obtained by solving the initial value problem
   $$y' = -\sqrt{100 - y^2} \text{ and } y = 10 \text{ when } t = 0.$$

   Since $y = 10 \cos t$ satisfies this problem, it follows that in a week and one-half (more precisely, $\frac{1}{2}\pi$ weeks) there will be no rats left. Dispute this claim mathematically.

9. Prove Theorem 14-1 with the symbol $\leq$ replaced by the symbol $\geq$ throughout.

10. The following theorem is the analogue of Theorem 14-1 in an interval to the left of the initial point x_0. Prove it. Suppose that f is continuous and f_2 is bounded in a plane domain D that contains the point (x_0, y_0). Let w be a solution of Initial Value Problem 14-1 in an interval $[a, x_0]$, and let v be a differentiable function such that $v(x_0) \leq y_0$, and for each $x \in [a, x_0]$, $(x, v(x)) \in D$ and $v'(x) \geq f(x, v(x))$. Then $v(x) \leq w(x)$ for each $x \in [a, x_0]$.

11. Show that Theorem 14-2 does not apply to the initial value problem $y' = |y|$ and $y = 0$ when $x = 0$. Nevertheless, this problem has a unique solution. Can you find it and show that it is unique?

12. Suppose that u is a continuous function such that the following integral inequality holds for $x \geq 0$:

(14-10) $$u(x) \leq 3 + \int_0^x 4u(t)dt.$$

(a) Set $v(x) = 3 + \int_0^x 4u(t)dt$, and show that Inequality 14-10 implies that

$$v'(x) \leq 4v(x).$$

(b) Now use Theorem 14-1 to show that $v(x) \leq 3e^{4x}$.

(c) Use the result of part (b), the definition of $v(x)$, and Inequality 14-10 to show that $u(x) \leq 3e^{4x}$.

(Integral inequalities of the type of Inequality 14-10—called **Gronwall-Bellman Inequalities**—have become an important tool in the modern theory of differential equations.)

15　FUNCTIONS DEFINED BY INITIAL VALUE PROBLEMS

In Section 4, we discussed the idea of defining functions by means of integrals; now we will extend this idea. The statement, "ln is the function defined by the equation $\ln x = \int_1^x \frac{du}{u}$," could equally well be phrased, "ln is the solution of the initial value problem

$$y' = 1/x \text{ and } y = 0 \text{ when } x = 1."$$

Our existence and uniqueness theorems tell us that this problem has exactly one solution, so it really does determine a function. Other initial value problems determine other functions, and we can learn a great deal about such functions by studying the initial value problems that give rise to them. For example, just as we use direct methods of integration (such as Simpson's Rule) to print tables of values of functions defined by integrals, so we can use direct methods of solving initial value problems (such as Euler-Cauchy polygons or more sophisticated techniques that we will introduce in Sections 16 and 17) to print tables of values of functions defined by initial value problems. In this section, we will concentrate on inferring non-numerical properties of such functions.

It will make our presentation clearer if we start off by discussing a particular example. So suppose that we think of the function Tangent as being *defined* as the solution of the initial value problem

(15-1) $y' = 1 + y^2$ and $y = 0$ when $x = 0$.

Because we have studied the calculus of the trigonometric functions, we know that $y = \mathrm{Tan}\ x$ really does satisfy Problem 15-1. But let us temporarily push this fact to the back of our mind. Our existence theorem tells us that there is an interval I in which Problem 15-1 has a solution, and our uniqueness theorem states that there is only one solution. We will name the solution function Tangent, and we will try to develop some of its properties. Of course, as these properties emerge, we can check to see that the function Tangent we learned about in trigonometry has them, too.

First, let us establish some simple properties of the graph of Tangent. Our differential equation says that $y' > 0$, so Tangent is an increasing function. Its graph rises. Since $y = 0$ when $x = 0$, it follows that $\mathrm{Tan}\ x > 0$ if $x > 0$, and $\mathrm{Tan}\ x < 0$ if $x < 0$. Now we differentiate both sides of the equation $y' = 1 + y^2$, and we find that $y'' = 2yy' = 2y(1 + y^2)$. Therefore, since x and y have the same sign, we see that x and y'' have the same sign. In other words, the graph of Tangent is concave upward in the first quadrant and concave downward in the third quadrant.

Our discussion in the last paragraph was pretty simple; now we will introduce a more sophisticated line of reasoning. We will show that Tangent is an *odd* function; that is, that $-\mathrm{Tan}\ (-x) = \mathrm{Tan}\ x$ for each x in an arbitrary symmetric subinterval $(-r, r)$ of I. We can establish this equation by showing that $y = -\mathrm{Tan}\ (-x)$ satisfies Problem 15-1, for our uniqueness theorem states that this problem has only one solution, and we are assuming that $y = \mathrm{Tan}\ x$ satisfies it. Since $y = -\mathrm{Tan}\ (-x)$ obviously satisfies the initial condition of Problem 15-1, we see that our argument will be complete when we show that $y = -\mathrm{Tan}\ (-x)$ also satisfies the differential equation; that is, that

$$-D_x \mathrm{Tan}\ (-x) = 1 + \mathrm{Tan}^2\ (-x).$$

The Chain Rule states that $D_x \mathrm{Tan}\ (-x) = \mathrm{Tan}'\ (-x)D_x(-x) = -\mathrm{Tan}'\ (-x)$, so we have to verify the equation

(15-2) $\mathrm{Tan}'\ (-x) = 1 + \mathrm{Tan}^2\ (-x).$

The statement that $y = \mathrm{Tan}\, x$ satisfies the differential equation $y' = 1 + y^2$ in the interval I means that for each $x \in I$,

(15-3) $$\mathrm{Tan}'\, x = 1 + \mathrm{Tan}^2 x.$$

Now if x is a point of our symmetric interval $(-r, r)$, so is $-x$, and when we replace x with $-x$ in Equation 15-3, we obtain Equation 15-2 and thus complete the demonstration that Tangent is an odd function.

We are engaged in a *qualitative* study of the behavior of the solution of Initial Value Problem 15-1. In a *quantitative* study we write down the solution, explicitly, or we compute a table of values. Here, we are developing properties of the solution directly from an initial value problem that it satisfies. Of course, we already are familiar with the function Tangent, because we have studied trigonometry. Our analysis doesn't add to our knowledge in this example. But we could apply the same kind of analysis to an initial value problem like $y' = 1 + y^4$ and $y = 0$ when $x = 0$, or to $y' = x^2 + y^2$ and $y = 0$ when $x = 0$, and so on, where we are not already familiar with the solution function.

Now we will use our theory of differential inequalities to study the solution of Initial Value Problem 15-1. In Exercise 15-2 we ask you to verify that the inequality

$$1 + y^2 \geq \tfrac{1}{2}(1 + y)^2$$

is valid for each real number y. If we replace y with $\mathrm{Tan}\, x$ in this inequality, we see from Equation 15-3 that

(15-4) $$\mathrm{Tan}'\, x \geq \tfrac{1}{2}(1 + \mathrm{Tan}\, x)^2.$$

Now Theorem 14-1 tells us that if w is the solution of the initial value problem

(15-5) $$y' = \tfrac{1}{2}(1 + y)^2 \text{ and } y = 0 \text{ when } x = 0,$$

then $\mathrm{Tan}\, x \geq w(x)$ for $x \geq 0$. It is a simple matter to solve the separable Problem 15-5 explicitly. We find that $y = x/(2 - x)$ satisfies it. Therefore, we have found a lower bound for $\mathrm{Tan}\, x$:

(15-6) $$\mathrm{Tan}\, x \geq x/(2 - x), \text{ if } x \geq 0.$$

According to Theorem 14-1, this inequality holds in any interval to the right of 0 in which Inequality 15-4 is valid and in which $y = x/(2 - x)$ satisfies Problem 15-5. Notice that $y = x/(2 - x)$ satisfies Problem 15-5 in the interval $[0, 2)$, but that $\lim\limits_{x \uparrow 2} x/(2 - x) = \infty$. Therefore, Inequality 15-6 tells us that the

Tangent function cannot be bounded in the interval $[0, 2)$. In fact, of course, $\lim_{x \uparrow \frac{1}{2}\pi} \text{Tan } x = \infty$.

When we say that the function Tangent is the *unique* solution of Problem 15-1, we are tacitly making an assumption that should be pointed out explicitly. Thus, Tangent is the restriction of the tangent function to the interval $(-\frac{1}{2}\pi, \frac{1}{2}\pi)$, and if we restrict tangent to some smaller domain, we get still another solution of Problem 15-1. For example, $w = \{(x, y): y = \tan x, x \in (-1, 1)\}$ also is a

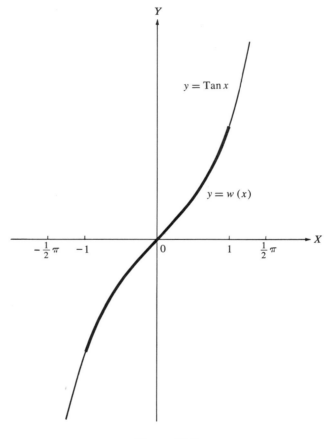

Figure 15-1

solution. Since w is a subset of Tangent (Fig. 15-1), we say that Tangent is an *extension* of w. Because no extension of Tangent is a solution of Problem 15-1, we refer to Tangent as a **fully extended** solution. Obviously, it is the fully extended solutions of differential equations that interest us, so when we say "solution" in this book, we mean "fully extended solution," unless we clearly indicate otherwise. Problem 15-1 has only one fully extended solution, though, of course, it has solutions, such as w, which are (according to the technical definition of a function) different from Tangent.

One of the greatest difficulties we face when we try to analyze an initial value problem is to find the domain of its (fully extended) solution. For Problem 15-1, this domain is the interval $(-\frac{1}{2}\pi, \frac{1}{2}\pi)$, as we know from trigonometry, but this fact is not easy to ascertain merely by looking at the problem. Inequality 15-6 tells us that the domain of Tangent must be a subinterval of $(-2, 2)$, and perhaps we could obtain a better result by using another differential inequality. But it is obviously hard to zero in on the exact interval $(-\frac{1}{2}\pi, \frac{1}{2}\pi)$, and it would be even harder in a more complicated initial value problem.

Roughly speaking, we can say that a fully extended solution curve reaches to the boundary of our basic domain D. In Problem 15-1, D is the entire XY-plane, so the statement that a fully extended solution curve reaches to the boundary of D has to be interpreted so as to include the possibility $\lim_{x \uparrow \frac{1}{2}\pi} \text{Tan } x = \infty$; that is, we think of the "point" $(\frac{1}{2}\pi, \infty)$ as belonging to the "boundary" of the XY-plane. Perhaps a better way of stating this characteristic of fully extended curves is expressed in the following theorem.

THEOREM 15-1

If K is a closed and bounded subset of D that contains the initial point (x_0, y_0) in its interior, then a fully extended solution curve must reach to the boundary of K.

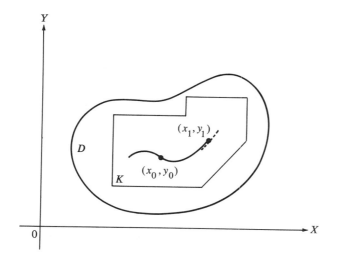

Figure 15-2

The basic ideas behind the proof of this theorem are easily stated. A fully extended solution curve cannot simply "stop short of the boundary of K" at a point (x_1, y_1), as shown in Fig. 15-2. For if it did, we could apply our existence theorem to the initial value problem

$$y' = f(x, y) \text{ and } y = y_1 \text{ when } x = x_1$$

to see that there is a solution curve that contains (x_1, y_1) in its interior (the dashed curve in the figure). Then we could adjoin this solution curve to our fully extended solution curve, thus performing the obviously impossible feat of extending the inextensible.

Here is an example of how Theorem 15-1 can be used in the qualitative analysis of the solution of an initial value problem.

Example 15-1.   Figure 14-3 suggests that if $w._5$ is the solution of the initial value problem

$$y' = y^2 - y \text{ and } y = .5 \text{ when } x = 0,$$

then $\lim\limits_{x \uparrow \infty} w._5(x) = 0$. Show that this statement is, in fact, correct.

Solution. Theorem 15-1 states that a fully extended solution curve reaches to the boundary of any closed and bounded subset that contains the initial point $(0, .5)$ in its interior. As such a subset, we draw in Fig. 14-3 the "box" bounded by the lines $y = 0$, $y = 1$, $x = -1$, and $x = b$ (where b is an arbitrary positive number). Theorem 15-1 says that the graph of $w._5$ must intersect the boundary of the box. But the uniqueness theorem states that the graph of $w._5$ cannot intersect the solution curves $y = 0$ and $y = 1$. Therefore, it must intersect the ends of the box. In particular, the graph of $w._5$ must intersect the line $x = b$. Because b can be *any* positive number, this statement implies that the domain of $w._5$ must include the entire interval $[0, \infty)$.

In Example 14-3, we pointed out that $w._5$ is a decreasing function, so if $y = w._5(x)$, then $y \le .5$, and therefore $y - 1 \le -.5$. Hence, since $y > 0$, and $y' = y(y - 1)$, it follows that $y' \le -.5y$. Therefore, according to Theorem 14-1, $w._5(x) \le u(x)$, where u is the solution of the initial value problem $y' = -.5y$ and $y = .5$ when $x = 0$. It is easy to see that $u(x) = .5e^{-.5x}$, and so $w._5(x) \le .5e^{-.5x}$. Since $w._5(x) > 0$, then $0 < w._5(x) \le .5e^{-.5x}$, from which it follows that $\lim\limits_{x \uparrow \infty} w._5(x) = 0$. (In Exercise 14-4, you found that $\lim\limits_{x \uparrow \infty} w._5(x) = 0$ by looking at an explicit formula for $w._5(x)$, so this qualitative analysis was not necessary. But we can often apply the same type of analysis to an initial value problem that we cannot solve explicitly.)

Example 15-2.   An egg at room temperature is dropped into a pot of boiling water. It is physically obvious that the temperature of the egg can never exceed 100°C. Is this fact equally obvious from the point of view of mathematical theory?

Solution. Yes. We will assume (with Newton) that the rate at which the temperature of the egg changes is proportional to the difference between the egg's temperature and that of the boiling water. If our egg is T degrees hot t seconds after we drop it into the pot, this physical assumption can be expressed as the differential equation

$$(15\text{-}7) \qquad\qquad D_t T = k(100 - T),$$

where k is a constant of proportionality. This differential equation has infinitely many solutions, one of which (the one that satisfies the initial condition $T =$ room temperature when $t = 0$) gives the temperature of our egg. But it is also obvious that $T = 100$ satisfies Equation 15-7. Therefore, since the uniqueness theorem does not permit solution curves to intersect, the graph of the egg's temperature cannot cross the line $T = 100$. The egg cannot get hotter than $100°$.

EXERCISE 15

1. What function is defined by the initial value problem $y' = 1 + y^2$ and $y = 0$ when $x = 3$? Be sure to state the domain of this function.

2. Show that $1 + y^2 \geq \frac{1}{2}(1 + y)^2$ for every real number y.

3. Let w be the solution of the initial value problem $y' = x^4 + y^4$ and $y = 2$ when $x = 0$.
   (a) Show that w is an increasing function.
   (b) Show that the part of the graph of w that lies in the first quadrant is concave upward.
   (c) Convince yourself that there is a number b (considerably less than 1) such that $\lim\limits_{x \uparrow b} w(x) = \infty$.

4. Would it be proper to say that the Cosine function is defined by the initial value problem $y' = -\sqrt{1 - y^2}$ and $y = 1$ when $x = 0$?

5. Let w_{-1} be the solution of the initial value problem $y' = y^2 - y$ and $y = -1$ when $x = 0$. Show qualitatively and by using an explicit formula for $w_{-1}(x)$ that $\lim\limits_{x \uparrow \infty} w_{-1}(x) = 0$.

6. Show that the solution of the initial value problem $y' = x^2 + y^2$ and $y = 0$ when $x = 0$ is an odd function, and the solution of the initial value problem $y' = x + y^3 \sin x$ and $y = 1$ when $x = 0$ is an even function.

7. (a) Your calculus book says that if w is a differentiable function with an inverse w^{-1}, then $D_x w^{-1}(x) = 1/w'(w^{-1}(x))$. Use this equation to show that:
   If w is a solution of the differential equation $y' = f(x, y)$, then w^{-1} is a solution of the differential equation $y' = 1/f(y, x)$.
   (b) Use the result of part (a) and the fact that Tangent is the solution of Problem 15-1 to show that Tan^{-1} is the solution of the initial value problem $y' = 1/(1 + x^2)$ and $y = 0$ when $x = 0$.

8. Suppose that w is the solution of the initial value problem $y' = e^{(y-x)}$ and $y = 1$ when $x = 1$. Show that w^{-1} exists. Use the result of part (a) of Exercise

15-7 to show that w^{-1} also is a solution of our initial value problem. Can you therefore conclude that $w^{-1} = w$? Solve the problem explicitly.

9. In this exercise, let us suppose that we know a great deal about the exponential function, and *define* the function ln as the solution of the initial value problem $y' = e^{-y}$ and $y = 0$ when $x = 1$.

(a) Show that ln is an increasing function.

(b) Show that the graph of ln is concave downward.

(c) From your knowledge of the exponential function, show that $e^{-y} \leq 1/(1 + y)$ for $y \geq 0$, and then use Theorem 14-1 to show that $\ln x \leq \sqrt{2x - 1} - 1$ for $x \geq 1$. Now infer that $\lim\limits_{x \uparrow \infty} \dfrac{\ln x}{x} = 0$.

(d) Use the result of Exercise 15-7(a) to show that the function $\ln^{-1}$ is the solution of the initial value problem $y' = e^x$ and $y = 1$ when $x = 0$. Now infer that $\ln^{-1} x = e^x$ and hence that $\ln = \exp^{-1}$.

10. Define the function Tan^{-1} as the solution of the initial value problem $y' = \cos^2 y$ and $y = 0$ when $x = 0$. Base your answers to the following questions on this initial value problem (but use your knowledge of trigonometry to show that they are correct).

(a) Since $y = \frac{1}{2}\pi$ and $y = -\frac{1}{2}\pi$ satisfy the differential equation $y' = \cos^2 y$, and solution curves do not intersect, infer that $-\frac{1}{2}\pi \leq \text{Tan}^{-1} x \leq \frac{1}{2}\pi$. Can we infer that the domain of Tan^{-1} is the entire interval $(-\infty, \infty)$?

(b) Show that Tan^{-1} is an odd function.

(c) Show that $|\text{Tan}^{-1} x| \leq |x|$ for each x.

(d) Show that $\cos^2 y \geq (1 - 2y/\pi)^2$ for each $y \in [0, \frac{1}{2}\pi]$, and then use Theorem 14-1 to show that $\text{Tan}^{-1} x \geq \frac{1}{2}\pi x/(\frac{1}{2}\pi + x)$ for $x \geq 0$. Now deduce that $\lim\limits_{x \uparrow \infty} \text{Tan}^{-1} x = \frac{1}{2}\pi$.

(e) Show that the graph of Tan^{-1} is concave downward in the first quadrant.

(f) Use the result of Exercise 15-7(a) to show that Tan is the solution of the initial value problem $y' = \sec^2 x$ and $y = 0$ when $x = 0$.

11. In Example 13-4, we showed that the initial value problem $y' = x^2 + y^2$ and $y = 0$ when $x = 0$ has a solution in the interval $[0, .5]$, but in Exercise 13-8 we pointed out that this argument cannot be used to infer that a solution exists in the interval $[0, 1]$. Nevertheless, in Example 14-1, we assume that such a solution *does* exist. Can you use Theorems 14-1 and 15-1 to show that this assumption is justified?

16   THE RUNGE-KUTTA METHOD OF SOLVING AN INITIAL VALUE PROBLEM DIRECTLY

We have just seen how a qualitative analysis of an initial value problem

(16-1) $$y' = f(x, y) \text{ and } y = y_0 \text{ when } x = x_0$$

can supply many of the properties of its solution function. But, by definition, a function is a set of pairs of numbers, so one of the really basic questions that we face when we tackle an initial value problem is, "What is a simple, efficient method of constructing a table of values of its solution?"

In Chapter Two, we studied some special differential equations whose solutions could be expressed in terms of functions defined by integrals. Our methods of direct integration then yielded tables of values of these functions. Now we want to introduce some methods of solving initial value problems that we can apply directly to Problem 16-1. We have already met one such direct method, the Euler-Cauchy polygonal approximation scheme. This method *is* simple, but there are better techniques for solving initial value problems numerically. We will discuss one such numerical method in this section and another in the next.

Suppose, then, that w is the solution of Problem 16-1, and we wish to make a table of its values at some points of an interval $[x_0, b]$. We first choose a positive integer n, set $h = (b - x_0)/n$, and divide the interval $[x_0, b]$ into n subintervals by means of the points $x_1 = x_0 + h$, $x_2 = x_0 + 2h$, . . . , $x_n = x_0 + nh = b$. Our goal is to find corresponding numbers $y_1, y_2, \ldots, y_n$ such that

$$y_k \approx w(x_k) \text{ for } k = 1, 2, \ldots, n.$$

Since $w'(x) = f(x, w(x))$, we see, by integrating from x_k to x_{k+1}, that, for each index k,

(16-2) $$w(x_{k+1}) = w(x_k) + \int_{x_k}^{x_{k+1}} f(x, w(x))dx.$$

We will base our development of recursion formulas for the approximating sequence $\{y_k\}$ on this equation.

For example, the Rectangle Rule says that we can approximate the integral in Equation 16-2 by replacing the integrand by its value at the left endpoint of the interval of integration:

$$w(x_{k+1}) \approx w(x_k) + hf(x_k, w(x_k)).$$

Since $y_k \approx w(x_k)$ and $y_{k+1} \approx w(x_{k+1})$, we are thus led to the Euler-Cauchy approximation relation

$$y_{k+1} = y_k + hf(x_k, y_k)$$

that we introduced in Section 12. Therefore, as we mentioned earlier, the Euler-Cauchy method can be viewed as a generalization of the Rectangle Rule.

Now let us see what happens when we approximate the integral in Equation 16-2 by a more accurate method, Simpson's Rule with $n = 1$. Here, we divide our interval $[x_k, x_{k+1}] = [x_k, x_k + h]$ into two subintervals, each $.5h$

units long, and then Simpson's Rule tells us that

$$(16\text{-}3) \quad \int_{x_k}^{x_{k+1}} f(x, w(x))dx \approx \frac{h}{6} [f(x_k, w(x_k))$$

$$+ 4f(x_k + .5h, w(x_k + .5h)) + f(x_k + h, w(x_k + h))].$$

Of course, we don't know the numbers $w(x_k)$, $w(x_k + .5h)$, and $w(x_k + h)$; these are numbers we are in the process of approximating. We are trying to find a sequence $\{y_k\}$ whose members approximate values of the solution w, so we naturally will replace $w(x_k)$ in Approximation 16-3 with y_k. Therefore, let us write

$$(16\text{-}4) \qquad\qquad a_k = f(x_k, y_k)$$

as an approximation to $f(x_k, w(x_k))$.

Now, how do we handle the term $4f(x_k + .5h, w(x + .5h))$? According to the Theorem of the Mean, there is a number m in the interval $(x_k, x_k + .5h)$ such that

$$(16\text{-}5) \qquad\qquad w(x_k + .5h) = w(x_k) + .5hw'(m).$$

We don't know m, but if h is small, it is close to x_k, and hence

$$w'(m) \approx w'(x_k) = f(x_k, w(x_k)) \approx f(x_k, y_k) = a_k.$$

So we replace $w'(m)$ with a_k in Equation 16-5 and obtain the approximation

$$w(x_k + .5h) \approx y_k + .5ha_k.$$

Therefore, if

$$(16\text{-}6) \qquad\qquad b_k = f(x_k + .5h, y_k + .5ha_k),$$

then

$$f(x_k + .5h, w(x_k + .5h)) \approx b_k.$$

Let us return to Equation 16-5. Since m is close to $x_k + .5h$, then

$$w'(m) \approx w'(x_k + .5h) = f(x_k + .5h, w(x_k + .5h)) \approx b_k.$$

So Equation 16-5 tells us that $w(x_k + .5h) \approx y_k + .5hb_k$. Therefore, if

$$(16\text{-}7) \qquad\qquad c_k = f(x_k + .5h, y_k + .5hb_k),$$

then

$$f(x_k + .5h, w(x_k + .5h)) \approx c_k,$$

too.

To approximate the third term on the right-hand side of Approximation 16-3, we use the Theorem of the Mean to see that

$$w(x_k + h) \approx w(x_k) + hw'(x_k + .5h) = w(x_k) + hf(x_k + .5h, w(x_k + .5h)).$$

But $f(x_k + .5h, w(x_k + .5h)) \approx c_k$, so $w(x_k + h) \approx y_k + hc_k$, and therefore if we set

(16-8) $$d_k = f(x_k + h, y_k + hc_k),$$

then

$$f(x_k + h, w(x_k + h)) \approx d_k.$$

Now we have approximations for all the terms on the right-hand side of Approximation 16-3. In fact, we have *two* approximations, b_k and c_k, for $f(x_k + .5h, w(x_k + .5h))$. Since this expression appears four times, we will replace it with $2b_k + 2c_k$. Therefore, from Equation 16-2 and Approximation 16-3, we are led to the recursion formula

(16-9) $$y_{k+1} = y_k + \frac{h}{6}[a_k + 2b_k + 2c_k + d_k], \qquad k = 0, 1, \ldots, n$$

where a_k, b_k, c_k, and d_k are computed successively from Formulas 16-4, 16-6, 16-7, and 16-8. Of course,

$$x_{k+1} = x_k + h.$$

Our "derivation" of Recursion Formula 16-9 is hardly a model of logical precision. It can be shown [2, 3], however, that the formula does yield quite accurate approximations to the solution of Problem 16-1. This approximation technique is called the **Runge-Kutta** method. It, and various modifications of it, are undoubtedly the best-known schemes for solving initial value problems numerically. To see how it compares with the Euler-Cauchy method, let us apply it to our "standard" example and compute some values of Tangent.

Example 16-1. Write a computer program that produces a table of values, at the points of the set $\{0.0, .05, .1, \ldots, 1.0\}$, of the solution of the initial value problem $y' = 1 + y^2$ and $y = 0$ when $x = 0$.

Solution. Figure 16-1 shows a flow chart and accompanying computer program for solving the problem by the Runge-Kutta method. It also lists the output of the

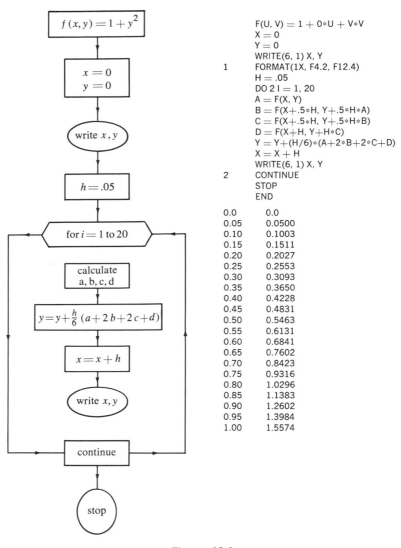

Figure 16-1

program, and you can compare these results with the results in Fig. 13-2 to see how much more accurate Runge-Kutta is than Euler-Cauchy. You might also compare the output in Fig. 16-1 with the table of values of Tangent that we calculated by a very different method in Exercise 9-12.

We are not going to talk about the absolute accuracy of the numerical methods we discuss in this book, but we will at least state something about their relative accuracy. Suppose that we are studying Initial Value Problem 16-1 in the interval $[x_0, b]$. It can be shown that there are numbers M and N such that the approximate value of the solution at $x = b$ computed by means of Euler-Cauchy polygons differs from the true value by no more than Mh, whereas the approximate value computed by the Runge-Kutta method differs from the true value by no more than Nh^4. Here, of course, h is the length of the subintervals into which we divide our basic interval $[x_0, b]$. Therefore, at least in theory, the Runge-Kutta method is considerably more sensitive to step size than is the Euler-Cauchy method. Halving the step size increases our confidence in the answer by a factor of 16 in the Runge-Kutta method, but it only doubles our confidence in the Euler-Cauchy method. On the other hand, the Runge-Kutta method requires substantially more computation than does the Euler-Cauchy method, and hence there is more opportunity for *round-off error*, error that arises from the fact that the computer uses only a few significant digits of the numbers it works with. Careful error analysis is a subtle and difficult business. A rough-and-ready approach is to run one's problem twice, once with a particular value of h and again with $.5h$. If the two answers do not differ too widely, we assume that they aren't too wrong.

EXERCISE 16

1. Show that the Runge-Kutta technique for solving Problem 16-1 reduces to Simpson's Rule if $f(x, y) = f(x)$.

2. Modify the computer program of Example 16-1 so that it will print *three* columns, the two it prints now, plus a column giving the "exact" solution.

3. Modify the computer program of Example 16-1 so that it *computes* the same approximations that it does now but *prints* only the values at the points of the set $\{0, .1, .2, \ldots, 1.0\}$.

4. Modify the program of the preceding exercise to obtain a program that uses a step size of .01 and still prints solution values at the points of the set $\{0, .1, \ldots, 1.0\}$.

5. In Example 13-3, we showed a program for finding a table of values of the solution of the initial value problem $y' = x^2 + y^2$ and $y = 0$ when $x = 0$ by using the Euler-Cauchy method. Write a similar program that uses the Runge-Kutta method. How do the outputs compare?

6. The Sine function is a solution of the initial value problem $y' = \sqrt{1 - y^2}$ and $y = 0$ when $x = 0$. Use the Runge-Kutta method to print a small table of values of this function, and compare the result with the table in your calculus book.

7. Modify the program of Fig. 16-1 so that it solves our initial value problem in the interval $[0, 1.55]$. Is the answer reliable near the right endpoint of this interval? Use the same program to solve the initial value problem $y' = 1 - y^2$

and $y = 0$ when $x = 0$. Now how good is your answer near the right end of the interval $[0, 1.55]$?

8. (a) Apply the Trapezoidal Rule to Equation 16-2 and obtain the approximation

$$w(x_{k+1}) \approx w(x_k) + \tfrac{1}{2}h[f(x_k, w(x_k)) + f(x_{k+1}, w(x_{k+1}))].$$

(b) Explain why this approximation suggests the two-stage scheme

$$z_k = y_k + hf(x_k, y_k)$$
$$y_{k+1} = y_k + \tfrac{1}{2}h[f(x_k, y_k) + f(x_{k+1}, z_k)].$$

(c) Use this method (and the computer) to solve the initial value problem $y' = x^2 + y^2$ and $y = 0$ when $x = 0$ in the interval $[0, 1]$. Compare the output with our earlier solutions of this problem.

17 MILNE'S METHOD OF SOLVING AN INITIAL VALUE PROBLEM NUMERICALLY

We do not intend to give a detailed discussion of numerical methods of solving an initial value problem of the form

$$(17\text{-}1) \qquad y' = f(x, y) \text{ and } y = y_0 \text{ when } x = x_0.$$

Therefore, in addition to the Runge-Kutta method, we will mention only one more technique that is widely used by professional solvers of initial value problems—*Milne's Method*.

Like Runge-Kutta, Milne's Method can be inspired by Simpson's Rule. As usual, we suppose that our basic interval $[x_0, b]$ is divided into n subintervals of length h by the points $x_1 = x_0 + h$, $x_2 = x_0 + 2h$, . . . , $x_n = x_0 + nh$, and we wish to find numbers $y_1, y_2, . . . , y_n$ that approximate the values $w(x_1)$, $w(x_2)$, . . . , $w(x_n)$ of the solution w of Problem 17-1. Let k be a given index, and integrate the equation $w'(x) = f(x, w(x))$ from x_k to x_{k+2}:

$$w(x_{k+2}) = w(x_k) + \int_{x_k}^{x_{k+2}} f(x, w(x))dx.$$

According to Simpson's Rule with $n = 1$,

$$w(x_{k+2}) \approx w(x_k) + \frac{h}{3}[f(x_k, w(x_k)) + 4f(x_{k+1}, w(x_{k+1})) + f(x_{k+2}, w(x_{k+2}))].$$

This approximation suggests that we take our desired approximations y_1, y_2, . . . , y_n as solutions of the equations

$$(17\text{-}2) \quad y_{k+2} = y_k + \frac{h}{3}[f(x_k, y_k) + 4f(x_{k+1}, y_{k+1}) + f(x_{k+2}, y_{k+2})]$$

$$(k = 0, 1, 2, \ldots, n - 2).$$

You will see immediately that Recursion Formula 17-2 presents us with difficulties. *Three* terms of our sequence $\{y_k\}$ appear, so we have to find two, y_k and y_{k+1}, before we can solve for y_{k+2}. In particular, if $k = 0$, we obtain the equation

$$(17\text{-}3) \qquad y_2 = y_0 + \frac{h}{3}[f(x_0, y_0) + 4f(x_1, y_1) + f(x_2, y_2)],$$

which involves y_0, y_1, and y_2. Of course, y_0 is given in advance, but we have to find y_1 somehow before we can even start to solve for y_2. Notice, though, that once we find y_1, we are all right. For then we solve for y_2 and set $k = 1$ in Formula 17-2. We thereupon get an equation in y_1, y_2, and y_3, which, since we now know y_1 and y_2, we can solve for y_3. Because our method uses two values of y while we calculate a third, it is a *two-step* method, in contrast to the *single-step* Runge-Kutta method. To get our new method started—that is, to find y_1 —we can use one of our former single-step methods, either Runge-Kutta or Euler-Cauchy. In this situation, many people use Runge-Kutta.

But even after y_1 has been found, we still have to solve Equation 17-3 for y_2, which is given *implicitly* rather than *explicitly*. Then we have a similar equation to solve for y_3, and so on. If we used, say, Newton's method to solve these equations, we would have an enormous computing job on our hands. What is usually done is to use a **predictor-corrector** technique. We first calculate, by some means or other, a "predicted" value z_2 that approximates y_2, and then substitute this value for y_2 in the right-hand side of Equation 17-3, thus obtaining a "corrected" value. There are various ways of calculating this predicted value. Because we have mentioned the Euler-Cauchy method earlier, we will use it to obtain our predicted value:

$$z_2 = y_1 + hf(x_1, y_1).$$

Since Euler-Cauchy isn't very accurate, we may be introducing a sizable error here, although the correcting process tends to "smooth out" this error. In practice, more accurate predictors are used.

Let us summarize the situation. We are given y_0 with our problem, and we calculate y_1 by Runge-Kutta or some other single-step method. Then we calculate $y_2, y_3, \ldots, y_n$ by means of the formulas

(17-4) $$z_{k+2} = y_{k+1} + hf(x_{k+1}, y_{k+1})$$

and

(17-5) $$y_{k+2} = y_k + \frac{h}{3}\left[f(x_k, y_k) + 4f(x_{k+1}, y_{k+1}) + f(x_{k+2}, z_{k+2})\right]$$

$$(k = 0, 1, 2, \ldots, n - 2).$$

Of course,

$$x_{k+2} = x_{k+1} + h.$$

Formula 17-4 is a **predictor** formula, and Formula 17-5 is a **corrector.** The method we have described is called **Milne's Method.** There are many modifications of Milne's Method and many other predictor-corrector methods. With a more accurate predictor than our simple Euler-Cauchy approximation, Milne's Method is comparable in accuracy to Runge-Kutta. But it is "unstable" for certain differential equations, and gross errors are possible, even with small step size, if the method is applied to such equations on an interval of reasonable length. In these situations, other predictor-corrector methods may be used.

Predictor-corrector formulas are used in place of Runge-Kutta formulas because we have to compute fewer values of f. Compare our versions of Runge-Kutta and Milne. At each stage of Runge-Kutta, we compute four values of f, the numbers a_k, b_k, c_k, and d_k. But in Milne, we have only to compute $f(x_{k+1}, y_{k+1})$ and $f(x_{k+2}, z_{k+2})$ at each stage (we have already computed $f(x_k, y_k)$). Since computing vaues of f may be complicated (after all, if f is very simple, we might not need a numerical method), and since it may be necessary to use many steps, it is advisable to eliminate as many computations of values of f as we can.

Let us use Milne's method to solve an initial value problem we have seen before.

Example 17-1.   Calculate the values of the solution of the initial value problem $y' = 1 + y^2$ and $y = 0$ when $x = 0$ at the points of the set $\{0.0, .05, .1, \ldots, 1.0\}$.

Solution. Figure 17-1 shows an annotated flow chart that explains the computer program of Fig. 17-2. The program clearly shows the computational improvement over Runge-Kutta. In each swing through the loop we calculate only two values of f. If you run this program on a computer, you will see that it gives good answers, almost as good as those of the Runge-Kutta program of Example 16-1.

References [**2**], [**3**], and [**10**] give a much fuller discussion of the numerical solution of initial value problems than we have given here. And they, in turn, refer to still more detailed sources of information. It is a big subject.

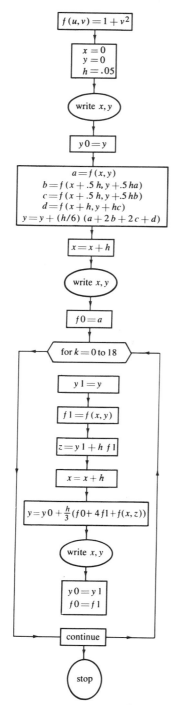

The flowchart shows the following boxes and annotations:

$f(u,v) = 1 + v^2$ —   SPECIFY THE FUNCTION F

$x = 0$
$y = 0$
$h = .05$ —   SELECT X_0, Y_0, AND H

write x, y —   WRITE X_0, Y_0

$y0 = y$ —   SAVE Y_0 FOR FUTURE REFERENCE

$a = f(x, y)$
$b = f(x + .5\,h, y + .5\,ha)$
$c = f(x + .5\,h, y + .5\,hb)$
$d = f(x + h, y + hc)$
$y = y + (h/6)\,(a + 2b + 2c + d)$ —   CALCULATE Y_1 BY RUNGE-KUTTA

$x = x + h$ —   CALCULATE X_1

write x, y —   WRITE X_1, Y_1

$f0 = a$ —   SAVE $F(X_0, Y_0)$ FOR FUTURE REFERENCE

for $k = 0$ to 18   —   CALCULATE (X_2, Y_2) TO (X_{20}, Y_{20})

$y1 = y$ —   PREVIOUS Y BECOMES Y_{K+1}

$f1 = f(x, y)$ —   CALCULATE $F(X_{K+1}, Y_{K+1})$

$z = y1 + h\,f1$ —   EQUATION 17-4

$x = x + h$ —   CALCULATE X_{K+2}

$y = y0 + \frac{h}{3}(f0 + 4f1 + f(x, z))$ —   EQUATION 17-5

write x, y —   WRITE X_{K+2}, Y_{K+2}

$y0 = y1$
$f0 = f1$ — Y_{K+1} BECOMES Y_K, AND $F(X_{K+1}, Y_{K+1})$ BECOMES $F(X_K, Y_K)$

continue

stop

Figure 17-1

```
           F(U, V) = 1 + 0*U + V*V
           X = 0
           Y = 0
           H = .05
           WRITE(6, 1) X, Y
    1      FORMAT(1X, F4.2, F12.4)
           Y0 = Y
           A = F(X, Y)
           B = F(X + .5*H, Y + .5*H*A)
           C = F(X+.5*H, Y+.5*H*B)
           D = F(X+H, Y+H*C)
           Y = Y + (H/6)*(A + 2*B + 2*C + D)
           X = X + H
           WRITE(6, 1) X, Y
           F0 = A
           DO 2 I = 1, 19
           Y1 = Y
           F1 = F(X, Y1)
           Z = Y1 + H*F1
           X = X + H
           Y = Y0 + (H/3)*(F0 + 4*F1 + F(X, Z))
           WRITE(6, 1) X, Y
           Y0 = Y1
           F0 = F1
    2      CONTINUE
           STOP
           END
```

Figure 17-2

EXERCISE 17

1. Use the Milne technique to print a table of values of the solution of the initial value problem $y' = x^2 + y^2$ and $y = 0$ when $x = 0$ at the points of the set $\{0, .05, \ldots, 1.0\}$, and compare it with the tables you have calculated by other methods.

2. The initial value problem $y' = \sqrt{1 - y^2}$ and $y = 0$ when $x = 0$ has the Sine function for a solution. Use the Milne method to print a table of values of this function, and compare it with the table you calculated in Exercise 16-6.

3. In Exercise 15-10 we saw that the function Tan^{-1} is the solution of the initial value problem $y' = \cos^2 y$ and $y = 0$ when $x = 0$. Use the Milne method to print a table of values of this function, and compare it with the table you computed in Exercise 6-6.

4. Show that if we apply Equation 17-2 to the linear problem $y' = x + y$ and $y = 0$ when $x = 0$, we obtain the *explicit* recursion formula

$$y_{k+2} = (1 - h/3)^{-1}\{y_k + (h/3)[x_k + y_k + 4(x_{k+1} + y_{k+1}) + x_{k+2}]\}.$$

Therefore, we need not use the predictor-corrector technique, although we still have to find y_1, perhaps by Runge-Kutta, to get us started. Another way of finding a starting value y_1 is to use Taylor's Formula without the remainder as an approximation. For example, we might use a three-term Taylor's Formula and write

$$(17\text{-}6) \qquad w(x_1) \approx w(x_0) + w'(x_0)h + w''(x_0)\frac{h^2}{2!} = y_1.$$

The numbers $w(x_0)$, $w'(x_0)$, and $w''(x_0)$ are easily computed, because w is a solution of our initial value problem. In other words, $w'(x) = x + w(x)$, and hence $w''(x) = 1 + w'(x)$. Therefore, $w(x_0) = y_0 = 0$, $w'(x_0) = x_0 + w(x_0) = x_0 + y_0 = 0 + 0 = 0$, $w''(x_0) = 1 + w'(x_0) = 1 + 0 = 1$, and so $y_1 = \frac{1}{2}h^2$.

(a) Write a computer program for printing the values of the solution of our initial value problem at the points of the set $\{0, .05, \ldots, 1\}$.

(b) Find y_1 by using a Taylor's Formula approximation with one more term.

5. If, in our computer program of Fig. 17-2, we replace the statement

$$y = y0 + (h/3) * (f0 + 4 * f1 + f(x, z))$$

with

do 3 $k = 1, 2$

$$y = y0 + (h/3) * (f0 + 4 * f1 + f(x, z))$$

$$z = y$$

3   continue

what do we accomplish? What would be the corresponding changes in Equations 17-4 and 17-5? What do we "pay" for any increased accuracy?

REVIEW EXERCISE, CHAPTER 3

Use the following exercises to test yourself on the material in this chapter.

1. Let w be the solution of the initial value problem

$$y' = \text{int } (\pi x) \text{ and } y = 2 \text{ when } x = 3.$$

(a) Find $w(\pi)$.

(b) What is the domain of w?

2. Find the differential equation of the family of curves $y = \tan (x + c)$.

3. Suppose that $y = w(x)$ satisfies the initial value problem $y' = f(y)$ and $y = 5$ when $x = 10$. Show that $y = w(x - 10)$ satisfies the initial value problem $y' = f(y)$ and $y = 5$ when $x = 20$.

4. Let w be the solution of the initial value problem $y' = \sin (xy)$ and $y = 1$ when $x = 0$.

(a) How do we know that $w(x) > 0$ for each x in the domain of w?

(b) Show that w is an even function.

(c) Show that $w(x) \leq x + 1$ for each $x \geq 0$.

(d) How do parts (a)–(c) and Theorem 15-1 imply that the domain of w is the interval $(-\infty, \infty)$?

(e) Does $y = -w(x)$ satisfy the initial value problem $y' = \sin(xy)$ and $y = -1$ when $x = 0$?

5. Let w be the solution of the initial value problem $y' = x^2 + y^2$ and $y = 0$ when $x = 0$, and let w_{20} be the twentieth Euler-Cauchy approximation in the interval $[0, 1]$. Can you convince yourself that $w_{20}(x) \leq w(x)$ for each $x \in [0, 1]$?

6. Do our existence and uniqueness theorems state that the initial value problem $y' = x|x| + y|y|$ and $y = 0$ when $x = 0$ has a unique solution?

7. Pick *two* pairs (a, b) so that $y = ax^b$ satisfies the initial value problem $y' = 6y^{2/3}$ and $y = 0$ when $x = 0$.

8. The exponential function is the solution of the initial value problem $y' = y$ and $y = 1$ when $x = 0$. Use the Runge-Kutta technique to print a table of values of exp at the points of the set $\{0, .1, .2, \ldots, 1.0\}$. Modify your program so that it also prints e^{-x} and $\sinh x$ at each of these points.

9. (a) Find a solution u of the integral equation $w(x) = 5 + \int_0^x \text{int } (w(t))dt$ in an interval $[0, b)$.

(b) What is the largest possible value of b such that $u'(x)$ exists for each $x \in [0, b)$?

(c) Find a solution v of the equation in an interval $(a, 0]$.

(d) What is the smallest possible choice of a such that $v'(x)$ exists for each $x \in (a, 0]$?

(e) If w is the function that is obtained by "patching" u and v together on the interval (a, b), show that w satisfies the integral equation.

(f) Does $y = w(x)$ satisfy the differential equation $y' = \text{int } (y)$ in the interval (a, b)?

10. (a) Apply the Tangent Rule to Equation 16-2 and obtain the approximation

$$w(x_{k+1}) \approx w(x_k) + hf(x_k + .5h, w(x_k + .5h)).$$

(b) Explain why this approximation suggests the predictor-corrector scheme

$$z_k = y_k + .5hf(x_k, y_k)$$

$$y_{k+1} = y_k + hf(x_k + .5h, z_k).$$

(c) Use this method (and the computer) to solve the initial value problem $y' = x^2 + y^2$ and $y = 0$ when $x = 0$ in the interval $[0, 1]$. Compare the results with our earlier solutions of this problem.

11. Suppose that u and v are solutions of an initial value problem $y' = f(x, y)$ and $y = y_0$ when $x = x_0$. Can you show that $y = \frac{1}{2}[|u(x) - v(x)| + u(x) +$

$v(x)$] also satisfies this problem? How does the graph of this latter equation compare with the graphs of u and v?

12. (a) If $f(x, y) = \sqrt{1 - y^2}$ for points of the set $\{(x, y): |y| \le 1\}$ and $f(x, y) = 0$ otherwise, can you convince yourself that f is continuous in the entire XY-plane?

(b) Thus, according to Theorem 15-1, a fully extended solution of the initial value problem $y' = f(x, y)$ and $y = 0$ when $x = 0$ must reach to the "boundary" of the XY-plane. Can you show that the equations

$$y = \sin x \text{ if } -\tfrac{1}{2}\pi \le x \le \tfrac{1}{2}\pi$$
$$= 1 \text{ if } x > \tfrac{1}{2}\pi$$
$$= -1 \text{ if } x < -\tfrac{1}{2}\pi$$

define a fully extended solution of our initial value problem?

13. Suppose that w is the solution of the initial value problem $y' = y$ and $y = 1$ when $x = 0$, and that a is a given number.

(a) Show that $y = w(a + x)$ and $y = w(a)w(x)$ satisfy the initial value problem $y' = y$ and $y = w(a)$ when $x = 0$.

(b) Now invoke the uniqueness theorem to show that $w(a + x) = w(a)w(x)$. Does this result surprise you?

(c) Can you use a similar argument to show that $w(rx) = (w(x))^r$ for each real number r?

CHAPTER 4

SYSTEMS

OF DIFFERENTIAL EQUATIONS

It would seem natural now to move up from a study of differential equations of the first order to differential equations of the second, and higher, orders. We will do so, but in a somewhat disguised way. In this chapter, we will discuss differential equations whose solutions are *vector-valued* functions, and it turns out that the theory of such differential equations includes the theory of scalar differential equations of order higher than 1. Furthermore, vector differential equations have some interesting applications of their own, and much of the modern literature on differential equations is written in vector language as a matter of course.

18 VECTORS AND MATRICES

We open this chapter with a review section devoted to vectors and matrices. Of course, we assume that you have met these important mathematical concepts before, but there is so much variation in notation and terminology in connection with linear algebra that a fairly detailed review is probably not out of place. We do not intend to go very deeply into the subject, however, and we will recall for you only those topics that will be directly useful to us in the present chapter. Some other ideas from linear algebra will be needed in Chapter Six, but we can wait till then to bring them in. It is fair to say that a specialist in differential equations spends almost as much time studying linear algebra (and its ramifications) as he devotes to the study of differential equations themselves.

When we introduce coordinates into the plane, we associate a pair of numbers with each point. Similarly, a coordinate system associates a triple of numbers with each point in three-space. We are so familiar with this association that we don't distinguish between points and pairs or triples of numbers. We say that (x, y, z) *is* a point, or that the plane *is* the set of pairs of real numbers. Because they are so useful, it is convenient to think of pairs and triples of real numbers as mathematical entities in their own right. The set of all pairs of real numbers is denoted by R^2, the set of all triples by R^3, the set of quadruples by R^4, and so on. Geometrically, R^1 is the number line, R^2 is the plane, and R^3 is three-space. Although there is no obvious geometric interpretation of R^4, R^5, and so on, that doesn't mean that they are not useful objects of study.

Because of the geometric background of some of these sets, the elements of a set R^n frequently are called *points*. For example, $(1, 2, -3, \pi)$ is a point of R^4. We will denote points of a set R^n by boldface letters. Thus, $\mathbf{x} = (x, y)$ is a point of R^2. The numbers x and y are the **components** of $\mathbf{x}$, and we often follow the convention of denoting the first component of the element $\mathbf{x}$ by the lightface letter x. We sometimes find it convenient to write elements as *columns*, rather than *rows*, of numbers. Thus, we might write $\mathbf{x} = \begin{pmatrix} x \\ y \end{pmatrix}$, instead of (x, y). This variation in notation represents no conceptual change; we are still dealing with an ordered pair of numbers and hence an element of R^2. The column notation merely helps us perform more easily some of the calculations that we will introduce shortly. There is another notational device we will use later. Suppose that $\mathbf{x}$ is the element of R^2 that we have just mentioned, and that t is a real number. Then we will write $(t, \mathbf{x})$ for the point (t, x, y) of R^3.

So far, we have been thinking of R^n merely as a *set;* now we are going to introduce arithmetic operations into this set. To keep from losing the main ideas (which are pretty simple) in a mass of subscripts, we will restrict our attention to R^2. Everything we say, however, applies in an obvious way to R^n, where n may be any positive integer. Thus, if $\mathbf{x}_1 = (x_1, y_1)$ and $\mathbf{x}_2 = (x_2, y_2)$ are elements of R^2, and if r is a real number, then we define the **sum** of $\mathbf{x}_1$ and $\mathbf{x}_2$ and the **product** of $\mathbf{x}_1$ by r by the equations

(18-1) $$\mathbf{x}_1 + \mathbf{x}_2 = (x_1 + x_2, y_1 + y_2)$$

and

(18-2) $$r\mathbf{x}_1 = (rx_1, ry_1).$$

It is a simple matter to show that $\mathbf{x}_1 + \mathbf{x}_2 = \mathbf{x}_2 + \mathbf{x}_1$, and, for any three elements $\mathbf{x}_1$, $\mathbf{x}_2$, and $\mathbf{x}_3$, $(\mathbf{x}_1 + \mathbf{x}_2) + \mathbf{x}_3 = \mathbf{x}_1 + (\mathbf{x}_2 + \mathbf{x}_3)$. The element $\mathbf{0} = (0, 0)$ plays the role of 0; that is, for any element $\mathbf{x}$, we have $\mathbf{x} + \mathbf{0} = \mathbf{0} + \mathbf{x} = \mathbf{x}$. The **negative** of an element $\mathbf{x} = (x, y)$ is the element $-\mathbf{x} = (-1)\mathbf{x} = (-x, -y)$, and we see that $\mathbf{x} + (-\mathbf{x}) = (-\mathbf{x}) + \mathbf{x} = \mathbf{0}$. You can easily check to see that, if $\mathbf{x}_1$ and $\mathbf{x}_2$ are elements of R^2, and r_1 and r_2 are real numbers, then

$$1\mathbf{x}_1 = \mathbf{x}_1,$$
$$(r_1 + r_2)\mathbf{x}_1 = r_1\mathbf{x}_1 + r_2\mathbf{x}_1,$$
(18-3) $$r_1(\mathbf{x}_1 + \mathbf{x}_2) = r_1\mathbf{x}_1 + r_1\mathbf{x}_2,$$
$$(r_1r_2)\mathbf{x}_1 = r_1(r_2\mathbf{x}_1).$$

With the arithmetic operations we have just introduced, the *set R^2* becomes an example of a **vector space** over the real numbers. When we have these operations in mind, we speak of the elements of R^2 as *vectors* and the real numbers r_1, r_2, and so on, as *scalars*.

But we can make our set R^2 into more than a mere vector space. In addition to the algebraic operations we have been talking about, we can introduce geometry into R^2. This introduction is accomplished by means of the **dot product**. If $\mathbf{x}_1 = (x_1, y_1)$ and $\mathbf{x}_2 = (x_2, y_2)$ are two elements of R^2, then the dot product of $\mathbf{x}_2$ by $\mathbf{x}_1$ is the number

(18-4) $$\mathbf{x}_1 \cdot \mathbf{x}_2 = x_1x_2 + y_1y_2.$$

Because the dot product of two vectors is simply a number, a scalar, it is often called the **scalar product**. Geometrically, if we think of $\mathbf{x}_1$ and $\mathbf{x}_2$ as two arrows in the plane, as shown in Fig. 18-1, then

(18-5) $$\mathbf{x}_1 \cdot \mathbf{x}_2 = |\mathbf{x}_1|\, |\mathbf{x}_2| \cos \theta,$$

where $|\mathbf{x}_1|$ and $|\mathbf{x}_2|$ are the lengths of $\mathbf{x}_1$ and $\mathbf{x}_2$, and θ is the angle between them. This same interpretation carries over to R^3, but of course it is hard to visualize the dot product in higher dimensions.

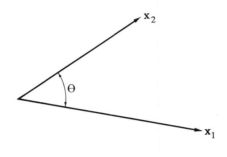

Figure 18-1

The dot product satisfies the "natural" laws of arithmetic. You may easily verify the following equations by going back to the defining Equation 18-4:

$$\mathbf{x}_1 \cdot \mathbf{x}_2 = \mathbf{x}_2 \cdot \mathbf{x}_1,$$

(18-6) $$(\mathbf{x}_1 + \mathbf{x}_2) \cdot \mathbf{x}_3 = \mathbf{x}_1 \cdot \mathbf{x}_3 + \mathbf{x}_2 \cdot \mathbf{x}_3,$$

$$(r\mathbf{x}_1) \cdot \mathbf{x}_2 = r(\mathbf{x}_1 \cdot \mathbf{x}_2),$$

$$\mathbf{x} \cdot \mathbf{x} \geq 0 \text{ and } \mathbf{x} \cdot \mathbf{x} = 0 \text{ only if } \mathbf{x} = \mathbf{0}.$$

The **norm**, or **length**, of an element $\mathbf{x} \in R^n$ is defined to be the number $|\mathbf{x}| = \sqrt{\mathbf{x} \cdot \mathbf{x}}$. From Equation 18-5, we see that two vectors $\mathbf{x}_1$ and $\mathbf{x}_2$ of R^2 are perpendicular ($\cos \theta = 0$) if, and only if, $\mathbf{x}_1 \cdot \mathbf{x}_2 = 0$. We carry this terminology over to higher dimensions and say that $\mathbf{x}_1$ and $\mathbf{x}_2$ are **orthogonal** (another word for perpendicular), provided that $\mathbf{x}_1 \cdot \mathbf{x}_2 = 0$.

Example 18-1. If $\mathbf{x}_1 = (2, -1)$ and $\mathbf{x}_2 = (1, 1)$, verify that

$$(3\mathbf{x}_1 - 2\mathbf{x}_2) \cdot \mathbf{x}_1 = 3|\mathbf{x}_1|^2 - 2(\mathbf{x}_1 \cdot \mathbf{x}_2).$$

Solution. We are to calculate the quantities on both sides of this equation separately and show that the results are the same. Thus, $3\mathbf{x}_1 - 2\mathbf{x}_2 = 3(2, -1) - 2(1, 1) = (4, -5)$, and so $(3\mathbf{x}_1 - 2\mathbf{x}_2) \cdot \mathbf{x}_1 = (4, -5) \cdot (2, -1) = 8 + 5 = 13$. On the other hand, $|\mathbf{x}_1|^2 = \mathbf{x}_1 \cdot \mathbf{x}_1 = 4 + 1 = 5$, and $\mathbf{x}_1 \cdot \mathbf{x}_2 = 2 - 1 = 1$, and so $3|\mathbf{x}_1|^2 - 2(\mathbf{x}_1 \cdot \mathbf{x}_2) = 3 \cdot 5 - 2 \cdot 1 = 13$, the same number.

For us, a **matrix** will be an array of numbers (just as a vector is a row or column of numbers), and we will be dealing only with square arrays. For example,

(18-7)
$$M = \begin{bmatrix} 1 & 2 \\ 3 & 4 \end{bmatrix}$$

is a 2 by 2 matrix; that is, a *square* matrix of *order* 2. The rows and columns of a matrix can be regarded as vectors. Thus, we can write a matrix $A = \begin{bmatrix} a & b \\ c & d \end{bmatrix}$ as

$$A = \begin{bmatrix} \mathbf{r}_1 \\ \mathbf{r}_2 \end{bmatrix} = [\mathbf{c}_1 \quad \mathbf{c}_2],$$

where $\mathbf{r}_1 = (a, b)$ and $\mathbf{r}_2 = (c, d)$ are the **row vectors** of A, and

$$\mathbf{c}_1 = \begin{pmatrix} a \\ c \end{pmatrix} \text{ and } \mathbf{c}_2 = \begin{pmatrix} b \\ d \end{pmatrix}$$

are the **column vectors** of A.

We will define the **product** of a vector $\mathbf{x} = (x, y) \in R^2$ by a 2 by 2 matrix $A = \begin{bmatrix} a & b \\ c & d \end{bmatrix}$. This product $A\mathbf{x}$ is a *vector;* that is, an element of R^2, so we must give the rule that assigns its two components. It is customary in this situation to write our vectors as columns, and we make the following definition of the product $A\mathbf{x}$:

(18-8)
$$\begin{bmatrix} a & b \\ c & d \end{bmatrix} \begin{pmatrix} x \\ y \end{pmatrix} = \begin{pmatrix} ax + by \\ cx + dy \end{pmatrix}.$$

It is often useful to think of the vector $A\mathbf{x}$ as a *linear combination* of the column vectors of A. Thus, we could also write Equation 18-8 as

$$A\mathbf{x} = x\mathbf{c}_1 + y\mathbf{c}_2.$$

Example 18-2. Find $M\mathbf{x}$, where M is the matrix of Equation 18-7, and $\mathbf{x} = (3, -2)$.

Solution. Here,

$$\begin{bmatrix} 1 & 2 \\ 3 & 4 \end{bmatrix} \begin{pmatrix} 3 \\ -2 \end{pmatrix} = \begin{pmatrix} 1 \cdot 3 + 2(-2) \\ 3 \cdot 3 + 4(-2) \end{pmatrix} = \begin{pmatrix} -1 \\ 1 \end{pmatrix}.$$

It is not difficult to show that for any vectors $\mathbf{x}_1$ and $\mathbf{x}_2$, and any scalars r_1 and r_2, we have the "linearity relation"

(18-9)
$$A(r_1\mathbf{x}_1 + r_2\mathbf{x}_2) = r_1 A\mathbf{x}_1 + r_2 A\mathbf{x}_2.$$

In other words, we end up with the same vector whether we first compute the linear combination $r_1\mathbf{x}_1 + r_2\mathbf{x}_2$ and then multiply by A or first multiply by A and then compute the linear combination of the resulting vectors.

Earlier in the section, we introduced algebraic operations into the set R^2; now we will briefly mention the algebra of square matrices. As usual, our *words* apply to the two-dimensional case, but our *ideas* are valid in any dimension. If A and B are 2 by 2 matrices, then their **sum** $A + B$ is the 2 by 2 matrix that is formed by adding corresponding elements of A and B. Similarly, if r is a scalar, the matrix rA (or Ar) is obtained from A by multiplying each of its components by r. The matrix $\begin{bmatrix} 0 & 0 \\ 0 & 0 \end{bmatrix}$ plays the role of zero in the algebra of 2 by 2 matrices, so we denote it by the symbol 0. Thus, $0 + A = A + 0 = A$. If we define $-A = (-1)A$, and $A - B = A + (-B)$, then $A - A = 0$. It is not difficult to show that the "natural" rules of arithmetic hold, so that, for example,

$$A + B = B + A, \; A + (B + C) = (A + B) + C,$$

$$r(A + B) = rA + rB, \text{ and } (p + q)A = pA + qA,$$

where A, B, and C are arbitrary matrices and r, p, and q are scalars.

Multiplication of matrices is more complicated. We define the **product** AB as the matrix whose column vectors are obtained by multiplying the column vectors of B by the matrix A. Thus, if $\mathbf{c}_1$ and $\mathbf{c}_2$ are the column vectors of B, we define AB by the equation

$$AB = [A\mathbf{c}_1 \quad A\mathbf{c}_2].$$

We use Equation 18-8 to compute the components of these column vectors, so our multiplication rule reads

(18-10) $$\begin{bmatrix} a & b \\ c & d \end{bmatrix} \begin{bmatrix} u & v \\ w & x \end{bmatrix} = \begin{bmatrix} au + bw & av + bx \\ cu + dw & cv + dx \end{bmatrix}.$$

Example 18-3.   Compute both AB and BA if

$$A = \begin{bmatrix} 2 & -1 \\ -4 & 2 \end{bmatrix} \text{ and } B = \begin{bmatrix} 1 & 5 \\ 2 & 10 \end{bmatrix}.$$

Solution. According to Equation 18-10,

$$AB = \begin{bmatrix} 2 & -1 \\ -4 & 2 \end{bmatrix} \begin{bmatrix} 1 & 5 \\ 2 & 10 \end{bmatrix} = \begin{bmatrix} 0 & 0 \\ 0 & 0 \end{bmatrix}$$

and

$$BA = \begin{bmatrix} 1 & 5 \\ 2 & 10 \end{bmatrix} \begin{bmatrix} 2 & -1 \\ -4 & 2 \end{bmatrix} = \begin{bmatrix} -18 & 9 \\ -36 & 18 \end{bmatrix}.$$

The preceding example shows that *it is not always true that AB and BA are equal.* Moreover, it is possible that $AB = 0$ without either A or B being the 0 matrix. Most of the other rules of arithmetic for multiplication, however, are valid for matrices. Thus, for example,

$$A(BC) = (AB)C \text{ and } A(B + C) = AB + AC.$$

These equations are consequences of the definition of matrix addition and multiplication, the linearity Equation 18-9, and the identity

$$(AB)\mathbf{x} = A(B\mathbf{x}).$$

This latter equation follows readily from our basic definitions and the linearity equation. It is also useful to observe that

$$(A + B)\mathbf{x} = A\mathbf{x} + B\mathbf{x}.$$

The **identity matrix** I that is defined by the equation

$$I = \begin{bmatrix} 1 & 0 \\ 0 & 1 \end{bmatrix}$$

acts like the number 1 of the real number system. In other words,

$$IA = AI = A \text{ and } I\mathbf{x} = \mathbf{x}$$

for any matrix A and any vector $\mathbf{x}$.

The matrix A^{-1} is the **inverse** of the matrix A if

(18-11) $$AA^{-1} = A^{-1}A = I.$$

Thus, $X = A^{-1}$ satisfies the two equations $AX = I$ and $XA = I$. In Exercise 18-8, we will ask you to show that these equations cannot have two different solutions; that is, if a matrix has an inverse, it has only one. Therefore, it is proper to speak of *the* inverse of a matrix, rather than *an* inverse. Furthermore, it can be shown that we need only solve the single equation $AX = I$ to find the inverse of A; the equation $XA = I$ will automatically be satisfied. From the symmetry of the definition of the inverse, it is clear that A is the inverse of A^{-1}; that is, $(A^{-1})^{-1} = A$. Notice that *not every matrix has an inverse.*

Example 18-4. Show that the matrix $A = \begin{bmatrix} 1 & 1 \\ 1 & 1 \end{bmatrix}$ does not have an inverse.

Solution. Let us take an arbitrary matrix $X = \begin{bmatrix} x & y \\ z & w \end{bmatrix}$ and consider the product

AX. We have

$$AX = \begin{bmatrix} 1 & 1 \\ 1 & 1 \end{bmatrix} \begin{bmatrix} x & y \\ z & w \end{bmatrix} = \begin{bmatrix} x+z & y+w \\ x+z & y+w \end{bmatrix}.$$

It is clear that no choice of x, y, z, and w will make this product the identity matrix I. We simply cannot, for example, choose x and z so that $x + z = 1$ *and* $x + z = 0$.

It is true that a matrix A has an inverse if, and only if, a certain number det A, called the **determinant** of A, is not 0. For a 2 by 2 matrix $A = \begin{bmatrix} a & b \\ c & d \end{bmatrix}$, we have

$$\det A = \begin{vmatrix} a & b \\ c & d \end{vmatrix} = ad - bc.$$

For matrices of higher order, the expression for det A is much more complicated, as you know. You also know another useful criterion for determining which matrices have inverses.

THEOREM 18-1

A square matrix A has an inverse if, and only if, **0** is the only solution of the equation $A\mathbf{x} = \mathbf{0}$.

EXERCISE 18

1. Let $A = \begin{bmatrix} 1 & -2 \\ 2 & 1 \end{bmatrix}$, $\mathbf{x} = (2, 1)$, and $\mathbf{y} = (1, 1)$. Compute the following quantities
   (a) $A\mathbf{x} \cdot \mathbf{y}$
   (b) $A^2\mathbf{x} + 2\mathbf{y}$
   (c) $|A^2\mathbf{x}| - |A\mathbf{x}|^2$
   (d) $\det A\mathbf{x}$
   (e) $|\mathbf{x}|^2|\mathbf{y}|^2 - (\mathbf{x} \cdot \mathbf{y})^2$
   (f) $\det (3A) - 3 \det A$
   (g) $|2\mathbf{x} - 3\mathbf{y}|$
   (h) $\left| \dfrac{1}{|\mathbf{x}|} \mathbf{x} \right|$

2. If $A = \begin{bmatrix} 0 & 1 \\ -1 & 0 \end{bmatrix}$, find A^{1492}.

3. Let A, B, and C be 2 by 2 matrices such that $AB = AC$. Does it necessarily follow that $B = C$?

4. (a) If $A = \begin{bmatrix} a & b \\ c & d \end{bmatrix}$, show that $A^{-1} = \dfrac{1}{\det A} \begin{bmatrix} d & -b \\ -c & a \end{bmatrix}$.
   (b) Compute $P^{-1}AP$ if $P = \begin{bmatrix} 2 & 1 \\ 1 & 1 \end{bmatrix}$ and $A = \begin{bmatrix} 1 & 4 \\ -2 & 7 \end{bmatrix}$.

5. Let P and A be n by n matrices and k be a positive integer. Explain why $(P^{-1}AP)^k = P^{-1}A^kP$.

6. Show that $D_x \begin{vmatrix} f(x) & g(x) \\ h(x) & k(x) \end{vmatrix} = \begin{vmatrix} f'(x) & g'(x) \\ h(x) & k(x) \end{vmatrix} + \begin{vmatrix} f(x) & g(x) \\ h'(x) & k'(x) \end{vmatrix}$.

7. (a) Show that if $A^2 = 0$, then $(I - A)^{-1} = I + A$.

    (b) Use the matrix $A = \begin{bmatrix} -4 & 16 \\ -1 & 4 \end{bmatrix}$ to illustrate the statement in part (a).

8. Show that if $AX = I$ and $YA = I$, then $X = Y$. How does this result imply that the inverse of a matrix (if it has one) is unique?

9. Let $\mathbf{x}(t) = (\cos t, \sin t)$. Show that $\mathbf{x}(t) \cdot \mathbf{x}'(t) = 0$. Show that, in general, if $|\mathbf{x}(t)| = 1$, then $\mathbf{x}(t) \cdot \mathbf{x}'(t) = 0$.

10. Let t be any real number and $R(t) = \begin{bmatrix} \cos t & \sin t \\ -\sin t & \cos t \end{bmatrix}$, and let $R^*(t)$ be the matrix whose column vectors are the row vectors of $R(t)$. Show that $R^*(t)R(t) = R(t)R^*(t) = I$. Show that $Y = R(t)$ satisfies the matrix differential equation $Y' = \begin{bmatrix} 0 & 1 \\ -1 & 0 \end{bmatrix} Y$.

11. Let $A(t) = \begin{bmatrix} t & e^t \\ 1 & e^t \end{bmatrix}$.

    (a) Find a number t_0 such that $A(t_0)$ does *not* have an inverse.
    (b) Solve the equation $A(t_0)\mathbf{x} = \mathbf{0}$.
    (c) If $t_1 \neq t_0$, solve the equation $A(t_1)\mathbf{x} = \mathbf{0}$.
    (d) How do the results of parts (b) and (c) fit in with Theorem 18-1?

19   INITIAL VALUE PROBLEMS IN SPACES OF HIGHER DIMENSIONS

We are going to introduce some new ideas in this section, but first we will look at an old idea in new clothing.

Example 19-1. Solve the initial value problem

$$x' = 3x + 4 \text{ and } x = 2 \text{ when } t = 0.$$

Solution. In our earlier chapters, we would have written this problem as

$$y' = 3y + 4 \text{ and } y = 2 \text{ when } x = 0,$$

but here we have x playing the role formerly played by y, and t taking the place of x. This change in notation is obviously of no conceptual importance; we are still dealing with an initial value problem with a simple linear equation. However, this new notation is the one we will be using in this chapter, so you may as well get used to it. In adopting it here, we are simply conforming to custom.

In Section 8, we learned that we should multiply both sides of our given differential equation by e^{-3t} and write the result in the form

$$D_t(e^{-3t}x) = 4e^{-3t}.$$

Hence,

$$e^{-3t}x = 2 + 4 \int_0^t e^{-3u}du = 2 - \tfrac{4}{3}e^{-3u} \Big|_0^t$$

$$= 2 - \tfrac{4}{3}e^{-3t} + \tfrac{4}{3}.$$

Therefore, $x = \tfrac{10}{3}e^{3t} - \tfrac{4}{3}$ satisfies our initial value problem.

More generally, in Chapter Three we studied initial value problems of the form

(19-1) $x' = f(t, x)$ and $x = x_0$ when $t = t_0$.

Here, f is a function whose domain D is a subset of R^2 and whose range is a subset of R^1. The initial point (t_0, x_0) belongs to D.

This idea of an initial value problem can be extended to higher dimensional spaces in an obvious way. Thus, suppose that D is a domain in R^3 that contains a given point $(t_0, \mathbf{x}_0)$, and let $\mathbf{f}$ be a function whose domain is D and whose range is a subset of R^2. Then we can consider the initial value problem

(19-2) $\mathbf{x}' = \mathbf{f}(t, \mathbf{x})$ and $\mathbf{x} = \mathbf{x}_0$ when $t = t_0$,

and we can go to still higher dimensions in exactly the same way.

Although the *concept* of a vector initial value problem is simple enough, a detailed explanation of one is likely to be a little complicated. For example, if $\mathbf{x} = (x, y)$, $\mathbf{f}(t, \mathbf{x}) = (3x - 2y + 2t - 2e^t, x + 3y + 1 - e^t - 3t)$, $\mathbf{x}_0 = (1, 0)$, and $t_0 = 0$, then the component form of Problem 19-2 is

(19-3)
$$\begin{aligned} x' &= 3x - 2y + 2t - 2e^t \\ y' &= x + 3y + 1 - e^t - 3t \end{aligned}$$
and $(x, y) = (1, 0)$ when $t = 0$.

Notice that the *single* vector equation $\mathbf{x}' = \mathbf{f}(t, \mathbf{x})$ is equivalent to a *system* of scalar equations in its components. We will therefore use the terms "vector equation" and "system of equations" interchangeably.

It is simply a matter of substitution to show that $(x, y) = (e^t, t)$ satisfies Problem 19-3. In other words, if we replace x with e^t and y with t, the system of differential equations is satisfied, and when $t = 0$ we have $(x, y) = (e^0, 0) = (1, 0)$. In general, a solution $\mathbf{u}$ of Problem 19-2 is a vector-valued function whose domain is an interval I that contains t_0 and is such that

and

(i) for each $t \in I$, $(t, \mathbf{u}(t)) \in D$ and $\mathbf{u}'(t) = \mathbf{f}(t, \mathbf{u}(t))$

(ii) $\mathbf{u}(t_0) = \mathbf{x}_0$.

Statements (i) and (ii) merely say that $\mathbf{x} = \mathbf{u}(t)$ should satisfy both the differential equation of Problem 19-2 and its initial condition.

The following example shows how vector initial value problems might arise in practice. You can easily imagine similar problems involving rocket trajectories, and so on.

Example 19-2. At a certain instant, a rabbit starts from the origin and runs along the positive X-axis at 30 miles per hour. At the same moment, a dog sets out from the point $(0, 1)$ at 40 miles per hour, always heading straight for the rabbit. How can we find the position of the dog at any later time?

Solution. Figure 19-1 shows the position of the dog and the rabbit t hours after they start running. The dog is at the terminal point of the vector $\mathbf{x}$, and the rabbit's position vector is $30t\mathbf{i}$ (where we have, as is customary, denoted the vector $(1, 0)$ by $\mathbf{i}$). The dog is headed straight for the rabbit, and so the vector $30t\mathbf{i} - \mathbf{x}$ is tangent to the dog's path. Since $\mathbf{x}$ is the dog's position vector, we know from calculus that the vector $\mathbf{x}'$ is also tangent to the dog's path and that its length $|\mathbf{x}'|$ is the dog's speed. Therefore, $\mathbf{x}'$ has the same direction as the vector $30t\mathbf{i} - \mathbf{x}$,

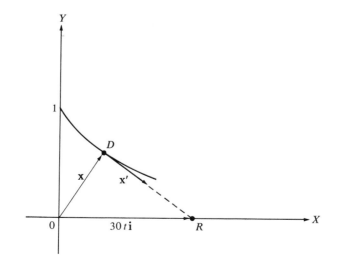

Figure 19-1

and it is 40 units long. In symbols, this statement becomes the differential equation

$$\mathbf{x}' = \frac{40}{|30t\mathbf{i} - \mathbf{x}|} (30t\mathbf{i} - \mathbf{x}).$$

To this differential equation we adjoin the initial condition $\mathbf{x} = (0,\ 1)$ when $t = 0$, and hence obtain an initial value problem whose solution gives us the position of the dog at any time.

It is easy to prove theorems on the existence and uniqueness of solutions of Problem 19-2 that are completely analogous to those we stated for the scalar case in Chapter 3. In fact, one of the real advantages of vector notation is that we can use some of the same proofs practically word for word [**6**, Chapters 1 and 2]. For example, we can set up Euler-Cauchy polygonal approximations and show that they (or, at least, a subsequence of them) converge to a solution of Problem 19-2, thus establishing the existence of a solution and proving the following vector version of Theorem 12-1.

THEOREM 19-1

If $\mathbf{f}$ is continuous in D, then Initial Value Problem 19-2 has a solution.

The statement of our previous uniqueness theorem (Theorem 14-2) is modified in the obvious way, but the proof we suggested before will not work. A new proof is easy, but somewhat tedious, to construct, and we will spare you the details. Most proofs of the following uniqueness theorem, for example, the one in Reference [**2**], are based on differential inequalities (Theorem 14-1), but not in the way our proof of Theorem 14-2 was.

THEOREM 19-2

Suppose that $\mathbf{f}$ is continuous in D, and the partial derivatives of the components of $\mathbf{f}(t,\ \mathbf{x})$ with respect to the components of $\mathbf{x}$ are bounded. If $\mathbf{u}$ and $\mathbf{v}$ are solutions of Problem 19-2 in an interval I, then $\mathbf{u}(t) = \mathbf{v}(t)$ for each $t \in I$.

Now we will show that initial value problems that deal with *single* differential equations of order higher than 1 are equivalent to initial value problems whose differential equations are *systems* of equations of the first order. We have already used this technique to solve Problem 7-4, and for certain special differential equations of the second order in Section 10. Now let us look at the general problem of the second order:

(19-4) $x'' = f(t, x, x')$ and $x = x_0$, $x' = y_0$ when $t = t_0$.

To write this problem as a first order problem in higher dimensional space, we simply let $y = x'$. Therefore, $y' = x'' = f(t, x, y)$, and so

(19-5)
$$x' = y$$
$$y' = f(t, x, y)$$
and $(x, y) = (x_0, y_0)$ when $t = t_0$.

Problem 19-5 is the component form of Problem 19-2 if $\mathbf{x} = (x, y)$ and $\mathbf{f}(t, \mathbf{x}) = (y, f(t, x, y))$. It is equivalent to Problem 19-4 in the sense that if $x = u(t)$ satisfies Problem 19-4, then $(x, y) = (u(t), u'(t))$ satisfies Problem 19-5, and if $(x, y) = (u(t), v(t))$ satisfies Problem 19-5, then $x = u(t)$ satisfies Problem 19-4.

Example 19-3.   Find a vector initial value problem that is equivalent to the scalar problem

$$x'' + 2x' - 3x = 5e^{2t} \text{ and } x = 3, \, x' = 0 \text{ when } t = 0.$$

Solution. Our differential equation can be written as $x'' = 3x - 2x' + 5e^{2t}$, and so $f(t, x, x') = 3x - 2x' + 5e^{2t}$. Since $x_0 = 3$, $y_0 = 0$, and $t_0 = 0$, System 19-5 therefore becomes

$$x' = y$$
$$y' = 3x - 2y + 5e^{2t}$$
and $(x, y) = (3, 0)$ when $t = 0$.

What we have done here, of course, is to replace a scalar problem of the second order that we cannot solve with a first order problem in two dimensions that we cannot solve either. We will learn how to handle these problems later on in this chapter.

The theoretical advantage of writing scalar problems of higher order as vector problems of the first order is considerable, for it enables us to apply our existence and uniqueness theorems, which we can prove with relatively simple first order techniques. Thus, since Theorems 19-1 and 19-2 tell us that Problem 19-5 has a unique solution (if f is a "reasonable" function), it follows that the equivalent Problem 19-4 has a unique solution. Among other things, this result shows us that we must specify *two* initial conditions to guarantee the uniqueness of the solution of a scalar problem of the *second* order. Of course, the same trick can be used to write, say, a scalar initial value problem in which the differential equation has order 12 as a vector problem of the first order, in which the vectors are elements of R^{12}.

EXERCISE 19

1. Write the following initial value problems involving differential equations of the second order as equivalent initial value problems involving systems of equations of the first order.

   (a) $x'' = txx'$
   $x = 3$, $x' = 4$ when $t = 0$

   (b) $x'' = e^{t+x^2+x'}$
   $x = 2$, $x' = 5$ when $t = 0$

   (c) $x'' + p(t)x' + q(t)x = r(t)$
   $x = x_0$, $x' = y_0$ when $t = t_0$

2. Eliminate y and hence write the following initial value problems involving systems of equations of the first order as equivalent initial value problems involving a single differential equation of the second order.

   (a) $x' = y$
   $y' = t \sin(x + y)$
   $(x, y) = (-1, 2)$ when $t = 0$

   (b) $x' = tx + y$
   $y' = e^{2x+y}$
   $(x, y) = (3, 4)$ when $t = 5$

   (c) $x' = 2x + 5y$
   $y' = x + 3y$
   $(x, y) = (3, 1)$ when $t = 0$

3. Verify that $x = e^t + e^{-3t} + e^{2t}$ satisfies the scalar second order initial value problem of Example 19-3. What is the solution of the equivalent first order system?

4. Find vectors (p, q) and (r, s) and numbers λ and μ such that $(x, y) = e^{\lambda t}(p, q) + e^{\mu t}(r, s)$ satisfies the initial value problem

$$x' = 2y$$
$$y' = 8x$$

   and $(x, y) = (4, -4)$ when $t = 0$.

5. First multiply both sides of the differential equation by e^{-3t} and then continue to use the techniques of Section 8 to solve the initial value problem

$$\mathbf{x}' = 3\mathbf{x} + 6(1, 0) \text{ and } \mathbf{x} = (2, -1) \text{ when } t = 0.$$

6. Show that the general recursion formula for the Euler-Cauchy polygonal approximations to the solution of Problem 19-2 is $\mathbf{x}_{k+1} = \mathbf{x}_k + h\mathbf{f}(t_k, \mathbf{x}_k)$. Here, $\mathbf{x}_k = (x_k, y_k)$; what is t_k?

7. (a) Show that the computer program in Fig. 19-2 gives an Euler-Cauchy approximation to the solution of Problem 19-3.

   (b) Modify this program so that it also prints the correct answer.

8. Problem 19-4 is a scalar problem, so we visualize Euler-Cauchy approximations to its solutions as polygonal graphs in the TX-plane. Show that if $\{(t_k, x_k)\}$ is the set of vertices of such a graph, then $t_{k+1} = t_k + h$, and the members of the sequence $\{x_k\}$ (after x_0) are calculated from the system of equations

$$x_{k+1} = x_k + hy_k$$

$$y_{k+1} = y_k + hf(t_k, x_k, y_k).$$

```
      X = 1
      Y = 0
      T = 0
      WRITE(6, 1) T, X, Y
1     FORMAT(1X, F3.1, 2F12.4)
      DO 2 I = 1, 5
      X = X + .1*(3*X − 2*Y + 2*T − 2*EXP(T))
      Y = Y + .1*(X + 3*Y + 1 − EXP(T) − 3*T)
      T = T + .1
      WRITE(6, 1) T, X, Y
2     CONTINUE
      STOP
      END
```

Figure 19-2

9. (a) Set $\mathbf{u} = 30t\mathbf{i} - \mathbf{x}$ in the identity $D_t|\mathbf{u}|^2 = D_t(\mathbf{u} \cdot \mathbf{u}) = 2\mathbf{u} \cdot D_t\mathbf{u}$, and then use the differential equation of Example 19-2 to replace $\mathbf{x}'$ in terms of $\mathbf{x}$ to obtain the equation

$$D_t|30t\mathbf{i} - \mathbf{x}|^2 = 60\mathbf{i} \cdot (30t\mathbf{i} - \mathbf{x}) - 80|30t\mathbf{i} - \mathbf{x}|.$$

(b) Now use the vector inequality $\mathbf{u} \cdot \mathbf{v} \le |\mathbf{u}| \, |\mathbf{v}|$ to show that

$$D_t|30t\mathbf{i} - \mathbf{x}|^2 \le -20|30t\mathbf{i} - \mathbf{x}|.$$

(c) Observe that $D_t|30t\mathbf{i} - \mathbf{x}|^2 = 2|30t\mathbf{i} - \mathbf{x}|D_t|30t\mathbf{i} - \mathbf{x}|$, and hence infer that

$$D_t|30t\mathbf{i} - \mathbf{x}| \le -10.$$

(d) Common sense tells us that our superdog (who can spot a rabbit a mile off) must catch the rabbit. How long does it take?

10. Show that the initial value problem

$$x' = -3ty^{1/3}$$
$$y' = -3tx^{1/3}$$

and $(x, y) = (0, 0)$ when $t = 0$

is satisfied by $(x, y) = (0, 0)$, $(x, y) = (-t^3, t^3)$, and $(x, y) = (t^3, -t^3)$.

20   LINEAR SYSTEMS WITH CONSTANT COEFFICIENTS

From our previous work with differential equations, it is clear that we will have a hard time solving a vector initial value problem

(20-1) $\mathbf{x}' = \mathbf{f}(t, \mathbf{x})$ and $\mathbf{x} = \mathbf{x}_0$ when $t = t_0$

unless $f(t, x)$ has a particularly simple form. Among the simplest useful scalar differential equations are the *linear* ones, and that same statement is true for vector equations.

A **linear** vector initial value problem has the form

(20-2)
$$x' = A(t)x + r(t)$$
$$x = x_0 \text{ when } t = t_0.$$

We are supposing that $A(t) = \begin{bmatrix} a(t) & b(t) \\ c(t) & d(t) \end{bmatrix}$ and that $r(t) = (r(t), s(t))$, where the functions a, b, c, d, r, and s are continuous in an interval J that contains the initial point t_0. The vector $x_0 = (x_0, y_0)$ is a given initial vector. The vector-valued function f that is defined by the equation $f(t, x) = A(t)x + r(t)$ is continuous, and the partial derivatives of the components of $A(t)x + r(t)$ with respect to the components of x are continuous, so our existence and uniqueness theorems apply. In fact, more is true. Theorem 19-1 tells us only that there is a *subinterval* of J (containing t_0) in which a solution exists. Because linear equations are so simple, it is not hard to show that the domain of a fully extended solution of Problem 20-2 is the *entire* interval J.

Example 20-1. Show that $x = (\cos t, 0)$ satisfies the initial value problem

$$x' = \begin{bmatrix} \tan t & \ln t \\ t^2 & 5 \end{bmatrix} x - (2 \sin t, t^2 \cos t)$$

$$x = (\tfrac{1}{2}, 0) \text{ when } t = \tfrac{1}{3}\pi.$$

Solution. In order that all the components of the given matrix make sense, we will naturally suppose that our basic interval is $J = (0, \tfrac{1}{2}\pi)$. Now we observe that $(\cos \tfrac{1}{3}\pi, 0) = (\tfrac{1}{2}, 0)$, so the initial condition is satisfied. To show that the differential equation also is satisfied, we merely have to verify the equation

$$\begin{pmatrix} -\sin t \\ 0 \end{pmatrix} = \begin{bmatrix} \tan t & \ln t \\ t^2 & 5 \end{bmatrix} \begin{pmatrix} \cos t \\ 0 \end{pmatrix} - \begin{pmatrix} 2 \sin t \\ t^2 \cos t \end{pmatrix}.$$

In Section 8, we learned that the first step in solving the *scalar* version of Problem 20-2 is to write $P(t) = \int_{t_0}^{t} A(v)dv$ and then multiply both sides of the given equation by $e^{-P(t)}$. In general, this trick does *not* work in higher dimensions, but it does work in the case of *constant coefficients*. So let us postpone further study of the general linear differential equation to Section 22 and suppose for the remainder of this section that

$$A = \begin{bmatrix} a & b \\ c & d \end{bmatrix}$$

is a 2 by 2 matrix of real numbers. The function $\mathbf{r}$, however, need not be a constant function. We will study the initial value problem

(20-3)
$$\mathbf{x}' = A\mathbf{x} + \mathbf{r}(t)$$
$$\mathbf{x} = \mathbf{x}_0 \text{ when } t = 0.$$

(Notice that we have set $t_0 = 0$; it makes our formulas a little simpler.)

Leaving the justification till the end, let us blindly apply the techniques we learned in Section 8 to solve this problem. We first multiply both sides of the given differential equation by e^{-At} and write the result as

$$e^{-At}\mathbf{x}' - e^{-At}A\mathbf{x} = e^{-At}\mathbf{r}(t).$$

We observe that the left-hand side of this equation is $D_t(e^{-At}\mathbf{x})$, so

$$D_t(e^{-At}\mathbf{x}) = e^{-At}\mathbf{r}(t),$$

an equation which suggests the substitution $\mathbf{z} = e^{-At}\mathbf{x}$. When we take the initial condition $\mathbf{x} = \mathbf{x}_0$ when $t = 0$ into account, and use the equation $e^{-A0} = I$, we see that $\mathbf{z} = \mathbf{x}_0$ when $t = 0$. Thus, our initial value problem is equivalent to the initial value problem

$$D_t\mathbf{z} = e^{-At}\mathbf{r}(t) \text{ and } \mathbf{z} = \mathbf{x}_0 \text{ when } t = 0.$$

This problem is obviously satisfied by $\mathbf{z} = \mathbf{x}_0 + \int_0^t e^{-As}\mathbf{r}(s)ds$, and when we replace $\mathbf{z}$ with $e^{-At}\mathbf{x}$, we find that

$$\mathbf{x} = e^{At}\mathbf{x}_0 + e^{At}\int_0^t e^{-As}\mathbf{r}(s)ds.$$

Since e^{At} is independent of the variable of integration s, we can take this factor inside the sign of integration, and we have the following theorem.

THEOREM 20-1

Initial Value Problem 20-3 is satisfied by

(20-4) $$\mathbf{x} = e^{At}\mathbf{x}_0 + \int_0^t e^{A(t-s)}\mathbf{r}(s)ds.$$

It would be stretching the truth to assert that we have *proved* Theorem 20-1. The trouble, of course, is that we have not said what e^{At} means. We know that e^2 means $e \cdot e$, that $e^{1/2}$ means $\sqrt{e}$, and so on. But what does it mean to raise e to a *matric* power? A careful analysis of the arguments which led us to

Theorem 20-1 shows that these arguments *do* constitute a proof if we can define matrix powers of e in such a way that

$$\text{(i) } \exp\left(\begin{bmatrix} 0 & 0 \\ 0 & 0 \end{bmatrix}\right) = \begin{bmatrix} 1 & 0 \\ 0 & 1 \end{bmatrix},$$

$$\text{(ii) } e^{A(u+v)} = e^{Au}e^{Av},$$

and

$$\text{(iii) } D_t e^{At} = e^{At}A.$$

So now we will produce such a definition.

Since $e^{at} = \sum\limits_{k=0}^{\infty} \dfrac{t^k}{k!} a^k$ if a is a scalar, it is natural to *define* e^{At} as the sum of the analogous series of powers of matrices:

$$(20\text{-}5) \qquad e^{At} = I + tA + \frac{t^2}{2!} A^2 + \frac{t^3}{3!} A^3 + \cdots = \sum_{k=0}^{\infty} \frac{t^k}{k!} A^k.$$

This definition requires a little comment. By $\sum\limits_{k=0}^{\infty} \dfrac{t^k}{k!} A^k$ we mean, of course, $\lim\limits_{K \uparrow \infty} \sum\limits_{k=0}^{K} \dfrac{t^k}{k!} A^k$. Now $\sum\limits_{k=0}^{K} \dfrac{t^k}{k!} A^k$, being the sum of 2 by 2 matrices, is itself a 2 by 2 matrix, with four components. Equation 20-5 therefore means that each of these four components converges, and the limit of each component is the corresponding component of the limit matrix e^{At}. We won't bother to stop to prove it, but it is really quite easy to show that the series in Equation 20-5 converges for each choice of A and t. (You can find a proof in Reference [3].)

Example 20-2. If $A = \begin{bmatrix} 0 & 1 \\ -1 & 0 \end{bmatrix}$, what is e^{At}?

Solution. As you can readily check, $A^2 = -I$, $A^3 = -A$, $A^4 = I$, and so on. Hence,

$$e^{At} = I + tA - \frac{t^2}{2!} I - \frac{t^3}{3!} A + \frac{t^4}{4!} I + \cdots$$

$$= \left(1 - \frac{t^2}{2!} + \frac{t^4}{4!} - \cdots\right) I + \left(t - \frac{t^3}{3!} + \frac{t^5}{5!} - \cdots\right) A$$

$$= \cos tI + \sin tA.$$

(Here, we simply recalled from our calculus course that the sums of the two scalar series multiplying I and A are $\cos t$ and $\sin t$.) Thus, we have the following useful result:

(20-6)
$$\exp\left(\begin{bmatrix} 0 & 1 \\ -1 & 0 \end{bmatrix} t\right) = \begin{bmatrix} \cos t & \sin t \\ -\sin t & \cos t \end{bmatrix}.$$

Now we must show that e^{At}, as defined by Equation 20-5, has the required properties (i), (ii), and (iii). For example, if we set $t = 0$, our series reduces to the single term I, so property (i) holds. We will give some hints on how to verify property (ii) in Exercise 20-9.

The verification of property (iii) is easy. In Section 30, we review some of the basic facts about power series that you learned in calculus. One of these facts is that the "operators" D_t and $\sum_{k=0}^{\infty}$ commute (a more precise statement is given in Theorem 30-2), and it follows that

$$D_t e^{At} = D_t \sum_{k=0}^{\infty} \frac{t^k}{k!} A^k = \sum_{k=0}^{\infty} D_t \left(\frac{t^k}{k!} A^k\right) = \sum_{k=1}^{\infty} \frac{t^{k-1}}{(k-1)!} A^k$$

$$= \left(\sum_{k=1}^{\infty} \frac{t^{k-1}}{(k-1)!} A^{k-1}\right) A = \left(\sum_{k=0}^{\infty} \frac{t^k}{k!} A^k\right) A = e^{At} A,$$

thus completing the proof of Theorem 20-1. Incidentally, since $AA^k = A^k A$ for any positive integer k, then $e^{At} A = A e^{At}$, and hence $D_t e^{At} = A e^{At}$, too.

Example 20-3. Solve the initial value problem

$$\mathbf{x}' = \begin{bmatrix} 0 & 1 \\ -1 & 0 \end{bmatrix} \mathbf{x} + (2, -1) \text{ and } \mathbf{x} = (1, 1) \text{ when } t = 0.$$

Solution. Because of our calculations in Example 20-2, we know what e^{At} is in this example. For simplicity, we chose $\mathbf{r}$ to be a constant function, and so Equation 20-4 becomes

$$\mathbf{x} = \begin{bmatrix} \cos t & \sin t \\ -\sin t & \cos t \end{bmatrix}\begin{pmatrix} 1 \\ 1 \end{pmatrix} + \int_0^t \begin{bmatrix} \cos(t-s) & \sin(t-s) \\ -\sin(t-s) & \cos(t-s) \end{bmatrix}\begin{pmatrix} 2 \\ -1 \end{pmatrix} ds$$

$$= \begin{pmatrix} \cos t + \sin t \\ \cos t - \sin t \end{pmatrix} + \int_0^t \begin{pmatrix} 2\cos(t-s) - \sin(t-s) \\ -2\sin(t-s) - \cos(t-s) \end{pmatrix} ds$$

$$= \begin{pmatrix} \cos t + \sin t \\ \cos t - \sin t \end{pmatrix} + \begin{pmatrix} -2\sin(t-s) - \cos(t-s) \\ -2\cos(t-s) + \sin(t-s) \end{pmatrix}\Big|_0^t$$

$$= \begin{pmatrix} \cos t + \sin t \\ \cos t - \sin t \end{pmatrix} + \begin{pmatrix} -1 \\ -2 \end{pmatrix} - \begin{pmatrix} -2\sin t - \cos t \\ -2\cos t + \sin t \end{pmatrix}$$

$$= \begin{pmatrix} 2\cos t + 3\sin t - 1 \\ 3\cos t - 2\sin t - 2 \end{pmatrix}.$$

Example 20-4. Solve the homogeneous linear initial value problem with constant coefficients $\mathbf{x}' = A\mathbf{x}$ and $\mathbf{x} = \mathbf{x}_0$ when $t = 0$.

Solution. Problem 20-2 is called **homogeneous** if $\mathbf{r}(t) = 0$. Here, we have constant coefficients, so Theorem 20-1 applies. Thus, Equation 20-4 tells us that $\mathbf{x} = e^{At}\mathbf{x}_0$ satisfies our problem.

Example 20-5. Show that $X = e^{At}$ satisfies the homogeneous *matrix* initial value problem

$$(20\text{-}7) \qquad\qquad X' = AX \text{ and } X = I \text{ when } t = 0.$$

Solution. Since $D_t e^{At} = A e^{At}$ and $e^0 = I$, it is clear that $X = e^{At}$ *does* satisfy the given problem. Furthermore, it is very easy to see that the problem has only one solution. Thus, we could have defined the matrix exponential function as the solution of Initial Value Problem 20-7, instead of basing the definition on an infinite series.

EXERCISE 20

1. Let $A(t) = \begin{bmatrix} -2\tan t & -2\sin t \\ \sec t \tan t & 2\tan t \end{bmatrix}$ and $\mathbf{r}(t) = (-\sin t, \tan t)$.

   (a) In what interval J of the T-axis would you expect to be able to find a solution of the initial value problem

   $$\mathbf{x}' = A(t)\mathbf{x} + \mathbf{r}(t) \text{ and } \mathbf{x} = (1, -1) \text{ when } t = 0?$$

   (b) Show that $\mathbf{x} = (\cos t, -1)$ satisfies this initial value problem.
   (c) Show that $\mathbf{x} = (2\cos t, -1)$ and $\mathbf{x} = (-1, \sec t)$ both satisfy the homogeneous vector differential equation $\mathbf{x}' = A(t)\mathbf{x}$.
   (d) Show that the equation $U(t) = \begin{bmatrix} 2\cos t & -1 \\ -1 & \sec t \end{bmatrix}$ defines a solution of the matrix linear differential equation $X' = A(t)X$.
   (e) Show that if C is any matrix, then $X = U(t)C$ satisfies the matrix differential equation of part (d).
   (f) By actually computing $U(t)^{-1}$, show that $X = U(t)^{-1}$ satisfies the matrix differential equation $X' = -XA(t)$.

2. Show that if $L = \begin{bmatrix} \lambda_1 & 0 \\ 0 & \lambda_2 \end{bmatrix}$ is a *diagonal matrix*, then $e^{Lt} = \begin{bmatrix} e^{\lambda_1 t} & 0 \\ 0 & e^{\lambda_2 t} \end{bmatrix}$.

3. Verify Equation 20-6 by showing that $X = \begin{bmatrix} \cos t & \sin t \\ -\sin t & \cos t \end{bmatrix}$ satisfies the matrix initial value problem $X' = \begin{bmatrix} 0 & 1 \\ -1 & 0 \end{bmatrix} X$ and $X = I$ when $t = 0$.

4. Let $S = \begin{bmatrix} 1 & 1 \\ 1 & 1 \end{bmatrix}$.

    (a) Show that $X = I + \frac{1}{2}(e^{2t} - 1)S$ satisfies the initial value problem

$$X' = SX \text{ and } X = I \text{ when } t = 0.$$

    What is e^{St}?

    (b) Use a power series to verify your answer to the last question.

    (c) Solve the initial value problem

$$\mathbf{x}' = S\mathbf{x} + (e^t, -e^t) \text{ and } \mathbf{x} = (1, -1) \text{ when } t = 0.$$

5. Let $K = \begin{bmatrix} 0 & 1 \\ 1 & 0 \end{bmatrix}$.

    (a) Show that $e^{Kt} = \begin{bmatrix} \cosh t & \sinh t \\ \sinh t & \cosh t \end{bmatrix}$.

    (b) Solve the initial value problem $\mathbf{x}' = K\mathbf{x}$ and $\mathbf{x} = (2, -3)$ when $t = 0$.

    (c) Solve the initial value problem $\mathbf{x}' = K\mathbf{x} + (-1, 1)$ and $\mathbf{x} = (2, -3)$ when $t = 0$.

6. (a) Find $\exp\left(\begin{bmatrix} 1 & 1 \\ -1 & -1 \end{bmatrix} t\right)$.

    (b) Solve the initial value problem

$$\mathbf{x}' = \begin{bmatrix} 1 & 1 \\ -1 & -1 \end{bmatrix} \mathbf{x} + (-t^2 - 3, \ t^2 + 2t + 5) \text{ and } \mathbf{x} = (1, 2) \text{ when } t = 0.$$

7. Find $\exp\left(\begin{bmatrix} 1 & 1 \\ 3 & 3 \end{bmatrix} t\right)$.

8. Show that if $A^r = 0$ for some positive integer r, then the components of e^{At} are simply polynomials in t.

9. Check each step of the following verification of the equation $e^{Au}e^{Av} = e^{A(u+v)}$:

$$e^{Au}e^{Av} = \sum_{k=0}^{\infty} \frac{u^k}{k!} A^k \sum_{k=0}^{\infty} \frac{v^k}{k!} A^k. \qquad \text{(Equation 20-5)}$$

$$= \sum_{k=0}^{\infty} \left(\sum_{j=0}^{k} \frac{u^{k-j}v^j}{(k-j)!\,j!} \right) A^k \qquad \text{(Equation 30-3)}$$

$$= \sum_{k=0}^{\infty} \left(\sum_{j=0}^{k} \frac{k!}{(k-j)!\,j!} u^{k-j}v^j \right) \frac{1}{k!} A^k \qquad \left(\text{Since } \frac{k!}{k!} = 1 \right)$$

$$= \sum_{k=0}^{\infty} \frac{(u+v)^k}{k!} A^k \qquad \text{(The Binomial Theorem)}$$

$$= e^{A(u+v)} \qquad \text{(Equation 20-5)}$$

21 MORE ABOUT e^{At}

In Example 20-2, we were able to compute the sum of the series $\sum_{k=0}^{\infty} \frac{t^k}{k!} A^k$ and thus obtain a simple formula for e^{At} when $A = \begin{bmatrix} 0 & 1 \\ -1 & 0 \end{bmatrix}$. Of course, our success was due to the special form of A. Now we will show that the problem of finding the sum for a general matrix can *always* be reduced to the problem of finding the sum for a special matrix.

Suppose that A is a given matrix and P and L are matrices such that

(21-1) $AP = PL.$

We are going to assume that P is an invertible matrix (that is, P^{-1} exists) and L is in some sense "simpler" than A, and we will show that the problem of finding e^{At} can be reduced to finding the sum $\sum_{k=0}^{\infty} \frac{t^k}{k!} L^k$.

We write Equation 21-1 as

$$A = PLP^{-1}$$

and notice that

$$A^2 = (PLP^{-1})(PLP^{-1}) = PL(P^{-1}P)LP^{-1} = PL^2P^{-1}.$$

In fact, if we continue this calculation, we find that

$$A^k = PL^kP^{-1}$$

for each positive integer k. Thus, for a given K,

$$\sum_{k=0}^{K} \frac{t^k}{k!} A^k = \sum_{k=0}^{K} \frac{t^k}{k!} PL^kP^{-1} = P\left(\sum_{k=0}^{K} \frac{t^k}{k!} L^k \right) P^{-1}.$$

Now if we let $K \uparrow \infty$, we see that

(21-2) $e^{At} = Pe^{Lt}P^{-1}.$

This equation states that if we can find e^{Lt}, we can find e^{At}. For example, we saw in Exercise 20-2 that

$$\exp\left(\begin{bmatrix} \lambda_1 & 0 \\ 0 & \lambda_2 \end{bmatrix} t \right) = \begin{bmatrix} e^{\lambda_1 t} & 0 \\ 0 & e^{\lambda_2 t} \end{bmatrix},$$

so if there is an invertible matrix P and a *diagonal* matrix $L = \begin{bmatrix} \lambda_1 & 0 \\ 0 & \lambda_2 \end{bmatrix}$ such that Equation 21-1 is satisfied, then

(21-3) $$e^{At} = P \begin{bmatrix} e^{\lambda_1 t} & 0 \\ 0 & e^{\lambda_2 t} \end{bmatrix} P^{-1}.$$

We will therefore look into the question of finding such a P and L; that is, of *diagonalizing* our given matrix A.

Suppose that we can diagonalize A. Then if the columns of P are the vectors $\mathbf{u}_1$ and $\mathbf{u}_2$, Equation 21-1 becomes $A[\mathbf{u}_1 \quad \mathbf{u}_2] = [\mathbf{u}_1 \quad \mathbf{u}_2] \begin{bmatrix} \lambda_1 & 0 \\ 0 & \lambda_2 \end{bmatrix}$, or

$$A\mathbf{u}_1 = \lambda_1 \mathbf{u}_1 \text{ and } A\mathbf{u}_2 = \lambda_2 \mathbf{u}_2.$$

In other words, the vectors $\mathbf{u}_1$ and $\mathbf{u}_2$ are *characteristic vectors* of A corresponding to the *characteristic values* λ_1 and λ_2. So let us recall some facts about characteristic values and characteristic vectors.

In algebra, you learned that a **characteristic vector u** of the matrix $A = \begin{bmatrix} a & b \\ c & d \end{bmatrix}$ is a non-zero vector that is transformed by A into a scalar multiple of itself. That is, there is a number λ (a **characteristic value** of A) such that

(21-4) $$A\mathbf{u} = \lambda\mathbf{u}.$$

For example, $(1, 2)$ is a characteristic vector of the matrix $\begin{bmatrix} 3 & 1 \\ 2 & 4 \end{bmatrix}$ corresponding to the characteristic value 5, because

$$\begin{bmatrix} 3 & 1 \\ 2 & 4 \end{bmatrix} \begin{pmatrix} 1 \\ 2 \end{pmatrix} = 5 \begin{pmatrix} 1 \\ 2 \end{pmatrix}.$$

Since Equation 21-4 can also be written as $(\lambda I - A)\mathbf{u} = \mathbf{0}$, we are asking that the equation $(\lambda I - A)\mathbf{x} = \mathbf{0}$ have a non-zero solution $\mathbf{u}$. According to Theorem 18-1, the existence of such a solution is equivalent to the statement that $\lambda I - A$ does not have an inverse; that is, that $\det (\lambda I - A) = 0$. In terms of the components of A, this equation is

(21-5) $$\lambda^2 - (a + d)\lambda + ad - bc = 0,$$

and we call it the **characteristic equation** of A. Thus, a number is a characteristic value of A if, and only if, it is a solution of the characteristic equation of A. Since the characteristic equation of a 2 by 2 matrix is a quadratic equation (the characteristic equation of an n by n matrix is always of degree n), it will have two solutions. Thus, unless the characteristic equation has a double zero, a 2 by 2 matrix has two characteristic values.

Example 21-1. Find the characteristic values and corresponding characteristic vectors of the matrix

$$A = \begin{bmatrix} 1 & 3 \\ 2 & 2 \end{bmatrix}.$$

Solution. The characteristic equation of this matrix is

$$\lambda^2 - 3\lambda - 4 = (\lambda - 4)(\lambda + 1) = 0;$$

hence its characteristic values are $\lambda_1 = 4$ and $\lambda_2 = -1$. To the first of these characteristic values there corresponds a characteristic vector $\mathbf{u}_1 = (p, q)$ that satisfies the equation $(4I - A)\mathbf{u}_1 = 0$; that is,

$$\begin{bmatrix} 3 & -3 \\ -2 & 2 \end{bmatrix} \begin{pmatrix} p \\ q \end{pmatrix} = \begin{pmatrix} 0 \\ 0 \end{pmatrix}.$$

Clearly, $\mathbf{u}_1 = (1, 1)$ will satisfy this equation. To find a characteristic vector that corresponds to the characteristic value -1, we solve the equation

$$\begin{bmatrix} -2 & -3 \\ -2 & -3 \end{bmatrix} \begin{pmatrix} p \\ q \end{pmatrix} = \begin{pmatrix} 0 \\ 0 \end{pmatrix},$$

and we see that we can take our second characteristic vector to be $\mathbf{u}_2 = (3, -2)$. You should check to see that $A\mathbf{u}_1 = 4\mathbf{u}_1$ and $A\mathbf{u}_2 = -\mathbf{u}_2$.

Let us see what we have just accomplished. By writing Equation 21-1 in the form $A[\mathbf{u}_1 \quad \mathbf{u}_2] = [\mathbf{u}_1 \quad \mathbf{u}_2] \begin{bmatrix} \lambda_1 & 0 \\ 0 & \lambda_2 \end{bmatrix}$, we found that the column vectors $\mathbf{u}_1$ and $\mathbf{u}_2$ of a matrix P that transforms A to diagonal form are characteristic vectors of A, and that the diagonal elements of the resulting matrix L are the corresponding characteristic values λ_1 and λ_2. It now appears that the "typical" 2 by 2 matrix has two characteristic values and corresponding characteristic vectors, exactly the quantities we need to diagonalize it.

Example 21-2. Illustrate Equation 21-1 for the matrix of Example 21-1.

Solution. We have found that characteristic vectors for the matrix in Example 21-1 that correspond to the characteristic values $\lambda_1 = 4$ and $\lambda_2 = -1$ are $\mathbf{u}_1 = (1, 1)$ and $\mathbf{u}_2 = (3, -2)$, so the matrices P and L that are to appear in Equation 21-1 are

$$P = \begin{bmatrix} 1 & 3 \\ 1 & -2 \end{bmatrix} \text{ and } L = \begin{bmatrix} 4 & 0 \\ 0 & -1 \end{bmatrix}.$$

Therefore, Equation 21-1 becomes

$$\begin{bmatrix} 1 & 3 \\ 2 & 2 \end{bmatrix} \begin{bmatrix} 1 & 3 \\ 1 & -2 \end{bmatrix} = \begin{bmatrix} 1 & 3 \\ 1 & -2 \end{bmatrix} \begin{bmatrix} 4 & 0 \\ 0 & -1 \end{bmatrix},$$

and you can easily verify that this equation is correct.

Example 21-3. Find e^{At} for the matrix A of Example 21-1.

Solution. We have found a diagonalizing matrix P and diagonal elements λ_1 and λ_2, so we can use Equation 21-3 to calculate e^{At} as soon as we find P^{-1}. It is easy to see (you can use the formula in Exercise 18-4(a) if you want to) that

$$P^{-1} = \begin{bmatrix} \frac{2}{5} & \frac{3}{5} \\ \frac{1}{5} & -\frac{1}{5} \end{bmatrix},$$

and so Equation 21-3 yields

(21-6) $\qquad \exp\left(\begin{bmatrix} 1 & 3 \\ 2 & 2 \end{bmatrix} t\right) = \begin{bmatrix} 1 & 3 \\ 1 & -2 \end{bmatrix} \begin{bmatrix} e^{4t} & 0 \\ 0 & e^{-t} \end{bmatrix} \begin{bmatrix} \frac{2}{5} & \frac{3}{5} \\ \frac{1}{5} & -\frac{1}{5} \end{bmatrix}$

$$= \frac{1}{5} \begin{bmatrix} 2e^{4t} + 3e^{-t} & 3e^{4t} - 3e^{-t} \\ 2e^{4t} - 2e^{-t} & 3e^{4t} + 2e^{-t} \end{bmatrix}.$$

If you try it, you will agree that it is not an easy matter to get this result by finding the sum of the series $\sum_{k=0}^{\infty} \dfrac{t^k}{k!} A^k$ directly.

In applications, an initial value problem usually describes some "process." The value **x** of a solution is the result of the process t seconds after it starts. Frequently, we are interested in what happens after a long interval, as t gets large. Equation 21-3 is often used to answer such a question. For example, if λ_1 and λ_2 are negative numbers (more generally, are complex numbers with negative real parts), then Equation 21-3 shows that $\lim_{t \uparrow \infty} e^{At} = 0$. As time goes on, then, the effects of the process diminish. If one (or both) of the numbers λ_1 and λ_2 is positive, however, we have a completely different situation; the process may "blow up."

Example 21-4. Find a non-zero solution of the differential equation

$$\mathbf{x'} = A\mathbf{x},$$

where A is the matrix of Example 21-1, that is bounded for t in the interval $[0, \infty)$.

Solution. Each solution of our differential equation is given by an equation of the form $\mathbf{x} = e^{At}\mathbf{x}_0$, where $\mathbf{x}_0$ is the initial value. Therefore, our problem is to determine a vector $\mathbf{x}_0$ such that $e^{At}\mathbf{x}_0$ is bounded for $t \in [0, \infty)$. (We have specifically ruled out the trivial choice $\mathbf{x}_0 = \mathbf{0}$.) Equation 21-6 tells us that

$$e^{At} = P\begin{bmatrix} e^{4t} & 0 \\ 0 & e^{-t} \end{bmatrix} P^{-1},$$

so we must pick $\mathbf{x}_0$ so that the vector

$$\mathbf{x} = P\begin{bmatrix} e^{4t} & 0 \\ 0 & e^{-t} \end{bmatrix} P^{-1}\mathbf{x}_0$$

is bounded. In other words, we must eliminate e^{4t} from this expression. Therefore, we will choose $\mathbf{x}_0$ so that $P^{-1}\mathbf{x}_0 = (0, 1)$. Then $\mathbf{x} = P(0, e^{-t})$; that is,

$$\mathbf{x} = \begin{bmatrix} 1 & 3 \\ 1 & -2 \end{bmatrix}\begin{pmatrix} 0 \\ e^{-t} \end{pmatrix} = e^{-t}\begin{pmatrix} 3 \\ -2 \end{pmatrix}.$$

We have been talking as if every matrix were diagonable, but this statement is not quite true. For certain exceptional matrices, there is no invertible matrix P such that $P^{-1}AP$ is diagonal. For a 2 by 2 exceptional matrix A, the nearest we can get to diagonal form is to find a matrix P and a number λ such that

(21-7) $$P^{-1}AP = \begin{bmatrix} \lambda & 1 \\ 0 & \lambda \end{bmatrix},$$

and there is an analogous, but more complicated, "almost" diagonal form for nondiagonable matrices of higher orders. Although it would be easy to provide a complete discussion of the diagonability of 2 by 2 matrices (it is hard to do it in general), nondiagonable matrices are too rare and unimportant to make such a discussion worthwhile for us. A simple test for showing that a matrix is diagonable is to look at its characteristic equation. If this equation has no multiple zeros, then the matrix is surely diagonable. It is easy to see from Equation 21-7 that for the matrix A that appears there, we have

(21-8) $$e^{At} = P\begin{bmatrix} e^{\lambda t} & te^{\lambda t} \\ 0 & e^{\lambda t} \end{bmatrix} P^{-1}.$$

Thus, for a 2 by 2 matrix A, e^{At} is given either by Equation 21-3 or, in exceptional cases, by Equation 21-8.

While it is true that "most" matrices are diagonable, it need not be true that the components of the diagonalizing matrix P or the diagonal matrix

$P^{-1}AP$ are real numbers, even though the components of the given matrix are real. For example, the characteristic values of a 2 by 2 matrix are solutions of a quadratic equation, and you know that such equations can have complex solutions. Of course, there is nothing wrong with using complex numbers, and we often do. There are times, however, when we prefer to deal only with real numbers, so let us see what modifications in our arguments are necessary to keep us in the real field.

We will assume as usual that A is a 2 by 2 matrix whose components are real numbers, but now we will also suppose that one of the characteristic values of A is the complex number $\lambda = \sigma + i\tau$, where $\tau > 0$ (it is easy to see that the other characteristic value is therefore $\sigma - i\tau$). Let $\mathbf{u} = \mathbf{p} + i\mathbf{q}$ be a corresponding characteristic vector. Thus,

$$A(\mathbf{p} + i\mathbf{q}) = (\sigma + i\tau)(\mathbf{p} + i\mathbf{q})$$
$$A\mathbf{p} + iA\mathbf{q} = (\sigma\mathbf{p} - \tau\mathbf{q}) + i(\tau\mathbf{p} + \sigma\mathbf{q}),$$

where we are assuming that the vectors $\mathbf{p}$ and $\mathbf{q}$ have real components and that σ and τ are real numbers. Therefore, this one equation between complex vectors is equivalent to two equations between real vectors:

(21-9)
$$A\mathbf{p} = \sigma\mathbf{p} - \tau\mathbf{q}$$
$$A\mathbf{q} = \tau\mathbf{p} + \sigma\mathbf{q}.$$

Now if we let P be the matrix whose columns are $\mathbf{p}$ and $\mathbf{q}$ (that is, $P = [\mathbf{p} \quad \mathbf{q}]$), then Equations 21-9 can be written as the matrix equation

$$AP = P\begin{bmatrix} \sigma & \tau \\ -\tau & \sigma \end{bmatrix}.$$

It is not hard to show that P is invertible (Exercise 21-12), so we have found a matrix P with real components such that Equation 21-1 is satisfied with

$$L = \begin{bmatrix} \sigma & \tau \\ -\tau & \sigma \end{bmatrix}.$$

Although this matrix L is not as simple as a diagonal matrix, it is the "best" matrix into which we can transform A if we insist that our transforming matrix P have only real components.

Now Equation 21-2 tells us that the problem of finding e^{At} is reduced to finding e^{Lt}. Let us write $L = \sigma I + \tau J$, where $J = \begin{bmatrix} 0 & 1 \\ -1 & 0 \end{bmatrix}$. Hence, $e^{Lt} = e^{(\sigma I + \tau J)t}$, and so we would hope that $e^{Lt} = e^{\sigma It}e^{\tau Jt}$. Since σI is a diagonal matrix,

$e^{\sigma It} = e^{\sigma t}I$, and we can refer to Example 20-2 to find that

$$e^{\tau Jt} = \begin{bmatrix} \cos \tau t & \sin \tau t \\ -\sin \tau t & \cos \tau t \end{bmatrix}.$$

It would therefore appear that

(21-10) $\qquad \exp\left(\begin{bmatrix} \sigma & \tau \\ -\tau & \sigma \end{bmatrix} t\right) = \begin{bmatrix} e^{\sigma t} \cos \tau t & e^{\sigma t} \sin \tau t \\ -e^{\sigma t} \sin \tau t & e^{\sigma t} \cos \tau t \end{bmatrix}.$

This equation is, in fact, correct, but the reasoning that we used to arrive at it is incomplete. We simply took it for granted that $e^{(\sigma I + \tau J)t} = e^{\sigma It}e^{\tau Jt}$. You know, however, that matrices do not obey all the usual laws of algebra, and one of the "natural" equations that is not always true for matrices is $e^{(A+B)t} = e^{At}e^{Bt}$. But we will help you show in Exercise 21-9 that this equation does hold if $AB = BA$, and since $(\sigma I)(\tau J) = (\tau J)(\sigma I)$, our derivation of Equation 21-10 is actually all right. A direct way to check the validity of Equation 21-10 is to show that $X = \begin{bmatrix} e^{\sigma t} \cos \tau t & e^{\sigma t} \sin \tau t \\ -e^{\sigma t} \sin \tau t & e^{\sigma t} \cos \tau t \end{bmatrix}$ satisfies the initial value problem $X' = (\sigma I + \tau J)X$ and $X = I$ when $t = 0$. Since this problem has only one solution, it must be true that $X = \exp(\sigma I + \tau J)t$.

Example 21-5. What is $\exp\left(\begin{bmatrix} 0 & 1 \\ -a^2 & 0 \end{bmatrix} t\right)$, where a is a positive number?

Solution. It is easy to see that

$$\begin{bmatrix} 1 & 0 \\ 0 & 1/a \end{bmatrix} \begin{bmatrix} 0 & 1 \\ -a^2 & 0 \end{bmatrix} \begin{bmatrix} 1 & 0 \\ 0 & a \end{bmatrix} = a \begin{bmatrix} 0 & 1 \\ -1 & 0 \end{bmatrix}.$$

Therefore,

$$\exp\left(\begin{bmatrix} 0 & 1 \\ -a^2 & 0 \end{bmatrix} t\right) = \begin{bmatrix} 1 & 0 \\ 0 & a \end{bmatrix} \exp\left(a\begin{bmatrix} 0 & 1 \\ -1 & 0 \end{bmatrix} t\right) \begin{bmatrix} 1 & 0 \\ 0 & 1/a \end{bmatrix} \qquad \text{(Equation 21-2)}$$

$$= \begin{bmatrix} 1 & 0 \\ 0 & a \end{bmatrix} \begin{bmatrix} \cos at & \sin at \\ -\sin at & \cos at \end{bmatrix} \begin{bmatrix} 1 & 0 \\ 0 & 1/a \end{bmatrix} \qquad \text{(Equation 21-10)}$$

$$= \begin{bmatrix} \cos at & \dfrac{1}{a} \sin at \\ -a \sin at & \cos at \end{bmatrix}.$$

EXERCISE 21

1. Let $A = \begin{bmatrix} -7 & 10 \\ -5 & 8 \end{bmatrix}$.

(a) Find the characteristic values of A.

  (b) Find corresponding characteristic vectors.

  (c) Find a matrix P such that $P^{-1}AP$ is diagonal.

  (d) Find e^{At}.

  (e) Solve the initial value problem $\mathbf{x}' = A\mathbf{x}$ and $\mathbf{x} = (1, -1)$ when $t = 0$.

  (f) Find a non-trivial solution of the differential equation $\mathbf{x}' = A\mathbf{x}$ that is bounded in the interval $[0, \infty)$.

2. Let $K = \begin{bmatrix} 0 & 1 \\ 1 & 0 \end{bmatrix}$.

  (a) Find a matrix P such that $P^{-1}KP$ is diagonal.

  (b) Find e^{Kt}, and compare the result with what you found in Exercise 20-5.

3. Let $J = \begin{bmatrix} 0 & 1 \\ -1 & 0 \end{bmatrix}$.

  (a) Find the characteristic values of J.

  (b) Since the characteristic values are different, there is a matrix P such that $P^{-1}JP$ is a diagonal matrix. What is $P^{-1}JP$?

  (c) Find characteristic vectors corresponding to the characteristic values you found in part (a).

  (d) Find a matrix P such that $P^{-1}JP$ is diagonal.

  (e) Find e^{Jt}, and compare the result with Equation 20-6.

4. Solve the initial value problem

$$\mathbf{x}' = \begin{bmatrix} 1 & 2 \\ 0 & 3 \end{bmatrix} \mathbf{x} + (e^{-t}, 0) \text{ and } \mathbf{x} = (2, -1) \text{ when } t = 0.$$

5. Solve the initial value problem with nondiagonable coefficient matrix

$$\mathbf{x}' = \begin{bmatrix} -2 & 1 \\ 0 & -2 \end{bmatrix} \mathbf{x} + (2t, 2) \text{ and } \mathbf{x} = (1, 2) \text{ when } t = 0.$$

6. Prove that the matrix $\begin{bmatrix} 2 & 1 \\ 0 & 2 \end{bmatrix}$ is *not* diagonable.

7. Show that every constant scalar multiple of the solution we found in Example 21-4 is bounded in the interval $[0, \infty)$. Can you show that, conversely, every bounded solution is a constant scalar multiple of the one we found? Can you find solutions of this same equation that are bounded in the interval $(-\infty, 0]$?

8. Show that if $\lambda < 0$ in Equation 21-8, then $\lim\limits_{t \uparrow \infty} e^{At} = 0$.

9. Suppose that A and B are square matrices such that $AB = BA$.

  (a) Show that $X = e^{At}B$ and $X = Be^{At}$ both satisfy the initial value problem

$$X' = AX \text{ and } X = B \text{ when } t = 0.$$

  (b) Invoke the uniqueness theorem and the result of part (a) to show that $e^{At}B = Be^{At}$.

    (c) Verify the equation of part (b) directly by using the series expression for e^{At}.

    (d) Show that $X = e^{(A+B)t}$ and $X = e^{At}e^{Bt}$ both satisfy the initial value problem

$$X' = (A + B)X \text{ and } X = I \text{ when } t = 0.$$

    (e) Invoke the uniqueness theorem to show that $e^{(A+B)t} = e^{At}e^{Bt}$.

    (f) Verify the equation of part (e) directly by using the series expressions for $e^{(A+B)t}$, e^{At}, and e^{Bt}.

10. (a) Show, by means of an example, that the matrices $e^{(A+B)t}$ and $e^{At}e^{Bt}$ need not be equal.

    (b) Can you show that if $e^{(A+B)t} = e^{At}e^{Bt}$ for all t, then $AB = BA$?

11. Show that if the components of a 2 by 2 matrix A are real numbers, and if one of its characteristic values is $\lambda_1 = \sigma + i\tau$, where σ and τ are real numbers (with $\tau > 0$), then the other characteristic value is $\lambda_2 = \sigma - i\tau$.

12. (a) Explain why the statement "the matrix $[\mathbf{p} \quad \mathbf{q}]$ is not invertible" is equivalent to the statement "one of the vectors $\mathbf{p}$ and $\mathbf{q}$ is a scalar multiple of the other."

    (b) Show that if one of the vectors $\mathbf{p}$ and $\mathbf{q}$ in Equations 21-9 is a scalar multiple of the other, then the characteristic values of A are real numbers, contrary to our assumption.

    (c) From (a) and (b), infer that the matrix $P = [\mathbf{p} \quad \mathbf{q}]$ is invertible.

22   LINEAR SYSTEMS WITH NON-CONSTANT COEFFICIENTS

    Now we will return to the general linear initial value problem with non-constant coefficients

$$(22\text{-}1) \qquad\qquad \mathbf{x}' = A(t)\mathbf{x} + \mathbf{r}(t) \text{ and } \mathbf{x} = \mathbf{x}_0 \text{ when } t = t_0.$$

We treat this problem just as we treated the case of constant coefficients in Section 20 and the scalar case in Section 8. Thus, we will reduce our problem to the form $\mathbf{z}' = \mathbf{h}(t)$ and $\mathbf{z} = \mathbf{x}_0$ when $t = t_0$. Solving this latter problem is simply a matter of integration.

    To effect this reduction in the case of constant coefficients, we multiplied both sides of the given differential equation by $e^{-At} = (e^{At})^{-1}$, so our first step here is to find the proper multiplier to use in Problem 22-1. Since $X = e^{At}$ satisfies the matrix initial value problem $X' = AX$ and $X = I$ when $t = 0$, it is natural to hope that we can replace e^{-At} with $U(t)^{-1}$, where U is the solution of the initial value problem

(22-2) $X' = A(t)X$ and $X = I$ when $t = t_0$.

We will now show that $U(t)$ has exactly the properties we want.

Since we plan to multiply by $U(t)^{-1}$, we had better show that $U(t)$ is invertible; that is, that det $U(t) \neq 0$ for each t in our basic interval J. In component form, with $U(t) = \begin{bmatrix} u(t) & v(t) \\ w(t) & z(t) \end{bmatrix}$, the equation $U'(t) = A(t)U(t)$ becomes

(22-3) $\begin{bmatrix} u'(t) & v'(t) \\ w'(t) & z'(t) \end{bmatrix} = \begin{bmatrix} a(t)u(t) + b(t)w(t) & a(t)v(t) + b(t)z(t) \\ c(t)u(t) + d(t)w(t) & c(t)v(t) + d(t)z(t) \end{bmatrix}.$

Now

$$D_t \begin{vmatrix} u(t) & v(t) \\ w(t) & z(t) \end{vmatrix} = \begin{vmatrix} u'(t) & v'(t) \\ w(t) & z(t) \end{vmatrix} + \begin{vmatrix} u(t) & v(t) \\ w'(t) & z'(t) \end{vmatrix} \qquad \text{(Exercise 18-6)}$$

$$= \begin{vmatrix} a(t)u(t) + b(t)w(t) & a(t)v(t) + b(t)z(t) \\ w(t) & z(t) \end{vmatrix} \qquad \begin{matrix} \text{(Use Equation 22-3} \\ \text{to replace } u'(t) \text{ with} \end{matrix}$$

$$+ \begin{vmatrix} u(t) & v(t) \\ c(t)u(t) + d(t)w(t) & c(t)v(t) + d(t)z(t) \end{vmatrix} \qquad \begin{matrix} a(t)u(t) + b(t)w(t), \\ \text{and so on.)} \end{matrix}$$

$$= a(t) \begin{vmatrix} u(t) & v(t) \\ w(t) & z(t) \end{vmatrix} + d(t) \begin{vmatrix} u(t) & v(t) \\ w(t) & z(t) \end{vmatrix} \qquad \begin{matrix} \text{(Properties of} \\ \text{determinants)} \end{matrix}$$

$$= [a(t) + d(t)] \begin{vmatrix} u(t) & v(t) \\ w(t) & z(t) \end{vmatrix}.$$

Also, since $U(t_0) = I$, then det $U(t_0) = 1$. Thus we see that $y = \det U(t)$ satisfies the scalar linear initial value problem

$$y' = [a(t) + d(t)]y \text{ and } y = 1 \text{ when } t = t_0.$$

But the techniques we developed in Section 8 to solve this problem tell us that it is satisfied by $y = \exp \left(\int_{t_0}^t [a(s) + d(s)]ds \right)$, and so we have derived the interesting formula

(22-4) $\det U(t) = \exp \left(\int_{t_0}^t [a(s) + d(s)]ds \right).$

From this equation, we see that det $U(t) \neq 0$ for each $t \in J$.

Now that we know that $U(t)^{-1}$ exists, we will calculate $D_t U(t)^{-1}$. Since $U(t)U(t)^{-1} = I$ for each $t \in J$, then

$$
\begin{aligned}
0 = D_t I &= D_t[U(t)U(t)^{-1}] \\
&= [D_t U(t)]U(t)^{-1} + U(t)D_t U(t)^{-1} \quad \text{(Rule for differentiating a product)} \\
&= A(t)U(t)U(t)^{-1} + U(t)D_t U(t)^{-1} \quad \text{(Since $D_t U(t) = A(t)U(t)$)} \\
&= A(t) + U(t)D_t U(t)^{-1}.
\end{aligned}
$$

In other words, $U(t)D_t U(t)^{-1} = -A(t)$, and so

$$
(22\text{-}5) \qquad\qquad\qquad D_t U(t)^{-1} = -U(t)^{-1}A(t).
$$

Because the commutative law is not valid for matrix multiplication, you must take care not to interchange the order of $U(t)^{-1}$ and $A(t)$ in this equation.

Once we have established Equation 22-5, it is easy to solve Problem 22-1. We multiply both sides of the given differential equation by $U(t)^{-1}$ and write the resulting equation as

$$
U(t)^{-1}\mathbf{x}' - U(t)^{-1}A(t)\mathbf{x} = U(t)^{-1}\mathbf{r}(t).
$$

From Equation 22-5, we recognize that this equation can be written as

$$
D_t[U(t)^{-1}\mathbf{x}] = U(t)^{-1}\mathbf{r}(t).
$$

Therefore, since $U(t)^{-1}\mathbf{x} = I\mathbf{x}_0 = \mathbf{x}_0$ when $t = t_0$, we see that $\mathbf{z} = U(t)^{-1}\mathbf{x}$ satisfies the initial value problem

$$
\mathbf{z}' = U(t)^{-1}\mathbf{r}(t) \text{ and } \mathbf{z} = \mathbf{x}_0 \text{ when } t = t_0.
$$

Clearly, $\mathbf{z} = \mathbf{x}_0 + \int_{t_0}^{t} U(s)^{-1}\mathbf{r}(s)ds$ satisfies this initial value problem, too, so $U(t)^{-1}\mathbf{x} = \mathbf{x}_0 + \int_{t_0}^{t} U(s)^{-1}\mathbf{r}(s)ds$. Now we solve for $\mathbf{x}$ to complete the proof of the following generalization of Theorem 20-1.

THEOREM 22-1

Initial Value Problem 22-1 is satisfied by

$$
\begin{aligned}
(22\text{-}6) \qquad \mathbf{x} &= U(t)\mathbf{x}_0 + U(t) \int_{t_0}^{t} U(s)^{-1}\mathbf{r}(s)ds \\
&= U(t)\mathbf{x}_0 + \int_{t_0}^{t} U(t)U(s)^{-1}\mathbf{r}(s)ds.
\end{aligned}
$$

Notice that we can obtain Equation 20-4 by replacing $U(t)$ with e^{At} in Equation 22-6 and setting $t_0 = 0$.

When we use Equation 22-6 to construct a solution of Problem 22-1, we must have at hand a special solution of the matrix differential equation $X' = A(t)X$; namely, the solution U that takes the value I at a given point t_0. Sometimes a simple trick will help us find $U(t)$. Thus, suppose that V is some solution of the differential equation $X' = A(t)X$. Exactly the same arguments that produced Equation 22-4 lead to the formula

$$\det V(t) = \det V(t_0) \exp \left(\int_{t_0}^t [a(s) + d(s)] ds \right).$$

Since the exponential function never takes the value 0, this equation tells us that either $\det V(t) = 0$ for *every* $t \in J$ (in case $\det V(t_0) = 0$) or $\det V(t) \neq 0$ for *no* $t \in J$ (in case $\det V(t_0) \neq 0$). If $\det V(t) \neq 0$, then V is called a **fundamental solution** of the differential equation $X' = A(t)X$. Our function U is just one of infinitely many fundamental solutions, but it is easy to find U if we can somehow find *any* fundamental solution V. For it is simply a matter of checking to see that $X = V(t)V(t_0)^{-1}$ satisfies Problem 22-2, and hence

$$U(t) = V(t)V(t_0)^{-1}.$$

Thus, we can replace $U(t)$ with $V(t)V(t_0)^{-1}$ and $U(s)$ with $V(s)V(t_0)^{-1}$ in Equation 22-6 and thereby obtain a more general wording of Theorem 22-1.

COROLLARY 22-1

If V is a fundamental solution of the matrix differential equation $X' = A(t)X$, then

(22-7) $$\mathbf{x} = V(t)V(t_0)^{-1}\mathbf{x}_0 + \int_{t_0}^t V(t)V(s)^{-1}\mathbf{r}(s)ds$$

satisfies Initial Value Problem 22-1.

Example 22-1. Let $A(t) = \begin{bmatrix} 2 & -2e^{-t} \\ e^t & 0 \end{bmatrix}$, and show that the equation $V(t) = \begin{bmatrix} 2e^t & 1 \\ e^{2t} & e^t \end{bmatrix}$ defines a fundamental solution of the differential equation $X' = A(t)X$ in the interval $(-\infty, \infty)$. Solve the initial value problem

$$\mathbf{x}' = A(t)\mathbf{x} + (e^t, 2) \text{ and } \mathbf{x} = (1, -1) \text{ when } t = 0.$$

Solution. It is an easy calculation to verify that V is a solution of the equation $X' = A(t)X$, and since $\det V(t) = 2e^{2t} - e^{2t} = e^{2t} \neq 0$, it follows that V is a *fundamental* solution. Furthermore, $V(t)^{-1} = \begin{bmatrix} e^{-t} & -e^{-2t} \\ -1 & 2e^{-t} \end{bmatrix}$, and so Formula 22-7 tells us that

$$
\mathbf{x} = \begin{bmatrix} 2e^t & 1 \\ e^{2t} & e^t \end{bmatrix} \begin{bmatrix} 1 & -1 \\ -1 & 2 \end{bmatrix} \begin{pmatrix} 1 \\ -1 \end{pmatrix} + \int_0^t \begin{bmatrix} 2e^t & 1 \\ e^{2t} & e^t \end{bmatrix} \begin{bmatrix} e^{-s} & -e^{-2s} \\ -1 & 2e^{-s} \end{bmatrix} \begin{pmatrix} e^s \\ 2 \end{pmatrix} ds
$$

$$
= \begin{pmatrix} 4e^t - 3 \\ 2e^{2t} - 3e^t \end{pmatrix} + \begin{bmatrix} 2e^t & 1 \\ e^{2t} & e^t \end{bmatrix} \int_0^t \begin{pmatrix} 1 - 2e^{-2s} \\ 4e^{-s} - e^s \end{pmatrix} ds
$$

$$
= (2te^t + e^t + 2 - 2e^{-t}, \ te^{2t} + 2e^t - 3)
$$

satisfies the given initial value problem.

Example 22-2. Show that if V is a solution, but not a fundamental solution, of the equation $X' = A(t)X$, then one of the columns of $V(t)$ is a constant scalar multiple of the other.

Solution. Because V is not a fundamental solution, we know that for each t in our basic interval J, $\det V(t) = 0$. Therefore, Theorem 18-1 states that there is a vector $\mathbf{u}$ *that is not the vector* $\mathbf{0}$ such that $V(t)\mathbf{u} = \mathbf{0}$. One would naturally assume that because $V(t)$ is a different matrix for different choices of t, then the vector $\mathbf{u}$ would have to vary with t. But it needn't. For let t_0 be any point of J, and let $\mathbf{u}_0$ be a non-zero vector such that $V(t_0)\mathbf{u}_0 = \mathbf{0}$. Then, as you should check and see, $\mathbf{x} = V(t)\mathbf{u}_0$ satisfies the initial value problem $\mathbf{x}' = A(t)\mathbf{x}$ and $\mathbf{x} = \mathbf{0}$ when $t = t_0$. But $\mathbf{x} = \mathbf{0}$ also satisfies this problem, and since the problem has only one solution, it must therefore be true that $V(t)\mathbf{u}_0 = \mathbf{0}$ *for each* $t \in J$. If $\mathbf{u}_0 = (u_0, v_0)$, the equation $V(t)\mathbf{u}_0 = \mathbf{0}$ states that u_0 times the first column of $V(t)$ is equal to $-v_0$ times the second. Thus, if $u_0 \neq 0$, then the first column of $V(t)$ is $-v_0/u_0$ times the second, and if $v_0 \neq 0$, the second column of $V(t)$ equals $-u_0/v_0$ times the first.

EXERCISE 22

1. Let $A(t) = \begin{bmatrix} -\tan t & \sec t \\ \sec t & -\tan t \end{bmatrix}$.

   (a) Verify that the solution U of the homogeneous matrix initial value problem

$$
X' = A(t)X \text{ and } X = I \text{ when } t = 0
$$

   is defined by the equation $U(t) = \begin{bmatrix} 1 & \sin t \\ \sin t & 1 \end{bmatrix}$.

   (b) Solve the initial value problem $\mathbf{x}' = A(t)\mathbf{x}$ and $\mathbf{x} = (3, 1)$ when $t = 0$.

   (c) Solve the initial value problem $\mathbf{x}' = A(t)\mathbf{x} + (1, \sin t)$ and $\mathbf{x} = (1, 1)$ when $t = 0$.

2. Let $A(t) = \begin{bmatrix} -1 & 0 \\ (1-t)e^t & 1 \end{bmatrix}$.

   (a) Show that the vector-matrix differential equation $\mathbf{x}' = A(t)\mathbf{x}$ is equivalent to the system of differential equations

$$x' = -x$$
$$y' = y + (1-t)e^t x.$$

   (b) Find $u(t)$ and $v(t)$ if $(x, y) = (u(t), v(t))$ satisfies the differential system of part (a) and the initial condition $(x, y) = (1, 0)$ when $t = 0$.
   (c) Find $w(t)$ and $z(t)$ if $(x, y) = (w(t), z(t))$ satisfies the differential system of part (a) and the initial condition $(x, y) = (0, 1)$ when $t = 0$.
   (d) Show that $X = \begin{bmatrix} u(t) & w(t) \\ v(t) & z(t) \end{bmatrix}$ satisfies the matrix initial value problem

$$X' = A(t)X \text{ and } X = I \text{ when } t = 0.$$

   (e) Solve the initial value problem $\mathbf{x}' = A(t)\mathbf{x} + (1, e^t)$ and $\mathbf{x} = (2, -1)$ when $t = 0$.

3. Let X_0 be a given matrix and U be the solution of Problem 22-2. Show that $X = U(t)X_0$ satisfies the homogeneous matrix initial value problem $X' = A(t)X$ and $X = X_0$ when $t = t_0$.

4. What is $\det W(t)$ if W is the solution of the initial value problem

$$X' = \begin{bmatrix} 2t & e^t \\ \sin t & \cos t \end{bmatrix} X \text{ and } X = \begin{bmatrix} 1 & 2 \\ 3 & 4 \end{bmatrix} \text{ when } t = 0?$$

5. Solve the homogeneous linear matrix initial value problem

$$X' = \begin{bmatrix} 2 & 0 \\ 0 & -3 \end{bmatrix} X \text{ and } X = \begin{bmatrix} 2 & 3 \\ 2 & 3 \end{bmatrix} \text{ when } t = 1.$$

   Show explicitly that one of the columns of your solution matrix is a constant multiple of the other. Is one of the rows a constant multiple of the other?

6. Find a continuous matrix-valued function A such that $X = \begin{bmatrix} t & t^2 \\ t^3 & t^4 \end{bmatrix}$ satisfies the differential equation $X' = A(t)X$ (or explain why you can't).

7. Suppose that $\mathbf{x} = \mathbf{w}(t)$ satisfies the initial value problem

$$\mathbf{x}' = \begin{bmatrix} e^{-t} & \sin t \\ -\sin t & e^{-t} \end{bmatrix} \mathbf{x} \text{ and } \mathbf{x} = (1, -1) \text{ when } t = 0.$$

   (a) Show that $D_t(\mathbf{w}(t) \cdot \mathbf{w}(t)) = 2e^{-t}(\mathbf{w}(t) \cdot \mathbf{w}(t))$.
   (b) Conclude that $\mathbf{w}(t) \cdot \mathbf{w}(t) = 2 \exp(2 - 2e^{-t})$.

(c) What can you conclude about $\lim\limits_{t \uparrow \infty} |\mathbf{w}(t)|$?

8. Let $A(t) = \begin{bmatrix} 0 & 2t \\ 0 & 0 \end{bmatrix}$.

   (a) What is $\exp\left(\int_0^t A(s)\,ds\right)$?

   (b) Does $X = \exp\left(\int_0^t A(s)\,ds\right)$ satisfy the initial value problem $X' = A(t)X$ and $X = I$ when $t = 0$?

23   SCALAR INITIAL VALUE PROBLEMS OF THE SECOND ORDER WITH LINEAR DIFFERENTIAL EQUATIONS

It may not be obvious, but Theorem 22-1 covers a lot of ground. None of the arguments that prove it depend on an assumption that we are working in two-dimensional space; Theorem 22-1 is valid in R^{12}, R^{1776}, and so on. Furthermore, since scalar equations of order n are equivalent to systems of n equations of the first order, Theorem 22-1 applies to scalar problems of higher order, too. Let us look at this point more closely.

If the functions p, q, and r are continuous in some interval J, then $x'' + p(t)x' + q(t)x = r(t)$ is a **linear differential equation** of the second order. Now we select a point $t_0 \in J$, two numbers x_0 and y_0, and we have the initial value problem we want to study in this section:

(23-1)
$$x'' + p(t)x' + q(t)x = r(t)$$
$$x = x_0,\ x' = y_0 \text{ when } t = t_0.$$

In order to use our previously developed theory, we will replace this scalar problem of the second order with an equivalent first order system in two dimensions. We set

$$x' = y$$

so that our linear equation of the second order becomes

$$y' = -p(t)y - q(t)x + r(t).$$

Then we combine these last *two* equations into a *single* vector-matrix equation, and thus complete the transformation of Problem 23-1 into a first order problem in two dimensions:

(23-2)
$$\begin{pmatrix} x \\ y \end{pmatrix}' = \begin{bmatrix} 0 & 1 \\ -q(t) & -p(t) \end{bmatrix} \begin{pmatrix} x \\ y \end{pmatrix} + \begin{pmatrix} 0 \\ r(t) \end{pmatrix}$$
$$(x, y) = (x_0, y_0) \text{ when } t = t_0.$$

Now we are back to Problem 22-1 with

$$A(t) = \begin{bmatrix} 0 & 1 \\ -q(t) & -p(t) \end{bmatrix} \text{ and } \mathbf{r}(t) = \begin{pmatrix} 0 \\ r(t) \end{pmatrix}.$$

According to Corollary 22-1, we can define its solution in terms of $V(t)$, where V is a fundamental solution of the differential equation $X' = A(t)X$.

To find such a matrix $V(t)$, we proceed as follows. Let u and v be solutions of the **homogeneous** differential equation

(23-3) $$x'' + p(t)x' + q(t)x = 0.$$

(We get this equation by replacing $r(t)$ with 0 in the original linear differential equation $x'' + p(t)x' + q(t)x = r(t)$.) Then it is merely a matter of checking to see that $X = V(t)$, where

(23-4) $$V(t) = \begin{bmatrix} u(t) & v(t) \\ u'(t) & v'(t) \end{bmatrix},$$

satisfies the differential equation $X' = A(t)X$.

Example 23-1. Use the initial value problem

(23-5) $$x'' = e^t \text{ and } x = 1, \ x' = -1 \text{ when } t = 0$$

to illustrate the points we have just been talking about.

Solution. Of course, this problem is easy to solve without constructing any elaborate machinery, but it is a useful model to show what is going on. Here, $p(t) = q(t) = 0$, and $r(t) = e^t$. The homogeneous differential equation associated with this problem is simply $x'' = 0$, and so we can take $u(t) = 1$ and $v(t) = t$ as equations that define solutions. With these choices, $V(t) = \begin{bmatrix} 1 & t \\ 0 & 1 \end{bmatrix}$. Since $A(t) = \begin{bmatrix} 0 & 1 \\ 0 & 0 \end{bmatrix}$, it readily follows that $V'(t) = A(t)V(t)$.

For Corollary 22-1 to apply, we must make sure that the solution V is *fundamental;* that is, we insist that $\det V(t) \neq 0$. The determinant of the matrix in Equation 23-4 is called the **Wronskian** of u and v, and we write

$$W(u(t), v(t)) = \begin{vmatrix} u(t) & v(t) \\ u'(t) & v'(t) \end{vmatrix}.$$

Thus, we require that u and v be two solutions of the homogeneous Equation 23-3 whose Wronskian does not vanish in J. From our calculations in Example

22-2, it follows that V is a fundamental solution if, and only if, neither column of $V(t)$ is a constant multiple of the other. In the context of this section, this statement says that the Wronskian of u and v is non-vanishing if, and only if, neither $u(t)$ nor $v(t)$ is a constant multiple of the other in the interval J. We then say that u and v are **linearly independent** solutions of Equation 23-3.

Once we have found two linearly independent solutions u and v of the homogeneous equation, we can construct our matrix $V(t)$ and hence use Equation 22-7 to solve Problem 23-2. From the formula for the inverse of a 2 by 2 matrix given in Exercise 18-4(a), we see that

$$V(t)^{-1} = \frac{1}{W(u(t), v(t))} \begin{bmatrix} v'(t) & -v(t) \\ -u'(t) & u(t) \end{bmatrix},$$

and therefore Equation 22-7 states that

$$\begin{pmatrix} x \\ y \end{pmatrix} = \frac{1}{W(u(t_0), v(t_0))} \begin{bmatrix} u(t) & v(t) \\ u'(t) & v'(t) \end{bmatrix} \begin{bmatrix} v'(t_0) & -v(t_0) \\ -u'(t_0) & u(t_0) \end{bmatrix} \begin{pmatrix} x_0 \\ y_0 \end{pmatrix}$$
$$+ \int_{t_0}^{t} \frac{1}{W(u(s), v(s))} \begin{bmatrix} u(t) & v(t) \\ u'(t) & v'(t) \end{bmatrix} \begin{bmatrix} v'(s) & -v(s) \\ -u'(s) & u(s) \end{bmatrix} \begin{pmatrix} 0 \\ r(s) \end{pmatrix} ds$$

satisfies Problem 23-2. The first component of this vector satisfies our original Problem 23-1, and when you go through the details of calculating this component, you will find that you have proved the following theorem.

THEOREM 23-1

If u and v are linearly independent solutions of the homogeneous linear Differential Equation 23-3, then

$$(23\text{-}6) \quad x = \frac{x_0 v'(t_0) - y_0 v(t_0)}{W(u(t_0), v(t_0))} u(t) + \frac{y_0 u(t_0) - x_0 u'(t_0)}{W(u(t_0), v(t_0))} v(t)$$
$$+ \int_{t_0}^{t} \frac{v(t)u(s) - u(t)v(s)}{W(u(s), v(s))} r(s) ds$$

satisfies Problem 23-1.

Example 23-2.   Solve Problem 23-5.

Solution. In Example 23-1, we decided to take $u(t) = 1$ and $v(t) = t$, and so
$W(u(t), v(t)) = \begin{vmatrix} 1 & t \\ 0 & 1 \end{vmatrix} = 1$. Since $t_0 = 0$, $x_0 = 1$, $y_0 = -1$, and $r(t) = e^t$, Equa-

tion 23-6 becomes

$$x = 1 \cdot 1 + (-1)t + \int_0^t \frac{t \cdot 1 - 1 \cdot s}{1} e^s ds$$

$$= 1 - t + (te^s - se^s + e^s) \Big|_0^t = e^t - 2t.$$

Example 23-3. Use the theory of differential equations to derive the trigonometric identity

$$\sin (a + b) = \sin a \cos b + \cos a \sin b.$$

Solution. Let us first observe that $u(t) = \cos t$ and $v(t) = \sin t$ define linearly independent solutions of the homogeneous linear differential equation $x'' + x = 0$. (To show that they are solutions, simply substitute in the differential equation, and to show that they are linearly independent, convince yourself that $\cos t$ is not a constant multiple of $\sin t$.) Furthermore, it is merely a matter of checking to see that

$$x = \sin (a + t)$$

satisfies the initial value problem

$$x'' + x = 0 \text{ and } x = \sin a, \ x' = \cos a \text{ when } t = 0.$$

But Equation 23-6, with $r(t) = 0$, tells us that

$$x = \frac{\sin a \cos 0 - \cos a \sin 0}{1} \cos t + \frac{\cos a \cos 0 - \sin a (- \sin 0)}{1} \sin t$$

$$= \sin a \cos t + \cos a \sin t$$

also satisfies this problem. There is only one solution, so these two expressions for x must be equal for each choice of t, in particular, for $t = b$, which is what we were to prove.

Equation 23-6 certainly qualifies as a fearsome formula, so suppose that we analyze it a bit and see if we can simplify its application. First, we will look at the last term on the right-hand side,

(23-7) $$w(t) = \int_{t_0}^t \frac{v(t)u(s) - u(t)v(s)}{W(u(s), v(s))} r(s) ds.$$

Since this term is what we get when we set $x_0 = y_0 = 0$, we see that w is *the solution of the initial value problem*

(23-8) $x'' + p(t)x' + q(t)x = r(t)$ and $x = 0, \ x' = 0$ when $t = t_0$.

In this problem, the initial conditions of Problem 23-1 are replaced by the *homogeneous* initial conditions $x = 0$ and $x' = 0$ when $t = t_0$. Notice that the construction of $w(t)$, using Equation 23-7, is purely a routine matter, *after* we have found independent solutions u and v of the homogeneous Equation 23-3.

Theorem 23-1 states that we can build up the solution of our given initial value problem by adding to $w(t)$ a linear combination $cu(t) + dv(t)$ of $u(t)$ and $v(t)$. The numbers c and d are chosen so that

$$(23\text{-}9) \qquad\qquad x = cu(t) + dv(t) + w(t)$$

satisfies the initial conditions $x = x_0$ and $x' = y_0$ when $t = t_0$. In summary, then, *we solve Initial Value Problem* 23-1 *by following this sequence of steps:*

(i)   *Find two linearly independent solutions u and v of the homogeneous Equation 23-3,*
(ii) *Use Equation 23-7 to construct $w(t)$,*
(iii) *Find numbers c and d so that x, as expressed by Equation 23-9, satisfies the given initial conditions.*

Step (i) is the big one; after it has been taken, steps (ii) and (iii) are mechanical (although the details of step (ii) can sometimes become tedious). Notice that if our given Problem 23-1 has a homogeneous differential equation ($r(t) = 0$), then $w(t) = 0$, so we can bypass step (ii) in this case.

Example 23-4.   Given that the equations $x = t^2$ and $x = t^3$ define solutions of the differential equation $x'' - 4t^{-1}x' + 6t^{-2}x = 0$, solve the initial value problem

$$x'' - 4t^{-1}x' + 6t^{-2}x = 2t^{-1} \text{ and } x = 5,\ x' = 14 \text{ when } t = 1.$$

Solution. Here we are told that $u(t) = t^2$ and $v(t) = t^3$; step (i) of our solution scheme has been taken for us. Therefore, we proceed to step (ii). Since $W(t^2, t^3) = \begin{vmatrix} t^2 & t^3 \\ 2t & 3t^2 \end{vmatrix} = t^4$, our formula for $w(t)$ becomes

$$w(t) = \int_1^t \frac{t^3 s^2 - t^2 s^3}{s^4}\, 2s^{-1}ds = \int_1^t (2t^3 s^{-3} - 2t^2 s^{-2})ds$$

$$= -t^3 s^{-2} + 2t^2 s^{-1} \Big|_1^t = t + t^3 - 2t^2.$$

Now, according to step (iii), we are to choose numbers c and d so that

$$x = ct^2 + dt^3 + t + t^3 - 2t^2$$

satisfies the initial conditions. This equation tells us that

$$x' = 2ct + 3dt^2 + 1 + 3t^2 - 4t,$$

and hence, since we are to have $x = 5$ and $x' = 14$ when $t = 1$, our equations for c and d are

$$5 = c + d + 0$$

$$14 = 2c + 3d + 0.$$

It follows that $c = 1$ and $d = 4$, so

$$x = t^2 + 4t^3 + t + t^3 - 2t^2 = 5t^3 - t^2 + t$$

satisfies our initial value problem.

EXERCISE 23

1. What is the largest interval J in which we would consider the initial value problem with the differential equation

$$x'' + (\tan t)x' + (\ln t)x = \sin (t + 1)$$

and the following initial conditions?
(a) $x = 3$, $x' = 4$ when $t = 1$ (c) $x = 4$, $x' = 6$ when $t = 15$
(b) $x = 2$, $x' = -1$ when $t = \pi$ (d) $x = 7$, $x' = 9$ when $t = -1$

2. Are u and v linearly independent in the interval $[1, 2]$ if $u(t) = \ln t$ and $v(t) = \ln t^2$? In the interval $[-1, 1]$?

3. If $u(t)$ is a constant multiple of $v(t)$ in an interval J, does it necessarily follow that $v(t)$ is a constant multiple of $u(t)$?

4. Show by direct computation that if $u(t)$ is a constant multiple of $v(t)$ in an interval J, then $W(u(t), v(t)) = 0$ for each $t \in J$.

5. Show that the equations $u(t) = \cos 4t$ and $v(t) = \sin 4t$ define linearly independent solutions of the homogeneous linear differential equation $x'' + 16x = 0$. Solve the initial value problems that consist of this differential equation and the following initial conditions.
(a) $x = 0$, $x' = 0$ when $t = 0$ (c) $x = 3$, $x' = -4$ when $t = 0$
(b) $x = 0$, $x' = 1$ when $t = 0$ (d) $x = 2$, $x' = 3$ when $t = \pi$

6. Suppose we are told that $x = t$ and $x = e^t$ satisfy the differential equation $x'' + p(t)x' + q(t)x = 0$, where p and q are continuous in some interval J.
(a) Look at $W(t, e^t)$ and explain why J cannot contain the point 1.
(b) Can you find $p(t)$ and $q(t)$?
(c) Solve the initial value problem that consists of the given differential equation and the initial conditions $x = 2$, $x' = -1$ when $t = 0$.

(d) Same as (c), except that the initial conditions are $x = \ln 3$, $x' = \ln \frac{1}{2}$ when $t = \ln 5$.

7. Show that Equation 23-6 can be written in the form $x = a(t)u(t) + b(t)v(t)$.

8. Verify that $x = e^t$ and $x = e^{-2t}$ satisfy the homogeneous linear differential equation $x'' + x' - 2x = 0$. Do we have two linearly independent solutions? Solve the following initial value problems.

(a) $x'' + x' - 2x = 10e^{3t}$
   $x = 3$ and $x' = 8$ when $t = 0$

(b) $x'' + x' - 2x = 4$
   $x = -1$ and $x' = 3$ when $t = 0$

(c) $x'' + x' - 2x = 9e^t$
   $x = 0$ and $x' = 0$ when $t = 0$

(d) $x'' + x' - 2x = 1 - 2t$
   $x = 3$ and $x' = -2$ when $t = 0$

9. (a) Show that the initial value problem

$$x'' + x = r(t) \text{ and } x = x_0, \ x' = y_0 \text{ when } t = 0$$

is satisfied by

$$x = \left(x_0 - \int_0^t r(s) \sin s \, ds \right) \cos t + \left(y_0 + \int_0^t r(s) \cos s \, ds \right) \sin t$$
$$= x_0 \cos t + y_0 \sin t + \int_0^t \sin (t - s) r(s) ds.$$

(b) Find the explicit formula for x if $x_0 = 2$, $y_0 = -1$, and $r(t) = t$, and check to see that you really do have a solution of this initial value problem.

(c) Explain and run the computer program in Fig. 23-1 for printing a table of values of the solution of the initial value problem $x'' + x = \sqrt{t}$ and $x = 2$, $x' = -1$ when $t = 0$ at the points of the set $\{0, 1, 2, 3, 4\}$.

```
        F(U) = −SQRT(U)*SIN(U)
        G(V) = SQRT(V)*COS(V)
        T = 0
        X = 2
        WRITE(6, 1) T, X
  1     FORMAT(1X, F3.1, F20.4)
        A = 2
        B = −1
        DO 2 I = 1, 4
        T = I
        R = F(T−1) + 4*F(T−.75) + 2*F(T−.5) + 4*F(T−.25) + F(T)
        S = G(T−1) + 4*G(T−.75) + 2*G(T−.5) + 4*G(T−.25) + G(T)
        A = A + (.25/3)*R
        B = B + (.25/3)*S
        X = A*COS(T) + B*SIN(T)
        WRITE(6, 1) T, X
  2     CONTINUE
        STOP
        END
```

Figure 23-1

10. Suppose that u and v are two solutions of the homogeneous linear differential equation $x'' + p(t)x' + q(t)x = 0$ in an interval J in which the coefficients p and q are continuous. Suppose that there is a point $a \in J$ such that $u(a) = v(a) = 0$. Show that, in J, $u(t)$ is a constant multiple of $v(t)$ or that $v(t)$ is a constant multiple of $u(t)$.

11. Show that if u is a solution of the differential equation $x'' + p(t)x' + q(t)x = 0$ in an interval J, and $u(t) \neq 0$ for each $t \in J$, then the equation

$$ v(t) = u(t) \int_{t_0}^{t} u(s)^{-2} \exp\left(-\int_{t_0}^{s} p(z)dz \right) ds, $$

where t_0 is any point of J, defines a solution v that is independent of u. (What this result shows is that if we can find *one* solution u of the homogeneous equation $x'' + p(t)x' + q(t)x = 0$, then it is merely a mechanical matter to find a second solution v.)

24   LINEAR DIFFERENTIAL EQUATIONS OF THE SECOND ORDER WITH CONSTANT COEFFICIENTS

The key step in solving the linear Initial Value Problem 23-1 consists of finding two linearly independent solutions u and v of the *homogeneous* differential equation

(24-1) $$ x'' + p(t)x' + q(t)x = 0. $$

We have had enough experience with differential equations to know that unless $p(t)$ and $q(t)$ are pretty simple, we stand little chance of finding explicit formulas for $u(t)$ and $v(t)$. But if $p(t)$ and $q(t)$ *are* simple enough, we can solve Equation 24-1.

In particular, if p and q are constant functions, we can do the job, so let us suppose that a and b are real numbers and consider the differential equation

(24-2) $$ x'' + ax' + bx = 0. $$

For example, we might have

(24-3) $$ x'' + x' - 2x = 0. $$

We can solve Equation 24-2 by the techniques we learned in Section 10, or we can transform it into a system and apply what we learned in Sections 20 and 21.

Suppose we try this latter approach. As we found in the last section, Equation 24-2 is equivalent to $(x, y)' = A(x, y)$, where $A = \begin{bmatrix} 0 & 1 \\ -b & -a \end{bmatrix}$. In Example 20-4, we saw that solutions of this differential equation are given by the equation $(x, y) = e^{At}(x_0, y_0)$. Furthermore, we know that there is a matrix L, "simpler" than A, such that $e^{At} = Pe^{Lt}P^{-1}$, and so $(x, y) = Pe^{Lt}P^{-1}(x_0, y_0)$. This equation tells us that *if x satisfies Equation 24-2, then x is a linear combination of the elements of e^{Lt}.*

So let us recall what these elements look like. To find our simple matrix L, we first solve the characteristic equation of A:

(24-4) $$\lambda^2 + a\lambda + b = 0.$$

In Section 21, we discussed the three possible cases:

(i) If Equation 24-4 has two distinct real solutions λ_1 and λ_2, then

$$e^{Lt} = \begin{bmatrix} e^{\lambda_1 t} & 0 \\ 0 & e^{\lambda_2 t} \end{bmatrix}.$$

(ii) If Equation 24-4 has a "double zero" λ, it turns out that A is non-diagonable, and

$$e^{Lt} = \begin{bmatrix} e^{\lambda t} & te^{\lambda t} \\ 0 & e^{\lambda t} \end{bmatrix}.$$

(iii) If the solutions of Equation 24-4 are complex numbers $\sigma + i\tau$ and $\sigma - i\tau$, where $\tau > 0$, then

$$e^{Lt} = \begin{bmatrix} e^{\sigma t}\cos\tau t & e^{\sigma t}\sin\tau t \\ -e^{\sigma t}\sin\tau t & e^{\sigma t}\cos\tau t \end{bmatrix}.$$

Since values of solutions of Equation 24-2 are linear combinations of the elements of these matrices, you will not be surprised to be told that Table 24-1 gives us a pair of linearly independent building blocks $u(t)$ and $v(t)$ in every

TABLE 24-1

Given differential equation: $x'' + ax' + bx = 0$	
Associated algebraic equation: $\lambda^2 + a\lambda + b = 0$	
Solutions of the algebraic equation	Equations that define independent solutions of the differential equation
λ_1 and λ_2, two different real numbers	$u(t) = e^{\lambda_1 t}$ and $v(t) = e^{\lambda_2 t}$
λ, a double zero	$u(t) = e^{\lambda t}$ and $v(t) = te^{\lambda t}$
$\sigma + i\tau$ and $\sigma - i\tau$, σ and τ real and $\tau > 0$	$u(t) = e^{\sigma t}\cos\tau t$ and $v(t) = e^{\sigma t}\sin\tau t$

possible case. Our "derivation" of these results is admittedly a little sketchy, so you may want to verify the correctness of the tabular entries in a straight-forward manner; namely, substitute the alleged solution values in Equation 24-2 and show that they satisfy it. You should know this table by heart.

Example 24-1.   Find two linearly independent solutions of Equation 24-3.

Solution. Here, $a = 1$ and $b = -2$, so Equation 24-4 becomes $\lambda^2 + \lambda - 2 = (\lambda - 1)(\lambda + 2) = 0$. Hence, our two characteristic values are $\lambda_1 = 1$ and $\lambda_2 = -2$, so the equations $u(t) = e^t$ and $v(t) = e^{-2t}$ define two linearly independent solutions of Equation 24-3. Check and see.

It would be ridiculous to go through the whole business of transforming to matrix notation every time you want to solve Equation 24-2. What Table 24-1 really says is that solutions of this equation are defined by equations of the form $x = e^{\lambda t}$, so we simply substitute this expression in our given differential equation, and we get

$$\lambda^2 e^{\lambda t} + a\lambda e^{\lambda t} + b e^{\lambda t} = 0.$$

Now we divide by $e^{\lambda t}$, and we have Equation 24-4. This process reduces the problem of solving the *differential* Equation 24-2 to the problem of solving the *algebraic* Equation 24-4.

Example 24-2.   Solve the initial value problem

$$x'' + 4x' + 4x = 0 \text{ and } x = 3, x' = 4 \text{ when } t = 0.$$

Solution. Since our given differential equation is homogeneous, the theory we developed in the last section tells us that we need only find two linearly independent solutions u and v and then choose numbers c and d so that $x = cu(t) + dv(t)$ satisfies the initial conditions.

The algebraic equation associated with our differential equation is $\lambda^2 + 4\lambda + 4 = 0$, or $(\lambda + 2)^2 = 0$. This equation has -2 as a double zero, so we find from Table 24-1 that the equations

$$u(t) = e^{-2t} \text{ and } v(t) = te^{-2t}$$

define two linearly independent solutions of the differential equation. Therefore, we must determine the numbers c and d so that $x = ce^{-2t} + dte^{-2t} = (c + dt)e^{-2t}$ satisfies the initial conditions. Thus, since $x' = (-2c - 2dt + d)e^{-2t}$, the equations $x = 3$ and $x' = 4$ when $t = 0$ become

$$c = 3 \text{ and } -2c + d = 4.$$

It follows that $(c, d) = (3, 10)$, and so $x = (3 + 10t)e^{-2t}$ satisfies our problem.

When we say that solutions of Equation 24-2 are defined by equations of the form $x = e^{\lambda t}$, we have to allow for the possibility that λ is a complex number. You have probably seen the definition of complex exponentials in your calculus course, but the theory of differential equations provides us with another approach.

Example 24-3. Why is it "natural" to make the definition

(24-5) $$e^{it} = \cos t + i \sin t?$$

Solution. Since $i^2 = -1$, the usual rules of calculus tell us that $x = e^{it}$ satisfies the initial value problem $x'' + x = 0$ and $x = 1$, $x' = i$ when $t = 0$. Now let us solve this problem by our methods. The algebraic equation associated with the given differential equation is $\lambda^2 + 1 = 0$, and its solutions are the complex numbers i and $-i$. Therefore, Table 24-1 states that $u(t) = \cos t$ and $v(t) = \sin t$ define linearly independent solutions of the equation $x'' + x = 0$. So now we need to find numbers c and d such that the combination $x = c \cos t + d \sin t$ satisfies the initial conditions. Since $x' = -c \sin t + d \cos t$, the equations $x = 1$ and $x' = i$ when $t = 0$ become $c = 1$ and $d = i$. Therefore, $x = \cos t + i \sin t$ satisfies our given initial value problem. Because this problem has only one solution, we are led to Equation 24-5.

The reason we must treat Equation 24-5 as a definition, rather than as a theorem, is that we obviously cannot apply the rules of calculus to e^{it} until we know what this symbol means. What we have really shown in this example is that the only definition of e^{it} that is consistent with the rules of calculus (in particular, $D_t e^{it} = i e^{it}$) is the definition provided by Equation 24-5. Of course, we define e^{s+it} as $e^s(\cos t + i \sin t)$.

In the last example, we used our theory to suggest a new definition. Now let us use it to provide an alternative definition of some familiar functions. Since we know the rules of calculus for the trigonometric functions, we know that $x = \cos t$ satisfies the initial value problem

(24-6) $$x'' + x = 0 \text{ and } x = 1, x' = 0 \text{ when } t = 0,$$

and $x = \sin t$ satisfies the initial value problem

(24-7) $$x'' + x = 0 \text{ and } x = 0, x' = 1 \text{ when } t = 0.$$

But suppose we had not studied trigonometry. It would still be true, our existence and uniqueness theorems tell us so, that Problems 24-6 and 24-7 each determine exactly one solution function. We could name these functions *cosine* and *sine*, and we could, with a little ingenuity, develop all their properties. For instance, in Example 23-3 we derived the trigonometric identity sin

$(a + b) = \sin a \cos b + \cos a \sin b$, and we used only the facts that the cosine and sine functions satisfy these initial value problems and that $D_t \sin t = \cos t$. Let us see how we could derive this latter equation.

Example 24-4. Show that $\sin' t = \cos t$, where by $\sin'$, of course, we mean the derived function of the sine function.

Solution. Because of our uniqueness theorem, we need only show that $x = \sin' t$ satisfies Initial Value Problem 24-6 to see that $\sin'$ is the cosine function. We are supposing that the sine function is defined as the solution of Problem 24-7, so

$$(24\text{-}8) \qquad\qquad \sin'' t + \sin t = 0,$$

$$(24\text{-}9) \qquad\qquad \sin 0 = 0,$$

and

$$(24\text{-}10) \qquad\qquad \sin' 0 = 1.$$

From Equations 24-8 and 24-9, we immediately conclude that

$$(24\text{-}11) \qquad\qquad \sin'' 0 = 0.$$

Furthermore, if we differentiate both sides of Equation 24-8, we obtain the equation

$$(24\text{-}12) \qquad\qquad \sin''' t + \sin' t = 0.$$

Equations 24-12, 24-10, and 24-11 state that $y = \sin' t$ satisfies Problem 24-6, and so our proof is complete.

We could also use an initial value problem to define the exponential function and in this way build up the solutions of all initial value problems whose differential equations are linear with constant coefficients in terms of solutions of a few particular problems. We will not have time to pursue this idea any further, however.

EXERCISE 24

1. Find two linearly independent solutions of each of the following differential equations.
   (a) $x'' - 2x' + 5x = 0$ (c) $x'' - 2x' - 3x = 0$
   (b) $x'' - 2x' + x = 0$ (d) $x'' + 3x' = 0$

2. Solve the following initial value problems.
   (a) $x'' + 9x = 0$
       $x = 2,\ x' = 3$ when $t = 0$
   (b) $x'' + 2x' + 2x = 0$
       $x = -3,\ x' = 5$ when $t = 0$
   (c) $x'' - 9x = 18$
       $x = 0,\ x' = 3$ when $t = 0$
   (d) $x'' + 2x' + x = 9e^{2t}$
       $x = -1,\ x' = 3$ when $t = 0$

3. Table 24-1 tells us that every solution w of the differential equation $x'' + \tau^2 x = 0$ is defined by an equation of the form $w(t) = c \cos \tau t + d \sin \tau t$, where the numbers c and d are determined by the values of w and w' when $t = 0$. Can you show that there are numbers A and δ such that $w(t) = A \cos (\tau t - \delta)$?

4. The initial value problem

   $$x'' - 6x' + 10x = 0 \text{ and } x = 0 \text{ when } t = 2$$

   is "incomplete" in the sense that it has too few initial conditions to determine a *unique* solution. Show, however, that if w is any solution of this problem, then $w(2 + \pi) = 0$.

5. What can you say about the (real) numbers a and b if all solutions of the differential equation $x'' + ax' + bx = 0$ are periodic?

6. What can you say about the (real) number a if for each solution w of the differential equation $x'' + ax' + bx = 0$ it is true that $w(t) = 0$?
   $$t \uparrow \infty$$

7. Show that if $\sigma + \tau$ and $\sigma - \tau$ are solutions of the algebraic Equation 24-4, then $x = e^{\sigma t} \cosh \tau t$ and $x = e^{\sigma t} \sinh \tau t$ satisfy the differential Equation 24-2.

8. (a) Show that each solution of the differential equation $x'' + 2x' + 5x = r(t)$ is obtained from the equation

   $$x = e^{-t}(c \cos 2t + d \sin 2t) + .5 \int_0^t e^{-(t-s)} \sin 2(t - s)r(s)ds$$

   by selecting the numbers c and d.
   (b) Show that if there is a number M such that $|r(t)| \le M$ for all $t \ge 0$, then every solution of our differential equation is bounded in the interval $[0, \infty)$.
   (c) (This question is harder than the preceding one.) Suppose that $\lim r(t) = 0$.
   $$t \uparrow \infty$$
   0. Show that if w is any solution of our differential equation, then $\lim w(t) = 0$.
   $$t \uparrow \infty$$

9. We have seen that the substitution $x = e^{\lambda t}$ turns the differential equation $x'' + ax' + bx = 0$ into an algebraic equation. Show, similarly, that the substitution $x = t^r$ turns **Euler's Differential Equation**

   $$x'' + at^{-1}x' + bt^{-2}x = 0$$

   (where a and b are given numbers) into the algebraic equation

   $$r^2 + (a - 1)r + b = 0,$$

and use this technique to find two linearly independent solutions of each of the following differential equations.

(a) $x'' + 3t^{-1}x' - 3t^{-2}x = 0$ (c) $t^2x'' + tx' - 3x = 0$
(b) $x'' + 4t^{-1}x' + 2t^{-2}x = 0$ (d) $tx'' + 4x' = 0$

10. It is easy to see that $x = e^t$ satisfies the differential equation $x'' - 2x' + x = 0$. Use the formula given in Exercise 23-11 to find an independent solution.

25 THE LINEARIZED EQUATION OF THE PENDULUM

There are any number of "practical" problems that can be modeled by initial value problems in which the differential equations have constant coefficients. Suppose that we look at one now. In Section 10, we derived the differential equation that governs the motion of a pendulum:

(25-1)
$$\theta'' + \frac{k}{m}\theta' + \frac{g}{r}\sin\theta = 0.$$

Here, θ is the angular displacement (in radians) t seconds after we start measuring time, the pendulum is r meters long, the bob has a mass of m kilograms, $g \approx 9.8$ meters per second per second, and we assume that the medium in which the pendulum is swinging offers a resistance of k newtons per meter per second (see Fig. 25-1).

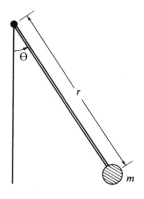

Figure 25-1

As it stands, Equation 25-1 is difficult to solve explicitly, and one way to get around this difficulty is to "linearize" it; that is, to replace sin θ with θ and thus obtain a linear equation. If θ is small, sin $\theta \approx \theta$, so this replacement seems reasonable. There is often, however, a line to be drawn between procedures that *seem* reasonable and procedures that *are* reasonable. We will leave the justification of this linearizing substitution for a later course in differential equations. Here, we will be content to see what it suggests about the behavior of the pendulum. In Section 28, we will look at the pendulum equation from a different point of view.

So let us study the **linearized equation of the pendulum**

$$\text{(25-2)} \qquad \theta'' + \frac{k}{m} \theta' + \frac{g}{r} \theta = 0.$$

To this equation we must adjoin *initial conditions*,

$$\theta = \theta_0 \text{ and } \theta' = \theta_1 \text{ when } t = 0,$$

to obtain the initial value problem that constitutes our mathematical model of the physical experiment of setting a pendulum in motion. (We would want to choose the initial angular displacement θ_0 and the initial angular velocity θ_1 to be small to make our approximation sin $\theta \approx \theta$ more realistic, at least for t near 0.)

To make matters even simpler, let us first investigate the case in which the medium offers no resistance at all, $k = 0$, and in which the initial velocity is 0. Then our initial value problem is

$$\theta'' + \frac{g}{r} \theta = 0 \text{ and } \theta = \theta_0, \ \theta' = 0 \text{ when } t = 0.$$

To solve this problem, we must find two linearly independent solutions of the given homogeneous differential equation and then combine them so that the initial conditions are satisfied. The algebraic equation associated with the differential equation $\theta'' + \frac{g}{r} \theta = 0$ is $\lambda^2 + \frac{g}{r} = 0$, and its solutions are $\sqrt{\frac{g}{r}} i$ and $-\sqrt{\frac{g}{r}} i$. Therefore, Table 24-1 tells us that $\theta = \cos \sqrt{\frac{g}{r}} t$ and $\theta = \sin \sqrt{\frac{g}{r}} t$ satisfy the differential equation. Thus, we must pick c and d so that

$$\text{(25-3)} \qquad \theta = c \cos \sqrt{\frac{g}{r}} t + d \sin \sqrt{\frac{g}{r}} t$$

satisfies the initial conditions $\theta = \theta_0$ and $\theta' = 0$ when $t = 0$. A short calculation produces the values $c = \theta_0$ and $d = 0$, and so we see that

$$\text{(25-4)} \qquad\qquad \theta = \theta_0 \cos \sqrt{\frac{g}{r}}\, t$$

satisfies our initial value problem.

This solution is about what we would expect. If we displace the pendulum
through a small angle that is θ_0 radians wide and release it from rest (give it
an initial velocity of 0), we would expect it to oscillate back and forth about the
vertical position. According to Equation 25-4, it does. The amplitude of the
motion is $|\theta_0|$; that is, the pendulum never makes a greater angle with the
vertical than it started with. Since the cosine function has a period of 2π, our
pendulum has a **period** of $2\pi \sqrt{\dfrac{r}{g}}$ seconds per complete oscillation. Its **fre-**
quency (the reciprocal of the period) is therefore $\sqrt{\dfrac{g}{r}} \Big/ 2\pi$ oscillations per second.

Notice that this expression is reasonable. For a long pendulum (r large) the
frequency is small, as we would expect. Notice, too, that $g \approx 9.8 \approx \pi^2$, and
suppose now that our pendulum is 1 meter long. Then its frequency is about
$\sqrt{\pi^2}/2\pi = \frac{1}{2}$; that is, the pendulum makes about one-half of a complete cycle
(the "tick" of "tick tock") in one second. From your experience with pendulums, this result should seem reasonable, too. Finally, we see from Equation
25-3 that the frequency of our pendulum is independent of the initial conditions. The initial displacement and velocity of the pendulum determine the
numbers c and d in Equation 25-3, but whatever these numbers turn out to be,
this equation defines a function with a period of $2\pi \sqrt{\dfrac{r}{g}}$ seconds per oscillation.

Now let us introduce resistance; suppose that $k > 0$. Then the algebraic
equation that goes with differential Equation 25-2 is

$$\text{(25-5)} \qquad\qquad \lambda^2 + \frac{k}{m}\lambda + \frac{g}{r} = 0.$$

The solutions of this equation are

$$\text{(25-6)} \quad \lambda_1 = -\frac{k}{2m} + \frac{1}{2}\sqrt{\frac{k^2}{m^2} - \frac{4g}{r}} \quad \text{and} \quad \lambda_2 = -\frac{k}{2m} - \frac{1}{2}\sqrt{\frac{k^2}{m^2} - \frac{4g}{r}}.$$

If our medium offers only slight resistance to the pendulum (k is small), the radicands will be negative, and the solutions will be complex numbers of the form $\lambda_1 = -\dfrac{k}{2m} + i\omega$ and $\lambda_2 = -\dfrac{k}{2m} - i\omega$. (For brevity, we have written $\omega = \dfrac{1}{2}\sqrt{\dfrac{4g}{r} - \dfrac{k^2}{m^2}}.$) Therefore, the equations $\theta = e^{-kt/2m}\cos \omega t$ and $\theta = e^{-kt/2m}\sin \omega t$ determine two solutions of Equation 25-2, and so the angular displacement of the pendulum will be

(25-7) $$\theta = e^{-kt/2m}(c \cos \omega t + d \sin \omega t),$$

where c and d are chosen so that the initial conditions are satisfied.

Notice that θ gets small as t gets large. The effect of the resistance of the medium is to *damp* the vibrations of the pendulum. Nevertheless, the motion is still oscillatory; the pendulum ticks back and forth every $2\pi/\omega$ seconds with, as we say, decreasing amplitude. Strictly speaking, the motion is not periodic, because each swing is not an exact repetition of its predecessor. Of course, we have to be somewhat suspicious of these results if t is large. Replacing sin θ with θ in Equation 25-1 may not be a great sin, but if we wait long enough, even a little error can grow into a big one.

Suppose we increase the density of the medium in which the pendulum is immersed until $\dfrac{k^2}{m^2} = \dfrac{4g}{r}$. Then Equation 25-5 has the double zero $-k/2m$, and two independent solutions of our differential equation are given by the equations $\theta = e^{-kt/2m}$ and $\theta = te^{-kt/2m}$. The displacement of the pendulum is then

$$\theta = e^{-kt/2m}(c + dt),$$

where c and d are chosen to satisfy the initial conditions. If, for example, we give the pendulum an initial displacement of θ_0 radians and start it from rest, then you can readily check that

(25-8) $$\theta = \theta_0 e^{-kt/2m}(1 + kt/2m).$$

This result is rather interesting. According to it, the pendulum never reaches the vertical position. Since we have increased the damping factor k until all oscillations cease, this case is called the case of **critical damping**. Again, we must caution you about relying on our results when t is large.

To complete the picture, we can briefly look at the case in which k is so large that $\dfrac{k^2}{m^2} - \dfrac{r}{4g} > 0$. Then the numbers λ_1 and λ_2 in Equations 25-6 are negative; let us call them $-\alpha_1$ and $-\alpha_2$. The displacement of the pendulum will be given by an equation of the form

$$\theta = ce^{-\alpha_1 t} + de^{-\alpha_2 t},$$

where, as usual, c and d are determined by the initial conditions. No matter what initial conditions we impose here, the pendulum cannot reach the vertical position more than once. There is no oscillation back and forth. This is the **overdamped** case. As in all cases of damped vibration, $\lim_{t \uparrow \infty} \theta = 0$. Because of the uncertain validity of our linearization procedure, we must not trust our results too much for large t. Physically, however, we believe this limit equation; in time, oscillations will die out if the medium offers resistance.

EXERCISE 25

1. Suppose that for a particular linearized pendulum $k = 1$, $m = 5$, and $\omega = 2$, and we start it in the "bob down" position with an initial velocity of .2 radians per second.
   (a) What does Equation 25-7 become in this case?
   (b) What is the maximum angular displacement from the vertical attained by the pendulum?

2. Does a linearized undamped pendulum with a .2 kilogram bob oscillate faster than one with a .1 kilogram bob? What about a damped pendulum?

3. Would a given linearized undamped pendulum oscillate faster on the moon or on the earth?

4. Show that Equation 25-8 implies that $\theta \in (0, \theta_0]$ for all $t \geq 0$.

5. Show that Equation 25-3 can be written as

$$\theta = \theta_0 \cos \sqrt{\frac{g}{r}} t + \theta_1 \sqrt{\frac{r}{g}} \sin \sqrt{\frac{g}{r}} t,$$

   where θ_0 and θ_1 are the initial angular displacement and velocity of the pendulum.
   (a) What is the amplitude of the oscillation?
   (b) Two identical undamped pendulums, one located on earth and one on the moon, are started with the same initial displacement and velocity. Which motion has the larger amplitude?
   (c) Two undamped pendulums (located at the same place), one .1 meter long and the other .2 meter long, are started with the same initial angular displacement and the same *linear* velocity (that is, meters per second, not radians per second). Which oscillates with the larger amplitude?

6. Show that there is a positive number A and a number δ such that Equation 25-7 can be written as

$$\theta = Ae^{-kt/2m} \cos (\omega t - \delta).$$

Is A the maximum angular displacement of the pendulum?

7. Suppose we start the (damped) pendulum of Exercise 25-1 with an initial angular displacement of $-.1$ radian. What should the initial velocity be so that it swings across the vertical position and stops at an angle of $.1$ radian? Then we could give it the reverse push to send it back, and we would have a clock. (You might want to use a computer on this problem; the arithmetic gets pretty fierce.)

8. Suppose that our pendulum is ticking away in a high wind in the plane of motion, so that a constant force is superimposed on the gravitational and resistance forces we are already assuming to be acting on the bob.

   (a) Convince yourself that the (linearized) differential equation of the pendulum has the form $\theta'' + \dfrac{k}{m} \theta' + \dfrac{g}{r} \theta = c$, where c is a number whose magnitude and sign depend on the speed and direction of the wind.

   (b) Can you show that if w is *any* solution of the equation of part (a), then

   $$\lim_{t \uparrow \infty} w(t) = \frac{rc}{g}?$$

26   TRAJECTORIES IN THE PHASE PLANE

Many physical experiments (swinging a pendulum is one) can be modeled by initial value problems with an **autonomous** differential equation

$$(26\text{-}1) \qquad\qquad \mathbf{x}' = \mathbf{f}(\mathbf{x}).$$

This equation differs from the more general differential equation $\mathbf{x}' = \mathbf{f}(t, \mathbf{x})$ in that $\mathbf{f}(\mathbf{x})$ is independent of t. If we choose a point $\mathbf{x}_0$ and adjoin to Equation 26-1 the initial condition $\mathbf{x} = \mathbf{x}_0$ when $t = 0$, we obtain an initial value problem with a solution $\mathbf{u}$ whose domain is some interval of the T-axis. In the rest of this chapter we will suppose that this interval is the half-axis $[0, \infty)$. Furthermore, we assume that each such initial value problem has only one solution.

We confine our attention to the two-dimensional case, so the equation $\mathbf{x} = \mathbf{u}(t)$ can be written in component form as

$$(26\text{-}2) \qquad\qquad x = u(t) \text{ and } y = v(t).$$

These two equations are parametric equations of an arc in the XY-plane. This arc is the **trajectory** of Equation 26-1 that starts at the point (x_0, y_0), and the XY-plane is the **phase plane** of the equation. In many applications, t measures time, and a trajectory is the path of a moving point. Thus, the point $(x, y) = (u(t), v(t))$ might represent the position of a rocket t seconds after launch. The set of all trajectories of a given differential equation is its **phase portrait.** (We should point out that in our efforts to compress a discussion of this very large topic into a few pages, we have departed slightly from the terminology used in the more complete References [2] and [4].) The autonomous vector Equation 26-1 is equivalent to a system of two scalar equations. For example,

(26-3)
$$x' = \sin y$$
$$y' = \sin x$$

is an autonomous system.

   If $\mathbf{c}$ is a vector such that $\mathbf{f}(\mathbf{c}) = \mathbf{0}$, then $\mathbf{x} = \mathbf{c}$ satisfies the initial value problem $\mathbf{x}' = \mathbf{f}(\mathbf{x})$ and $\mathbf{x} = \mathbf{c}$ when $t = 0$. The graph of the equation $\mathbf{x} = \mathbf{c}$ is simply the point $\mathbf{c}$ itself, so this particular trajectory is a short one. For example, $(\pi, 0)$, $(0, 3\pi)$, and so on, are "point trajectories" of System 26-3. In applications, such points may represent equilibrium positions of a system whose behavior is described by the differential equation (we will discuss an example in Section 28). We call them **critical points** of the differential equation, and it is useful to discuss trajectories in the neighborhoods of critical points.

   The simplest example of an autonomous differential equation is furnished by the homogeneous linear differential equation with constant coefficients

(26-4)
$$\mathbf{x}' = A\mathbf{x},$$

where A is a given matrix of real numbers. The origin $(0, 0)$ is a critical point of this equation, and to assure that it is the only critical point, we will assume that $\det A \neq 0$. We are going to spend this section studying the phase portraits of Equation 26-4 for various choices of the matrix A. Since the behavior of the trajectories of a nonlinear equation in the neighborhood of a critical point can often be pretty well established by replacing the given equation by a linear approximation, this study of linear equations will be useful for an understanding of nonlinear problems, too.

   As we know, Equation 26-4 is satisfied by $\mathbf{x} = e^{At}\mathbf{x}_0$, where $\mathbf{x}_0 = (x_0, y_0)$ is a given initial vector. The graph of this vector equation is the trajectory that starts at (x_0, y_0). Because e^{At} can be a complicated expression, it is not easy to picture such a trajectory in general. However, by transforming A into a simpler form, we can get an idea of its basic properties.

   Thus, suppose that P is a matrix of real numbers such that $P^{-1}AP = L$, where L has a "simpler" form than A. Then (see Equation 21-2) $e^{At} = Pe^{Lt}P^{-1}$, and the trajectory equation $\mathbf{x} = e^{At}\mathbf{x}_0$ becomes $\mathbf{x} = Pe^{Lt}P^{-1}\mathbf{x}_0$, or $P^{-1}\mathbf{x} = e^{Lt}P^{-1}\mathbf{x}_0$. So if we set $\bar{\mathbf{x}} = P^{-1}\mathbf{x}$ and $\bar{\mathbf{x}}_0 = P^{-1}\mathbf{x}_0$, our equation is $\bar{\mathbf{x}} = e^{Lt}\bar{\mathbf{x}}_0$. The equation $\bar{\mathbf{x}} = P^{-1}\mathbf{x}$ can be viewed as representing a fairly simple transformation of the XY-plane to the $\bar{X}\bar{Y}$-plane. While it is true that this transformation distorts shapes as it maps the trajectory $\mathbf{x} = e^{At}\mathbf{x}_0$ onto $\bar{\mathbf{x}} = e^{Lt}\bar{\mathbf{x}}_0$, it is also true that the "really important" properties of the trajectory are not changed by the mapping. In other words, we can get the basic facts about the phase portrait of Equation 26-4 by studying the phase portrait of the equation

(26-5) $$\mathbf{x}' = L\mathbf{x},$$

where $L = P^{-1}AP$. This latter portrait is just a somewhat skewed version of the former, and since we can choose P so that L is much simpler than A, it will save us a lot of work to study Equation 26-5 instead of Equation 26-4.

In Section 21, we saw that there were three "standard forms" into which A could be transformed by an invertible matrix P with real components. The simplest is *diagonal form:*

(26-6) $$P^{-1}AP = L = \begin{bmatrix} \lambda_1 & 0 \\ 0 & \lambda_2 \end{bmatrix},$$

where λ_1 and λ_2 are the characteristic values of A. Since we are assuming that $\det A \neq 0$, it follows that neither λ_1 nor λ_2 is 0. Let us look at possible phase portraits for Equation 26-5 with this choice of L. Here,

$$e^{Lt} = \begin{bmatrix} e^{\lambda_1 t} & 0 \\ 0 & e^{\lambda_2 t} \end{bmatrix},$$

so, in component form, the equation $\mathbf{x} = e^{Lt}\mathbf{x}_0$ becomes

(26-7) $$x = e^{\lambda_1 t}x_0 \text{ and } y = e^{\lambda_2 t}y_0.$$

To obtain one of the trajectories of Equation 26-5, we select the point (x_0, y_0) and sketch the graph of the parametric Equations 26-7 for $t \in [0, \infty)$. Let us see what these curves look like for various choices of λ_1 and λ_2.

One possibility is that λ_1 and λ_2 are equal; for example, we might have $\lambda_1 = \lambda_2 = -2$. Then our parametric equations are

(26-8) $$x = e^{-2t}x_0 \text{ and } y = e^{-2t}y_0.$$

If we eliminate t from these equations, we obtain the equation $y_0 x = x_0 y$, whose graph is simply a line that contains the origin. Notice, however, that the graph of Equations 26-8 does not contain the origin (if $(x_0, y_0) \neq (0, 0)$). Each trajectory is a half-open line segment that contains the initial endpoint (x_0, y_0) but not the endpoint $(0, 0)$. As $t \uparrow \infty$, $(x, y) \to (0, 0)$. In this case, we call the critical point $(0, 0)$ an **attractor.** Figure 26-1 shows the phase portrait of Equation 26-5 if $\lambda_1 = \lambda_2 < 0$. Notice that a trajectory inherits a positive direction

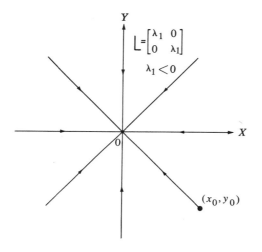

Figure 26-1

from the interval $[0, \infty)$, and in our figures we have used arrows to indicate this direction.

Suppose, now, that $\lambda_1 < \lambda_2 < 0$; for example, $\lambda_1 = -2$ and $\lambda_2 = -1$. Then the parametric equations of the trajectory that starts at (x_0, y_0) are

(26-9) $x = e^{-2t}x_0$ and $y = e^{-t}y_0.$

Again, the critical point $(0, 0)$ is an attractor; $(x, y) \to (0, 0)$ as $t \uparrow \infty$. When we eliminate t from Equations 26-9, we obtain the nonparametric equation $y^2 = x_0^{-1}y_0^2 x$. Thus, trajectories are parabolic arcs. For different choices of λ_1 and λ_2, we get somewhat similar curves, and the phase portrait of Equation 26-5 in this case is shown in Fig. 26-2.

Now we consider the possibility that $\lambda_1 < 0 < \lambda_2$; for example, $\lambda_1 = -1$ and $\lambda_2 = 2$. Here, $x = e^{-t}x_0$ and $y = e^{2t}y_0$ are parametric equations of the trajectory that starts at (x_0, y_0). The critical point $(0, 0)$ is not an attractor; unless $y_0 = 0$, $|y| \uparrow \infty$. This trajectory is part of the curve $y = y_0x_0^2 x^{-2}$, and Fig. 26-3 shows the phase portrait of our differential equation in this case.

If the characteristic values of A are $\sigma + i\tau$ and $\sigma - i\tau$, where $\tau > 0$, then

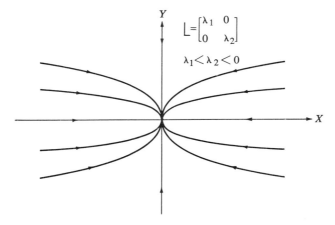

Figure 26-2

our "simple" matrix L has the form

$$L = \begin{bmatrix} \sigma & \tau \\ -\tau & \sigma \end{bmatrix},$$

and (see Equation 21-10)

(26-10) $$e^{Lt} = \begin{bmatrix} e^{\sigma t} \cos \tau t & e^{\sigma t} \sin \tau t \\ -e^{\sigma t} \sin \tau t & e^{\sigma t} \cos \tau t \end{bmatrix}.$$

Let us find the phase portrait of Equation 26-5 with this choice of L.

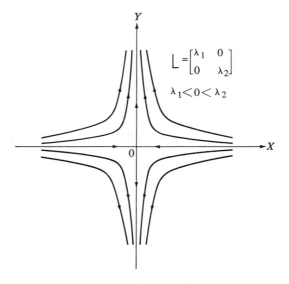

Figure 26-3

Suppose we start with the simplest case, $\sigma = 0$. Then the component form of the equation $\mathbf{x} = e^{Lt}\mathbf{x}_0$ is

$$x = x_0 \cos \tau t + y_0 \sin \tau t \text{ and } y = -x_0 \sin \tau t + y_0 \cos \tau t.$$

If we square and add, we find that $x^2 + y^2 = x_0^2 + y_0^2$. Therefore, our trajectories

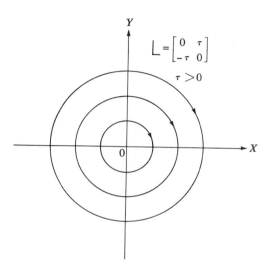

Figure 26-4

are circles, as shown in Fig. 26-4. How does the fact that $\tau > 0$ determine the direction of the arrows in this figure?

If $\sigma \neq 0$, the equation $\mathbf{x} = e^{Lt}\mathbf{x}_0$ becomes, in component form,

$$x = e^{\sigma t}(x_0 \cos \tau t + y_0 \sin \tau t) \text{ and } y = e^{\sigma t}(-x_0 \sin \tau t + y_0 \cos \tau t).$$

It is hard to eliminate t from these equations, but if we square and add, we find that

$$x^2 + y^2 = e^{2\sigma t}(x_0^2 + y_0^2).$$

Suppose that $\sigma < 0$. Then as t increases, $x^2 + y^2$ decreases; that is, the point (x, y) moves nearer to the origin. Thus, you will not be surprised to be told that the trajectories are spirals, as shown in Fig. 26-5.

We haven't quite exhausted all the possible cases. For example, it is possible that the signs of the numbers $\lambda_1, \lambda_2, \sigma$, and τ could be reversed. Such a reversal merely changes the directions of the trajectories, so we can suppose that these cases are taken care of. There is still one further case, the "exceptional"

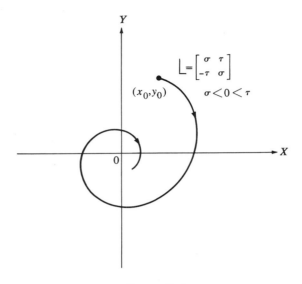

Figure 26-5

case that we mentioned in Section 21. It may be true that the simplest form into which we can transform A is

$$P^{-1}AP = L = \begin{bmatrix} \lambda & 1 \\ 0 & \lambda \end{bmatrix},$$

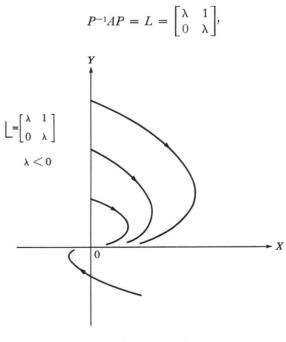

Figure 26-6

and this matrix leads to a phase portrait that we haven't seen before. Since we do not have time for a discussion of the details, let us merely remark that Fig. 26-6 shows some typical trajectories of Equation 26-5 in this case. As the figure indicates, if $\lambda < 0$, the point $(0, 0)$ is an attractor.

EXERCISE 26

1. Sketch the graphs of the following pairs of parametric equations for $t \in [0, \infty)$.
   (a) $(x, y) = (1 + t, 1 - 2t)$ (d) $(x, y) = (e^t, e^{-t})$
   (b) $(x, y) = (t, \sin t)$ (e) $(x, y) = (3 \cos t, 2 \sin t)$
   (c) $(x, y) = (t, t^2)$ (f) $(x, y) = (\cos (\text{Tan}^{-1} t), \sin (\text{Tan}^{-1} t))$

2. Plot the phase portrait of the differential equation $\mathbf{x}' = A\mathbf{x}$ for each of the following choices of A.

   (a) $\begin{bmatrix} -1 & 0 \\ 0 & -1 \end{bmatrix}$ (c) $\begin{bmatrix} -2 & 0 \\ 0 & 3 \end{bmatrix}$

   (b) $\begin{bmatrix} -2 & 0 \\ 0 & -3 \end{bmatrix}$ (d) $\begin{bmatrix} -1 & 1 \\ -1 & -1 \end{bmatrix}$

3. (a) Show that the initial value problem $\mathbf{x}' = \begin{bmatrix} 0 & 1 \\ 1 & 0 \end{bmatrix} \mathbf{x}$ and $\mathbf{x} = (x_0, y_0)$ when $t = 0$ is satisfied by

   $$(x, y) = (x_0 \cosh t + y_0 \sinh t, \ x_0 \sinh t + y_0 \cosh t).$$

   (b) Now use the identity $\cosh^2 t - \sinh^2 t = 1$ to show that the trajectories of the differential equation in part (a) are arcs of hyperbolas.

   (c) Find a matrix P such that $P^{-1} \begin{bmatrix} 0 & 1 \\ 1 & 0 \end{bmatrix} P = L$ is a diagonal matrix.

   (d) Sketch the phase portrait of the equation $\mathbf{x}' = L\mathbf{x}$, and compare it with the curves you got in part (b).

4. (a) Show that $(x, y) = (-t + x_0, -(x_0 - t)^3 + y_0 + x_0^3)$ satisfies the initial value problem $(x, y)' = (-1, 3x^2)$ and $(x, y) = (x_0, y_0)$ when $t = 0$.
   (b) Sketch the phase portrait of the given differential equation.

5. (a) Use the equation $D_x y = D_t y / D_t x$ to show that if

   $$\begin{pmatrix} x \\ y \end{pmatrix}' = \begin{bmatrix} \lambda_1 & 0 \\ 0 & \lambda_2 \end{bmatrix} \begin{pmatrix} x \\ y \end{pmatrix},$$

   then $D_x y = \dfrac{\lambda_2 \, y}{\lambda_1 \, x}$.

   (b) From the scalar equation in part (a), conclude that a trajectory of the vector equation has the form $x_0^{\lambda_2} y^{\lambda_1} = y_0^{\lambda_1} x^{\lambda_2}$.

6. How are the phase portraits of the equations $\mathbf{x}' = \begin{bmatrix} 0 & 1 \\ -1 & 0 \end{bmatrix} \mathbf{x}$ and $\mathbf{x}' = \begin{bmatrix} 0 & -1 \\ 1 & 0 \end{bmatrix} \mathbf{x}$ related?

7. How are the phase portraits of the equations $\mathbf{x}' = \begin{bmatrix} 1 & 2 \\ 3 & 4 \end{bmatrix} \mathbf{x}$ and $\mathbf{x}' = \begin{bmatrix} 2 & 4 \\ 6 & 8 \end{bmatrix} \mathbf{x}$ related?

8. Sketch the phase portrait of the following equation with an "exceptional" matrix:

$$\mathbf{x}' = \begin{bmatrix} -2 & 1 \\ 0 & -2 \end{bmatrix} \mathbf{x}.$$

9. Trajectories of scalar differential equations are plotted in one-dimensional space, so they are simply line segments (or points). Discuss the trajectories of the scalar equation $x' = -x + x^2$. (The formula for solutions of this equation is given in Example 14-3.)

10. The trajectory that starts at the point $\mathbf{x}_0$ is the graph of the equation $\mathbf{x} = \mathbf{u}(t)$, for $t \in [0, \infty)$, where $\mathbf{u}$ is the solution of the initial value problem $\mathbf{x}' = \mathbf{f}(\mathbf{x})$ and $\mathbf{x} = \mathbf{x}_0$ when $t = 0$. Therefore, if $\mathbf{x}_1$ is a point of this trajectory, there is a point $t_1 \in [0, \infty)$ such that $\mathbf{x}_1 = \mathbf{u}(t_1)$. Can you show that the trajectory that starts at $\mathbf{x}_1$ is the graph of the equation $\mathbf{x} = \mathbf{u}(t + t_1)$, for $t \in [0, \infty)$? How is this trajectory related to the trajectory that starts at $\mathbf{x}_0$?

27   STABILITY

A critical point $\mathbf{c}$ of an autonomous differential equation $\mathbf{x}' = \mathbf{f}(\mathbf{x})$ can be thought of as a point of equilibrium. Thus, since $\mathbf{f}(\mathbf{c}) = \mathbf{0}$, it follows that $\mathbf{x} = \mathbf{c}$ satisfies the initial value problem that consists of the given differential equation and the initial condition $\mathbf{x} = \mathbf{c}$ when $t = 0$. Hence, for all $t \geq 0$, we have $\mathbf{x} = \mathbf{c}$; the system remains in its initial state. Now we ask whether the equilibrium position is *stable* or not. We want to know if a solution of the differential equation whose *initial* value is near the point $\mathbf{c}$ *always* takes values near $\mathbf{c}$. For example, let us think of the pendulum (which we will discuss more fully in the next section). The "bob down" equilibrium position is stable. If we start the pendulum in a nearby position with a small velocity, it will not oscillate very widely. But the "bob up" position is unstable. If we could balance the pendulum with the bob absolutely straight up, it would (theoretically) stay there. But if we start it off even slightly displaced from the vertical, we get large oscillations.

Here is another example. Figure 27-1 shows graphs of solutions of the differential equation $x' = -x + x^2$ (this figure is simply Fig. 14-3 with different

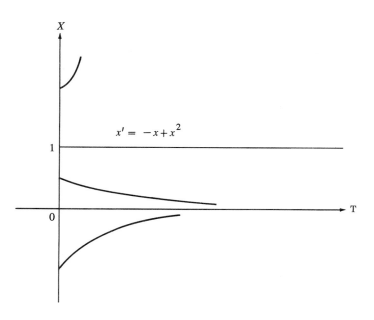

Figure 27-1

lettering). The critical points of this equation are 0 and 1 (since these numbers are the solutions of the equation $-x + x^2 = 0$). From the figure we see that the equation $x = 0$ defines what we would like to call a stable solution. If the value of a solution is near 0 when $t = 0$, then it will remain near 0 for all $t > 0$. The equation $x = 1$, however, does not define a stable solution. Solution values starting near 1 don't stay near 1.

In stability theory, we usually suppose that our critical point is **0**, because it is simply a matter of translating axes to transfer a non-zero critical point to the origin. Then $\mathbf{x} = \mathbf{0}$ satisfies our differential equation $\mathbf{x}' = \mathbf{f}(\mathbf{x})$, and we speak of the *zero solution* of this equation. The zero solution is stable if each solution $\mathbf{u}$ that has an initial value $\mathbf{u}(0)$ near **0** has all its values near **0**. In other words, if $|\mathbf{u}(0)|$ is small, we want $|\mathbf{u}(t)|$ to be small for all $t > 0$. More formally, we say that the zero solution of the differential equation $\mathbf{x}' = \mathbf{f}(\mathbf{x})$ is **stable** if for each number $p > 0$ there exists a number $r > 0$ such that each solution $\mathbf{u}$ for which $|\mathbf{u}(0)| \leq r$ has a domain that includes $[0, \infty)$, and the inequality $|\mathbf{u}(t)| \leq p$ holds for each $t \geq 0$. The solution $\mathbf{u}$ is **asymptotically stable** if it is stable and $\lim_{t \uparrow \infty} \mathbf{u}(t) = \mathbf{0}$.

It is plain from Fig. 27-1 that the zero solution of the equation $x' = -x + x^2$ is more than just stable; it is asymptotically stable. That is, not only do values of solutions that start near 0 stay near 0, but they actually approach 0 as time goes on.

The phase portrait of an autonomous system can tell us about the stability of its zero solution. Geometrically, our definition of stability says that if we draw a circular disk of radius p with 0 as its center, then there is a disk of radius r, also with 0 as its center, such that all trajectories that start in this latter disk never leave the former (Fig. 27-2). Asymptotic stability requires that, in addition, the trajectories approach 0 as $t \uparrow \infty$. Thus, Figs. 26-1, 26-2, 26-4, and

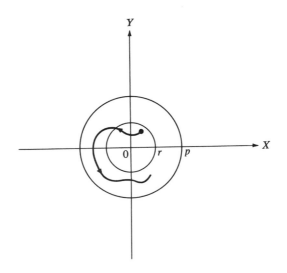

Figure 27-2

26-5 make it clear that the corresponding differential equations have stable zero solutions. Moreover, except for the differential equation corresponding to Fig. 26-4, these zero solutions are asymptotically stable. The zero solution of the differential equation whose phase portrait appears in Fig. 26-3 is unstable; a given disk will not hold all the trajectories that start in any other disk, no matter how small this latter disk may be. These remarks suggest that the zero solution of the homogeneous linear equation $\mathbf{x}' = A\mathbf{x}$ is asymptotically stable if, and only if, the characteristic values of A have negative real parts.

This statement is correct, and it is quite easy to prove it, although we will not give a complete proof here. If A is real diagonable, then we pointed out in the last section that e^{At} "behaves like" $\begin{bmatrix} e^{\lambda_1 t} & 0 \\ 0 & e^{\lambda_2 t} \end{bmatrix}$, where the real numbers λ_1 and λ_2 are the characteristic values of A. If these numbers are negative, then clearly $\lim\limits_{t \uparrow \infty} e^{At} = 0$. If A has a complex characteristic value $\sigma + i\tau$, then e^{At} "behaves like" the matrix of Equation 26-10, and thus its behavior is governed by the behavior of $e^{\sigma t}$. If $\sigma < 0$, then $\lim\limits_{t \uparrow \infty} e^{At} = 0$. As usual, the "exceptional case" must be treated separately, but in any event it is fairly easy to show that if $-\alpha$ is a negative number that is larger than the real part of either characteristic value of A, then there is a positive number K such that

$$(27\text{-}1) \qquad\qquad \left|e^{At}\mathbf{x}_0\right| \le Ke^{-\alpha t}|\mathbf{x}_0|$$

for each vector $\mathbf{x}_0$ and each $t \ge 0$.

Example 27-1. Discuss Inequality 27-1 in connection with the matrix

$$A = \begin{bmatrix} 0 & 1 \\ -13 & -4 \end{bmatrix}.$$

Solution. The characteristic equation of this matrix is

$$\det(\lambda I - A) = \begin{vmatrix} \lambda & -1 \\ 13 & \lambda + 4 \end{vmatrix} = \lambda^2 + 4\lambda + 13 = 0.$$

This equation has the solutions $\lambda_1 = -2 + 3i$ and $\lambda_2 = -2 - 3i$. Both these characteristic values have the real part -2. The number α in Inequality 27-1 can be chosen as any number such that $-\alpha > -2$; for example, we could choose $\alpha = 1$. Then we have said that there is a number $K > 0$ such that

$$\left| \exp\left(\begin{bmatrix} 0 & 1 \\ -13 & -4 \end{bmatrix} t \right) \mathbf{x}_0 \right| \le Ke^{-t}|\mathbf{x}_0|.$$

It is not too easy to determine the "best possible" value of K, but usually we are not concerned with a specific value. The existence of such a K is enough. In our present example, the number 10 could be used as a value of K.

Now we will use Inequality 27-1 to show that the zero solution of the equation $\mathbf{x}' = A\mathbf{x}$ is asymptotically stable if the characteristic values of A have negative real parts. First, we show that the zero solution is stable. Suppose that p is a given positive number. According to the definition of stability, we are to find a number r such that a solution whose initial value does not exceed r in magnitude never exceeds p in magnitude. We will choose $r = p/K$, where K is the number that appears in Inequality 27-1. Suppose we have a solution whose initial value $\mathbf{x}_0$ does not exceed r in magnitude. This solution will be given by the equation

$$\mathbf{x} = e^{At}\mathbf{x}_0, \text{ where } |\mathbf{x}_0| \le r.$$

Now, according to Inequality 27-1,

$$|\mathbf{x}| = |e^{At}\mathbf{x}_0| \leq Ke^{-\alpha t}|\mathbf{x}_0|$$

$$\leq Kre^{-\alpha t} \quad \text{(since } |\mathbf{x}_0| \leq r)$$

$$= pe^{-\alpha t} \quad \text{(we chose } r = p/K)$$

$$\leq p \quad \text{(since } e^{-\alpha t} \leq 1).$$

Furthermore, the inequality $|\mathbf{x}| \leq pe^{-\alpha t}$ that we have just derived shows us that $\lim_{t \uparrow \infty} \mathbf{x} = \mathbf{0}$, so the zero solution is asymptotically stable, as well as simply stable.

Of course, linear systems are especially simple systems of differential equations, but it turns out that the stability of the zero solution of a nonlinear system can often be inferred from the stability of the zero solution of a linear approximation. For example, the differential equation $x' = -x + x^2$ is approximated (for small x) by the linear equation $x' = -x$. The coefficient matrix of this equation is the 1 by 1 matrix $[-1]$. It has a negative characteristic value (-1), so the zero solution is stable. And when we looked at Fig. 27-1, we saw that the zero solution of the original equation is stable, too. This fact is not a coincidence.

Suppose that $\mathbf{f}$ is a vector-valued function such that $\mathbf{f}(\mathbf{0}) = \mathbf{0}$. Then (if the components of $\mathbf{f}(\mathbf{x})$ have sufficiently many derivatives) Taylor's Theorem says that

$$\mathbf{f}(\mathbf{x}) = A\mathbf{x} + \mathbf{g}(\mathbf{x}),$$

where the components of the matrix A are partial derivatives at $(0, 0)$ of the components of $\mathbf{f}(\mathbf{x})$, and $\mathbf{g}(\mathbf{x})$ has a quadratic polynomial in the components of $\mathbf{x}$ as a factor. Thus, $A\mathbf{x}$ is the "linear part" of $\mathbf{f}(\mathbf{x})$, compared to which, for small $|\mathbf{x}|$, $\mathbf{g}(\mathbf{x})$ is negligible. How this linear part determines the stability of the zero solution of the equation $\mathbf{x}' = \mathbf{f}(\mathbf{x})$ is the content of the following stability theorem, whose proof [4, p. 161] is just a bit too complicated to include in this short course.

THEOREM 27-1

If the characteristic values of the matrix A have negative real parts, and if there are positive numbers R and r such that $|\mathbf{g}(\mathbf{x})| \leq R|\mathbf{x}|^2$ for all $\mathbf{x}$ such that $|\mathbf{x}| \leq r$, then the zero solution of the equation

$$(27\text{-}2) \qquad\qquad \mathbf{x}' = A\mathbf{x} + \mathbf{g}(\mathbf{x})$$

is asymptotically stable.

Example 27-2. Discuss the stability of the zero solution of the scalar differential equation $x' = -\sin x$.

Solution. Here, $f(x) = -\sin x$, and we see that $x = 0$ is a critical point. Suppose we write $-\sin x = -x + (x - \sin x)$. In Exercise 27-7 we will ask you to show that $|x - \sin x| \leq \frac{1}{2}x^2$, so if we let $A = [-1]$, $g(x) = x - \sin x$, $R = \frac{1}{2}$ and $r = 1$, we see that the conditions of Theorem 27-1 are satisfied. Therefore, the zero solution of the given differential equation is asymptotically stable. In Exercise 27-10, we will give you some hints and ask you to verify this result directly.

If A is an invertible matrix, it is quite easy to show that $\mathbf{0}$ is an isolated critical point of Equation 27-2; that is, there is a circle whose center is the origin and which contains no other critical points of the equation. It can be shown that, in general, the phase portrait of Equation 27-2 is very similar to the phase portrait of the linear equation $\mathbf{x}' = A\mathbf{x}$ in a neighborhood of the origin. For example, if the trajectories of $\mathbf{x}' = A\mathbf{x}$ are spirals, as in Fig. 26-5, then the trajectories of Equation 27-2 will also spiral inward toward the origin. The only exception to the rule that trajectories of Equation 27-2 are determined by the linear approximation $\mathbf{x}' = A\mathbf{x}$ appears when A has complex characteristic values with real part 0, τi and $-\tau i$. Then the trajectories of the equation $\mathbf{x}' = A\mathbf{x}$ are ellipses (circles in Fig. 26-4), and it may be true that some of the trajectories of Equation 27-2 are spirals.

Although lack of space prevented us from giving proofs of most of our statements in this section, we tried to make the point that often it is possible to infer something about the behavior of the solutions of a nonlinear differential equation by studying the solutions of a linear equation that "approximates" it. Linear equations are a lot easier to work with than nonlinear ones, and consequently we already know a great deal about them. So we try to transfer that knowledge to nonlinear equations. It is an interesting effort and one that has many practical applications these days.

EXERCISE 27

1. For each of the following matrices, find conditions on the real number a that guarantee that the zero solution of the homogeneous linear differential equation $\mathbf{x}' = A\mathbf{x}$ is asymptotically stable.

   (a) $A = \begin{bmatrix} a & 0 \\ 0 & 3a \end{bmatrix}$ (b) $A = \begin{bmatrix} -1 & a \\ a & -2 \end{bmatrix}$ (c) $A = \begin{bmatrix} 0 & 1 \\ -4 & a \end{bmatrix}$

2. (a) Show that 1 is a critical point of the differential equation $x' = -x + 1$.
   (b) Show that the solution defined by the equation $x = 1$ is stable.

3. (a) Show that 1 is a critical point of the differential equation $x' = x - 1$.
   (b) Does the equation $x = 1$ define a stable solution of this differential equation?

4. Use Theorem 27-1 to show that the zero solution of the differential equation $x' = -x + \sin^2 x$ is asymptotically stable.

5. If $A = \begin{bmatrix} -2 & 0 \\ 0 & -3 \end{bmatrix}$, find numbers K and α such that

$$|e^{At}\mathbf{x_0}| \leq Ke^{-\alpha t}|\mathbf{x_0}| \text{ for arbitrary } \mathbf{x_0}.$$

6. Is the zero solution of the homogeneous linear system

$$x' = -2x - 4y$$
$$y' = x - 2y$$

asymptotically stable?

7. Let $g(x) = x - \sin x$. Use Taylor's Theorem to show that for each number x there is a number z such that $g(x) = \frac{1}{2}(\sin z)x^2$, and hence $|g(x)| \leq \frac{1}{2}x^2$ for each x.

8. Use Theorem 27-1 to show that the zero solution of the system

$$x' = -2x + y + xy^2$$
$$y' = x - 2y + x^2y$$

is asymptotically stable.

9. Show that the zero solution of the equation $x' = \sin x$ is not stable. Does the equation $x = \pi$ define a stable solution?

10. Verify that the equation

$$u(t) = \text{Sin}^{-1}[2(\csc x_0 - \cot x_0)e^{-t}/(1 + (\csc x_0 - \cot x_0)^2e^{-2t})]$$

defines the solution of the initial value problem $x' = -\sin x$ and $x = x_0$ when $t = 0$ (for x_0 near 0). Can you use this expression to convince yourself that the zero solution of the differential equation is asymptotically stable?

11. Let $J = \begin{bmatrix} 0 & 1 \\ -1 & 0 \end{bmatrix}$.

(a) Show that $|e^{Jt}\mathbf{x_0}| = |\mathbf{x_0}|$ for arbitrary $\mathbf{x_0}$.

(b) Use the result of part (a) to show that the zero solution of the differential equation $\mathbf{x'} = J\mathbf{x}$ is stable.

(c) Is this zero solution asymptotically stable?

28   AN ANALYSIS OF THE PENDULUM

In Sections 10 and 25, we saw that the angular displacement θ of a swinging pendulum satisfies the differential equation

(28-1)
$$\theta'' + \frac{k}{m}\theta' + \frac{g}{r}\sin \theta = 0,$$

where k, m, g, and r are certain positive numbers that depend on the physical aspects of the problem. We can learn a good deal about the motion of our pendulum if we convert this equation to a system and discuss its phase portrait and the stability of some of its solutions. So let us make the substitution $\omega = \theta'$ (thus, ω is the angular velocity of the pendulum, in radians per second), and then Equation 28-1 is equivalent to the following autonomous system of equations of the first order:

$$\theta' = \omega$$

(28-2)

$$\omega' = -\frac{g}{r} \sin \theta - \frac{k}{m} \omega.$$

It will simplify matters if we first assume that the resistance of the medium in which the pendulum is swinging is negligible; that is, that $k = 0$. Then our system reduces to

$$\theta' = \omega$$

(28-3)

$$\omega' = -\frac{g}{r} \sin \theta.$$

We can use the first of these equations to write the second as

$$\omega\omega' = -\frac{g}{r} (\sin \theta)\theta',$$

and so

$$D_t \left(\frac{1}{2} \omega^2 - \frac{g}{r} \cos \theta \right) = 0.$$

This equation states that the quantity in parentheses does not change with time. Thus, if a trajectory starts at a certain point (θ_0, ω_0), then, always,

$$\frac{1}{2} \omega^2 - \frac{g}{r} \cos \theta = \frac{1}{2} \omega_0^2 - \frac{g}{r} \cos \theta_0.$$

In other words, the trajectory that starts at the point (θ_0, ω_0) is an arc of the curve

(28-4)

$$\omega^2 = 2\frac{g}{r} \cos \theta + \omega_0^2 - 2\frac{g}{r} \cos \theta_0.$$

Now let us see what such a curve looks like. We will first choose $\theta_0 = 0$ (bob down), so that Equation 28-4 becomes

(28-5) $$\omega^2 = 2\frac{g}{r}\cos\theta + \omega_0^2 - 2\frac{g}{r},$$

and we get different trajectories by choosing different values of ω_0 (different initial angular velocities). For example, if $\omega_0 = 0$, then $\omega^2 = 2\frac{g}{r}(\cos\theta - 1)$. Since $\omega^2 \geq 0$ and $\cos\theta - 1 \leq 0$, this equation can hold only if both sides are 0. Hence, our trajectory consists of the single point $(\theta, \omega) = (0, 0)$. Physically, we are saying that if the pendulum starts at rest in the bob down position, it will remain there, a perfectly reasonable result.

Since the graph of Equation 28-5 is symmetric with respect to the Θ- and the Ω-axes, we can obtain the phase portrait of the equation of the undamped pendulum by plotting trajectories in the first quadrant and then reflecting about the coordinate axes. So let us suppose that $\omega_0 > 0$. As θ increases from 0 to π, $\cos\theta$ decreases, and therefore ω decreases as we move away from the Ω-axis (Fig. 28-1).

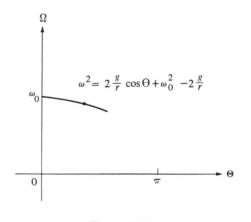

Figure 28-1

Suppose that ω decreases to 0, as in Fig. 28-2. Then when we reflect about the coordinate axes, we see that our trajectory is a closed curve. A closed trajectory represents a **periodic motion;** as time goes on (t increases), values of the displacement θ and angular velocity ω repeat. Thus, the initial state $(\theta, \omega) = (0, \omega_0)$ will lead to a periodic motion if at some later time $\omega = 0$.

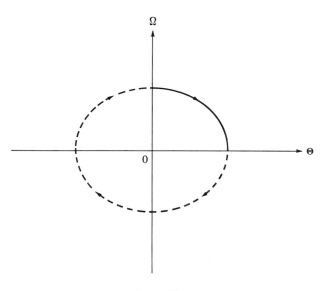

Figure 28-2

To find the value of θ when ω is 0, we solve the equation

$$2 \frac{g}{r} \cos \theta + \omega_0^2 - 2 \frac{g}{r} = 0;$$

that is,

(28-6) $$\cos \theta = 1 - \frac{r}{2g} \omega_0^2.$$

This equation has a solution only if $\omega_0 \leq 2 \sqrt{g/r}$; in other words, unless this inequality holds, ω never becomes 0. Therefore, if we want the pendulum to oscillate back and forth periodically, we cannot impart to it an initial velocity greater than $2 \sqrt{g/r}$.

If we do start the pendulum with a velocity greater than $2 \sqrt{g/r}$ radians per second, then ω will not reach 0. The angular displacement θ will continue to increase as t increases; that is, the pendulum goes round and round the pivot point (over the top), not back and forth. Trajectories are not closed curves.

In Fig. 28-3, we have sketched some of the trajectories of System 28-3. The critical point $(\pi, 0)$ is particularly interesting. The figure suggests that it is a part of the trajectory that starts at $(0, 2 \sqrt{g/r})$. Actually, it is not. It is a one-point trajectory in its own right. If (θ, ω) is a point of the trajectory that starts at $(0, 2 \sqrt{g/r})$, then $\lim_{t \uparrow \infty} (\theta, \omega) = (\pi, 0)$. Thus, we are starting the pen-

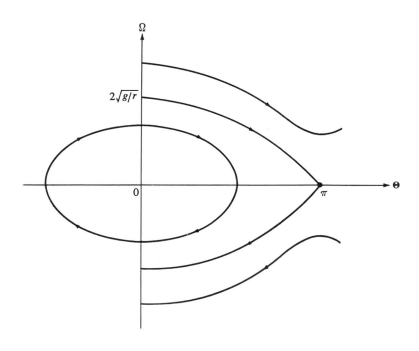

Figure 28-3

dulum in the bob down position and with a velocity that allows it to *approach*, but not reach, the vertical position. Needless to say, we would have some difficulty achieving this condition experimentally.

The critical points of System 28-3 form the set $\{(0, 0), (\pi, 0), (-\pi, 0),$ $(2\pi, 0), \ldots\}$. The points $(0, 0)$ and $(\pi, 0)$ represent different behaviors of the pendulum, but considerations of periodicity make it clear that $(0, 0)$ and $(2\pi, 0)$ are the same type of critical point. Thus, in the whole phase plane, trajectories of System 28-3 are as shown in Fig. 28-4. Can you read from the figure that the critical points $(0, 0)$, $(2\pi, 0)$, $(-2\pi, 0)$, and so on, represent stable (but not asymptotically stable) solutions of System 28-3, whereas the points $(\pi, 0)$, $(-\pi, 0)$, and so on, represent unstable solutions?

Now we will multiply both sides of Equation 28-4 by $\frac{1}{2}mr^2$ and rewrite the result a little:

$$(28\text{-}7) \quad \tfrac{1}{2}m(r\omega)^2 + mg(r - r\cos\theta) = \tfrac{1}{2}m(r\omega_0)^2 + mg(r - r\cos\theta_0).$$

Figure 28-5 shows our pendulum at a point of its swing. It is $r - r\cos\theta$ meters above the horizontal, so the second term on the left-hand side of Equation 28-7 represents the potential energy of the bob. The first term (one-half the product of the mass and square of the velocity) is the kinetic energy. Hence, Equation

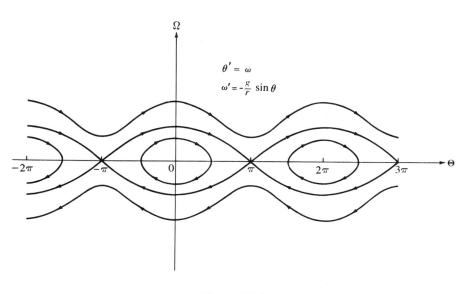

Figure 28-4

28-7 says that the energy of the system does not change; *energy is conserved.* Since the energy of the system is constant along trajectories, these curves are often called *energy curves.*

Let us return now to the equation of the damped pendulum, System 28-2. We will suppose that the damping constant k is a small positive number; that is, the pendulum meets with very little resistance from the medium in which it is swinging. Therefore, we would expect that the phase portrait of System 28-2 would be a slightly distorted version of Fig. 28-4. Let us see what

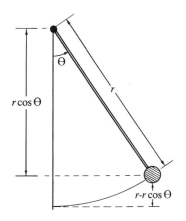

Figure 28-5

this distortion amounts to. If we replace $\sin \theta$ with θ, we obtain the following linearized version of our system:

$$\theta' = \omega$$

$$\omega' = -\frac{g}{r}\theta - \frac{k}{m}\omega.$$

The matrix of this system is $\begin{bmatrix} 0 & 1 \\ -g/r & -k/m \end{bmatrix}$, whose characteristic values are

$$-k/2m + \sqrt{k^2/4m^2 - g/r} \text{ and } -k/2m - \sqrt{k^2/4m^2 - g/r}.$$

We are assuming that k is small; in particular, we will suppose that it is so small that the radicand in the above expressions is negative. Hence, the real part of the characteristic values of our coefficient matrix is the negative number $-k/2m$. Therefore, as we pointed out in the last section, the zero solution of the linearized system is asymptotically stable. In fact, Theorem 27-1 tells us that this statement is also true for the original nonlinear system. Thus, solutions that start near the origin not only stay near the origin, but they actually approach it as time goes on. The ovals that surround the origin in Fig. 28-4 become spirals in the damped case.

Now we turn to the critical point $(\pi, 0)$. To linearize System 28-2 here, we first make the substitution $\theta_1 = \theta - \pi$ and obtain the system

$$\theta_1' = \omega$$

$$\omega' = \frac{g}{r}\sin\theta_1 - \frac{k}{m}\omega,$$

and then (since we are working in a region in which θ_1 is small) we replace $\sin \theta_1$ with θ_1:

$$\theta_1' = \omega$$

$$\omega' = \frac{g}{r}\theta_1 - \frac{k}{m}\omega.$$

The matrix of this system is $\begin{bmatrix} 0 & 1 \\ g/r & -k/m \end{bmatrix}$, and its characteristic values are the numbers

$$-k/2m + \sqrt{k^2/4m^2 + g/r} \text{ and } -k/2m - \sqrt{k^2/4m^2 + g/r}.$$

These two real numbers have opposite signs, and so the phase portrait of the linearized system is a skewed version of Fig. 26-3. Near the critical point, the phase portrait of the nonlinear system has the same aspect.

In Fig. 28-6, we have sketched a few of the trajectories of System 28-2

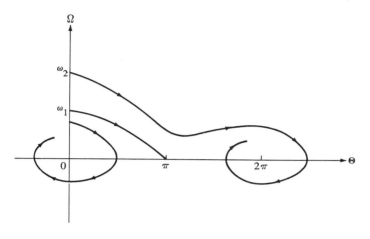

Figure 28-6

for small k. We can call the phase portrait of this system a slightly damped version of Fig. 28-4. As in Fig. 28-4, there is a velocity ω_1 (can you convince yourself that $\omega_1 > 2 \sqrt{g/r}$?) such that if we start the pendulum in the bob down position with a velocity of ω_1 radians per second, it will approach (but never reach) the vertical position. Any lesser initial velocity results in an oscillation with constantly decreasing amplitude. Suppose we start the pendulum with a slightly greater initial velocity, ω_2 radians per second. Then, as we have shown it, the pendulum goes over the top, but by the time it again reaches the bob down position ($\theta = 2\pi$), its velocity is less than ω_1, so it begins to oscillate with decreasing amplitude.

EXERCISE 28

1. Physically, what does it mean to start an undamped pendulum at the point $(\pi, 0)$ of the phase plane? What does Fig. 28-4 suggest will happen if you start the pendulum straight up but with a small positive velocity? A small negative velocity? What if you start it with velocity 0 but not quite straight up?

2. Physically, it is obvious that if we start a pendulum (damped or undamped) with velocity 0 in any position except straight up or down, then it will oscillate back and forth; that is, it will never go "over the top." How do Figs. 28-4 and 28-6 express this fact?

3. If we start an undamped pendulum so fast that it goes "over the top," then obviously, as it goes around and around, its speed is least when it is in the upright position and greatest in the "bob down" position. How do these facts show up in Fig. 28-4?

4. Suppose we start a pendulum in the "bob down" position with an initial velocity so great that it goes "over the top." Obviously, the pendulum slows as it approaches the vertical position and then speeds up as it comes down after having gone over the top. For the undamped pendulum, the minimum speed occurs just as the pendulum is vertical. For the damped pendulum, is the point of minimum speed before, at, or after the point of verticality?

5. Use System 28-2 to show that the differential equation that is satisfied by the family of curves shown in Fig. 28-6 is

$$D_\theta \omega = -\frac{k}{m} - \frac{g}{r}\frac{\sin\theta}{\omega}.$$

Do the figure and the differential equation seem to agree?

6. Show that $D_t[\frac{1}{2}m(r\omega)^2 + mg(r - r\cos\theta)] = -kr^2\omega^2$ along a trajectory of System 28-2. Interpret this equation physically.

7. (a) Show that the equation $x'' + x^3 = 0$ is equivalent to the system

$$x' = y$$
$$y' = -x^3.$$

(b) Follow the procedure we used to develop Equation 28-4 and show that trajectories of this system are members of the family $x^4 + 2y^2 = c$.

(c) How does the result of part (b) show that solutions of our given differential equation are periodic?

(d) Is the zero solution of the system in part (a) stable?

REVIEW EXERCISE, CHAPTER 4

Use the following exercises to test yourself on the material in this chapter.

1. Let $S = \begin{bmatrix} 1 & 1 \\ 1 & 1 \end{bmatrix}$.

(a) Find a matrix P such that $P^{-1}SP$ is a diagonal matrix.

(b) Use the result of part (a) to calculate e^{St}, and compare your answer with what we obtained in Exercise 20-4.

2. If $X = \begin{bmatrix} 2e^{5t} & e^t \\ e^t & e^{-3t} \end{bmatrix}$ satisfies the differential equation $X' = A(t)X$, what is $A(t)$?

3. In Section 22, we expressed det $V(t)$ in terms of the components of $A(t)$, where V is a solution of the differential equation $X' = A(t)X$. Use this formula to express the Wronskian of two solutions u and v of the scalar differential equation of the second order $x'' + p(t)x' + q(t)x = 0$. Explain why the Wronskian is a constant function if $p(t) = 0$ for each t in our basic interval J.

4. Although it need not be true that $e^{(A+B)t} = e^{At}e^{Bt}$, show that det $e^{(A+B)t} = $ det $(e^{At}e^{Bt})$.

5. Find a fundamental solution of the matrix differential equation $X' = 2t\begin{bmatrix} 0 & 1 \\ -1 & 0 \end{bmatrix}X$.

6. Solve the initial value problem $x'' + 4|x| = 0$ and $x = 0$, $x' = 2$ when $t = 0$.

7. Suppose that the sine function is defined as the solution of Initial Value Problem 24-7. Show that it is therefore an odd function.

8. Show that Equation 23-6 can be written as

$$x = \frac{\begin{vmatrix} x_0 & v(t_0) \\ y_0 & v'(t_0) \end{vmatrix}}{\begin{vmatrix} u(t_0) & v(t_0) \\ u'(t_0) & v'(t_0) \end{vmatrix}} u(t) + \frac{\begin{vmatrix} u(t_0) & x_0 \\ u'(t_0) & y_0 \end{vmatrix}}{\begin{vmatrix} u(t_0) & v(t_0) \\ u'(t_0) & v'(t_0) \end{vmatrix}} v(t) + \int_{t_0}^{t} \frac{\begin{vmatrix} u(s) & v(s) \\ u(t) & v(t) \end{vmatrix}}{\begin{vmatrix} u(s) & v(s) \\ u'(s) & v'(s) \end{vmatrix}} r(s)\,ds.$$

9. Discuss the phase portraits of the equations $\mathbf{x}' = \begin{bmatrix} -2 & 1 \\ -1 & -2 \end{bmatrix}\mathbf{x}$ and $\mathbf{x}' = \begin{bmatrix} 2 & -1 \\ 1 & 2 \end{bmatrix}\mathbf{x}$.

10. Obviously, $x = e^t$ satisfies the differential equation

$$x'' + 2e^{-2t}x' - (2e^{-2t} + 1)x = 0.$$

Use the formula of Exercise 23-11 to find another solution.

11. Find positive numbers K and α such that

$$\left| \exp\left(\begin{bmatrix} -2 & 1 \\ -1 & -2 \end{bmatrix} t\right)\mathbf{x}_0 \right| \le Ke^{-\alpha t}|\mathbf{x}_0|$$

for an arbitrary vector $\mathbf{x}_0$.

12. Show that the set of solutions of the homogeneous linear scalar differential equation of the second order $x'' + p(t)x' + q(t)x = 0$ is a vector space of dimension 2.

CHAPTER *5*

USING INFINITE SERIES TO SOLVE
DIFFERENTIAL EQUATIONS

When we can express the values of a solution of a differential equation in terms of integrals, we are happy. For we can, especially in these days of high speed computers, evaluate integrals easily. By the same token, since we can (again with the help of a computer) rather easily find sums of infinite series, we often try to express solutions of differential equations as sums of infinite series. In this chapter, we will look at a few of the standard techniques for applying the theory of infinite series to solve differential equations. In the process, we will introduce two classes of functions that are important in applied mathematics, the Legendre Polynomials and some Bessel Functions.

29 SEQUENCES AND SERIES

We led off the last chapter with a review section, and we preface the new material of this chapter with *two* review sections. In this first review section, we will refresh your memory of the basic ideas and terminology of sequences and series in general. In the next section, we specialize to power series.

A **sequence** is a function whose domain is a set of integers. Therefore, if we used regular functional notation to describe a sequence, we would name it with a letter such as a and denote by $a(n)$ the number that corresponds to the integer n. Sequences, however, have acquired a special notation of their own, and in this notation we denote the number that corresponds to n by a_n. Thus, since a function is a set of pairs, a sequence is a set of pairs $\{(n, a_n)\}$ whose first members are integers. It is customary to abbreviate this notation and simply speak of "the sequence $\{a_n\}$." Usually, we don't specifically mention the domain of a sequence. In our work, we will be dealing mostly with sequences whose domains are the non-negative integers. If a sequence has some other domain, it will be clear from the context what it is. The numbers $a_0, a_1, a_2, \ldots$ are the **terms** of the sequence $\{a_n\}$, and we speak of the *zeroth* term a_0, the *first* term a_1, the *second* term a_2, and so on.

As with any function, the most straightforward way to specify the terms of a sequence is by means of an explicit formula. For example, if $\{a_n\}$ is the sequence in which $a_n = (-1)^n/(2n + 1)!$, then $a_0 = 1/1! = 1$, $a_1 = -1/3! = -1/6$, $a_2 = 1/5! = 1/120$, and so on. From the point of view of the computer, however, it is better to describe this sequence by listing its first term, $a_0 = 1$, and then stating a *recursion formula* by which we go from one term to its successor:

$$a_n = -a_{n-1}/2n(2n + 1), \quad n = 1, 2, 3, \ldots.$$

It is easy to find such a recursion formula when we have an explicit expression for a_n. For example, if $a_n = f(n)$, then $a_{n-1} = f(n - 1)$, and hence

$$a_n = \frac{f(n)}{f(n - 1)} a_{n-1}.$$

Thus, if we apply this equation to our example of the preceding paragraph, we obtain the stated recursion formula:

$$a_n = \frac{(-1)^n/(2n + 1)!}{(-1)^{n-1}/(2n - 1)!} a_{n-1} = -\frac{(2n - 1)!}{(2n + 1)!} a_{n-1} = -a_{n-1}/2n(2n + 1).$$

It is considerably harder, in general, to go the other way; that is, to start with a recursion formula and end with a formula expressing a_n in terms of n. We will discuss this point more fully in connection with the sequence of the next example.

Example 29-1. Let $\{a_n\}$ be the sequence in which $a_0 = 1$ and $a_n = \frac{1}{3}a_{n-1} + 2$ for $n = 1, 2, 3, \ldots$. Find the first sixteen terms of this sequence.

Solution. In the computer program of Fig. 29-1, a represents the nth term of our sequence. We start with $a = 1$ (and set the index n at 0) and then simply apply the recursion formula

$$a_n = \tfrac{1}{3}a_{n-1} + 2$$

fifteen times, writing the result each time. The first column of the printout lists the index of the term of $\{a_n\}$, and the second column gives its value.

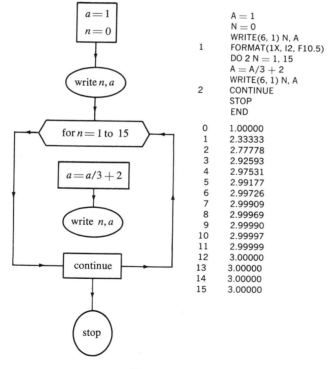

	A = 1
	N = 0
	WRITE(6, 1) N, A
1	FORMAT(1X, I2, F10.5)
	DO 2 N = 1, 15
	A = A/3 + 2
	WRITE(6, 1) N, A
2	CONTINUE
	STOP
	END

0	1.00000
1	2.33333
2	2.77778
3	2.92593
4	2.97531
5	2.99177
6	2.99726
7	2.99909
8	2.99969
9	2.99990
10	2.99997
11	2.99999
12	3.00000
13	3.00000
14	3.00000
15	3.00000

Figure 29-1

Now let us see how we would go about trying to find a formula for a_n, the nth term of the sequence in the example above. What we do is *guess* the formula and then verify our guess. Obviously, this "method" is not guaranteed to work for every sequence, but it does work in our present example. Here,

$$a_0 = 1, a_1 = \tfrac{1}{3} + 2 = \tfrac{7}{3}, a_2 = \tfrac{1}{3} \cdot \tfrac{7}{3} + 2 = \tfrac{25}{9}, a_3 = \tfrac{79}{27}, \ldots$$

Since $3^1 = 3$, $3^2 = 9$, $3^3 = 27$, and $3^4 = 81$, it appears that perhaps

$$a_n = \frac{3^{n+1} - 2}{3^n}.$$

This formula, at least, gives us a_0, a_1, a_2, and a_3. To verify that it holds for *all* indices, we must use *mathematical induction*. Specifically, we show that:

(i) The formula for a_n that we are testing yields the term a_0.
(ii) It satisfies the recursion relation.

We have already verified the first of these statements for the example at hand. To show that the second also holds, we observe that our "guessed" formula yields $a_{n-1} = \dfrac{3^n - 2}{3^{n-1}}$, and so terms calculated by this formula satisfy the equation

$$a_n - \frac{1}{3} a_{n-1} = \frac{3^{n+1} - 2}{3^n} - \frac{3^n - 2}{3 \cdot 3^{n-1}} = \frac{3^{n+1} - 3^n}{3^n} = 3 - 1 = 2,$$

which is simply another way of writing the given recursion relation. Thus, mathematical induction tells us that our guessed formula is correct in this case. Notice that our computer printout suggests, and our explicit formula confirms, that $\lim_{n \uparrow \infty} a_n = 3$.

With each sequence $\{a_n\}$, we can associate a sequence $\{S_n\}$ whose terms are defined by the equation

(29-1) $$S_n = \sum_{k=0}^{n} a_k = a_0 + a_1 + a_2 + \cdots + a_n.$$

This sequence $\{S_n\}$ is the sequence of **partial sums** of $\{a_n\}$. Clearly, its terms satisfy the recursion formula

(29-2) $$S_n = S_{n-1} + a_n.$$

If $\lim_{n \uparrow \infty} S_n = S$, we say, of course, that the infinite series $\sum_{k=0}^{\infty} a_k$ **converges**, and its **sum** is S.

Example 29-2. We know that $e = \sum_{k=0}^{\infty} \dfrac{1}{k!}$. Add a few terms of this series.

Solution. When we work with an infinite series, we are dealing with *two* sequences, the sequence $\{a_n\}$ of terms and the sequence $\{S_n\}$ of partial sums. In our example, $a_0 = 1$, and it is always true that $S_0 = a_0$, so these two equations become the first two statements of the computer program of Fig. 29-2. Suppose we want S_6. Then

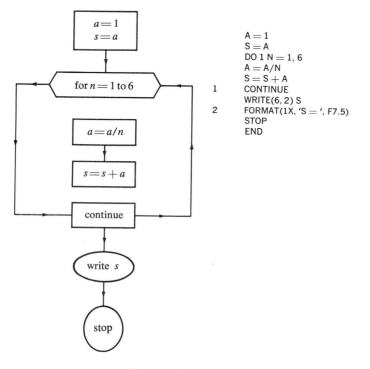

```
      A = 1
      S = A
      DO 1 N = 1, 6
      A = A/N
      S = S + A
1     CONTINUE
      WRITE(6, 2) S
2     FORMAT(1X, 'S = ', F7.5)
      STOP
      END
```

Figure 29-2

for $n = 1, 2, \ldots , 6$ we are to calculate the term a_n and add it to the previous partial sum S_{n-1}. Thus, the statement

$$a = a/n$$

in our program represents the recursion formula $a_n = a_{n-1}/n$ for calculating the nth term of the sequence $\{1/n!\}$, and the statement

$$s = s + a$$

is Equation 29-2.

When this program is run, it prints $s = 2.71805$, which compares quite well with the true (to 5 decimal places) value $e = 2.71828$. Our series converges very rapidly. For example, it takes only 72 terms to get the first 100 decimal places of e.

In calculus, you learned the ratio test and the root test for the convergence of a series $\sum_{k=0}^{\infty} a_k$. For brevity, we are combining them into one statement here, but we really have two tests, both based on the geometric series.

THEOREM 29-1

Suppose that

$$\lim_{k \uparrow \infty} \frac{|a_k|}{|a_{k-1}|} = L \text{ or that } \overline{\lim_{k \uparrow \infty}} \, |a_k|^{1/k} = L.$$

Then

(i) If $L < 1$, the series $\sum_{k=0}^{\infty} a_k$ converges absolutely.

(ii) If $L > 1$ or L is the symbol ∞, the series $\sum_{k=0}^{\infty} a_k$ diverges.

(iii) If $L = 1$, we need further information to determine whether or not the series converges.

Example 29-3. Discuss the convergence of the series $\sum_{k=0}^{\infty} e^{\sin k}$.

Solution. We might try to apply the root test, but we find that $\lim_{k \uparrow \infty} e^{(\sin k)/k} = 1$, so we are in case (iii) of Theorem 29-1. However, it is clear that $e^{\sin k} \geq e^{-1}$ for each k, so the terms of our series do not approach 0, and hence the series must diverge.

EXERCISE 29

1. (a) What is the difference between the sequences $\{2^k/k!\}$ and $\{2^{n+1}/(n+1)!\}$?
   (b) What are the limits of the sequences in part (a)?
   (c) What are the limits of their sequences of partial sums?
   (d) What is the difference between the sequences $\{2^k/k!\}$ and $\{2^m/m!\}$?

2. Suppose that $\{a_n\}$ is a sequence with $a_0 = 2$.
   (a) If $a_n = \frac{1}{3}a_{n-1}$, show that $a_n = 2/3^n$.
   (b) If $a_n = a_{n-1} + 5$, show that $a_n = 5n + 2$.
   (c) If $a_n = a_{n-1}^2$, show that $a_n = 2^{2^n}$.
   (d) If $a_n = a_{n-1}/n$, show that $a_n = 2/n!$.
   (e) If $a_n = a_{n-1}^{-1}$, show that $a_n = \dfrac{3 + (-1)^n}{3 + (-1)^{n-1}}$.

Which of these sequences converge (that is, have limits)? Can you find a formula for S_n in each case? Which of the sequences of partial sums converge? Write a computer program for finding a_{20} (using the recursion formula) and S_{20} in each case.

3. Test the following infinite series for convergence.

(a) $\displaystyle\sum_{k=0}^{\infty} \frac{k + (-1)^k}{3^k}$

(d) $\displaystyle\sum_{k=0}^{\infty} \frac{\exp\left(\int_0^k \sin x^2 dx\right)}{k!}$

(b) $\displaystyle\sum_{k=0}^{\infty} \frac{(2^k)!}{2^{k!}}$

(e) $\dfrac{1}{3} - \dfrac{1 \cdot 3}{3 \cdot 6} + \dfrac{1 \cdot 3 \cdot 5}{3 \cdot 6 \cdot 9} - \dfrac{1 \cdot 3 \cdot 5 \cdot 7}{3 \cdot 6 \cdot 9 \cdot 12} + \cdots$

(c) $\displaystyle\sum_{k=0}^{\infty} \frac{(-1)^k (k!)^2}{(2k)!}$

(f) $\dfrac{1}{2} + \dfrac{1 \cdot 3}{2 \cdot 4} + \dfrac{1 \cdot 3 \cdot 5}{2 \cdot 4 \cdot 6} + \cdots$

4. Show that $\displaystyle\sum_{k=0}^{\infty} x^k = \frac{1}{1-x}$ if $|x| < 1$. (If you have forgotten how to do this exercise, go back to your calculus book and look it up.)

5. Modify the program in Fig. 29-1 so that it prints three columns, n, a_n, and S_n, for n in the set $\{1, 2, \ldots, 20\}$.

6. Use the computer to calculate a number of terms of the sequence $\{a_n\}$, where $a_1 = \frac{3}{4}$, and $a_n = \dfrac{4n^2 - 1}{4n^2} a_{n-1}$ for $n > 1$. It is true that $\lim_{n \uparrow \infty} a_n = 2/\pi$. What does your computer printout suggest about the rapidity of convergence of this sequence?

7. Show that if $\lim_{k \uparrow \infty} \dfrac{|a_k|}{|a_{k-2}|} = L < 1$, then the series $\displaystyle\sum_{k=0}^{\infty} a_k$ converges absolutely.

8. The sequence $\{a_n\}$, where $a_0 = 1$, $a_1 = 1$, and $a_n = a_{n-1} + a_{n-2}$ for $n = 2, 3, 4, \ldots$ is an example of a **Fibonacci sequence.**
   (a) Write a computer program to find the first 20 terms of $\{a_n\}$.
   (b) Modify your program so that it also computes S_{20}.
   (c) Use mathematical induction to show that $S_n = a_{n+2} - 1$, and check this formula with your results in parts (a) and (b).
   (d) Show that if $a_n = r^n$ satisfies the *difference equation* $a_n = a_{n-1} + a_{n-2}$, then r is a solution of the quadratic equation $r^2 - r - 1 = 0$.
   (e) Show that if r_1 and r_2 are two solutions of the quadratic equation of part (d), then $a_n = cr_1^n + dr_2^n$ satisfies our difference equation, regardless of the choice of c and d.
   (f) Now choose c and d so that the "initial conditions" $a_0 = 1$ and $a_1 = 1$ are satisfied.
   (g) Use the formula for a_n you have just developed to find a_2 and a_3, and compare with the values calculated from the recursion formula.
   (h) Does the solution procedure in parts (d)–(f) remind you of a technique we have used in solving a certain type of homogeneous linear differential equation of the second order?

9. Can you show that $\lim\limits_{k\uparrow\infty} \dfrac{|a_k|}{|a_{k-1}|} = L$ implies that $\overline{\lim\limits_{k\uparrow\infty}} \, |a_k|^{1/k} = L$? What does this implication tell us about the relation between the ratio test and the root test?

30   POWER SERIES

Suppose we select a sequence $\{c_k\}$ of numbers and a number a. Then for each number x we can form the **power series** in $(x - a)$

$$(30\text{-}1) \qquad \sum_{k=0}^{\infty} c_k(x - a)^k = c_0 + c_1(x - a) + c_2(x - a)^2 + \cdots$$

The terms of the sequence $\{c_k\}$ are the *coefficients* of the series. We can use any number x when we form a power series, and we naturally want to know what numbers yield convergent series. In Exercise 30-10, we suggest how to use the root test to answer this question. As a result, we can state the following theorem that you learned in calculus.

THEOREM 30-1

For a power series $\sum\limits_{k=0}^{\infty} c_k(x - a)^k$, one of the following statements is true:

(i) The series converges only for the "trivial" choice $x = a$.

(ii) The series converges absolutely for every number x.

(iii) There is a positive number r (the *radius of convergence* of the series) such that the series converges absolutely for every number x in the open *interval of convergence* $(a - r, a + r)$ and diverges for every number x outside the closed interval $[a - r, a + r]$.

While, theoretically, we can always use the root test to find the interval of convergence of a power series, you probably recall from your calculus course that it is usually easier to use the ratio test.

Example 30-1. Discuss the convergence of the power series

$$\sum_{k=1}^{\infty} \frac{(-1)^k 2^k (x - 5)^k}{k^2}.$$

Solution. Here,

$$\frac{|a_k|}{|a_{k-1}|} = \frac{2^k|x-5|^k}{k^2} \cdot \frac{(k-1)^2}{2^{k-1}|x-5|^{k-1}}$$

$$= 2\left(\frac{k-1}{k}\right)^2 |x-5|.$$

Therefore,

$$\lim_{k\uparrow\infty} \frac{|a_k|}{|a_{k-1}|} = \lim_{k\uparrow\infty} 2\left(\frac{k-1}{k}\right)^2 |x-5| = 2|x-5|.$$

According to Theorem 29-1, our series will converge when this limit $2|x-5|$ is less than 1 and diverge when it is greater than 1. Hence, the radius of convergence is $\frac{1}{2}$, and so the interval of convergence of our series is $(\frac{9}{2}, \frac{11}{2})$.

Suppose that $\sum_{k=0}^{\infty} c_k(x-a)^k$ and $\sum_{k=0}^{\infty} d_k(x-a)^k$ are two power series, both of which are convergent in the interval $(a-r, a+r)$. Then their sum and product are defined by the following equations, and it is quite easy to prove that these newly defined power series also converge in $(a-r, a+r)$:

$$(30\text{-}2) \qquad \sum_{k=0}^{\infty} c_k(x-a)^k + \sum_{k=0}^{\infty} d_k(x-a)^k = \sum_{k=0}^{\infty} (c_k+d_k)(x-a)^k$$

and

$$(30\text{-}3) \qquad \sum_{k=0}^{\infty} c_k(x-a)^k \sum_{k=0}^{\infty} d_k(x-a)^k = \sum_{k=0}^{\infty} \left(\sum_{j=0}^{k} c_j d_{k-j}\right)(x-a)^k.$$

Example 30-2. Find $\left(\sum_{k=0}^{\infty} x^k\right)^2$.

Solution. Here, we use Equation 30-3, with $a = 0$, and $c_k = d_k = 1$ for all k:

$$\left(\sum_{k=0}^{\infty} x^k\right)^2 = \sum_{k=0}^{\infty}\left(\sum_{j=0}^{k} 1 \cdot 1\right) x^k = \sum_{k=0}^{\infty} (k+1)x^k.$$

There is a close analogy between infinite series and integrals (both are "sums," after all). For example, the index of summation, like the variable of integration, is really a "dummy." Thus, $\sum_{k=0}^{\infty} (k+1)x^k = \sum_{j=0}^{\infty} (j+1)x^j$. And, as in integrals, we can change the index of summation by a substitution. For instance, if we set $j = k + 1$, then $\sum_{k=0}^{\infty} (k + 1)x^k = \sum_{j=1}^{\infty} jx^{j-1} = \sum_{k=1}^{\infty} kx^{k-1}$. You are going to see many such manipulations with series in the pages ahead.

Let us denote by I the interval of convergence of Series 30-1. For each number $x \in I$, the series converges, so it pairs with x a number, the sum of the series. In other words, Series 30-1 defines a function. If we name this function f, then

$$(30\text{-}4) \qquad\qquad f(x) = \sum_{k=1}^{\infty} c_k(x - a)^k$$

for each $x \in I$.

Some functions are not as "nicely behaved" as we would like. For example, the graph of the greatest integer function has breaks in it, the graph of the absolute value function has a kink in it, and so on. But functions defined by power series *are* nicely behaved. It is shown in advanced calculus that Equation 30-4 defines a differentiable function, in fact, a function that has derivatives of all orders. That is, $f^{(n)}(x)$ exists if x is any point of I and n is any positive integer.

Moreover, it is very easy to calculate derivatives of $f(x)$. You know that the differential operator D_x is *linear* in the sense that if u and v are differentiable functions and c and d are numbers, then

$$(30\text{-}5) \qquad D_x(cu(x) + dv(x)) = cD_xu(x) + dD_xv(x).$$

Thus, we can form a linear combination of $u(x)$ and $v(x)$ first and then apply the operator D_x, or apply the operator and then form the linear combination. The result is the same in either case. It is a simple matter to extend Equation 30-5 to apply to a sum of 10, 100, or 1,000,000 terms, but, in general, it does not extend to an "infinite sum"; that is, to an infinite series. For *power* series, however, this equation is still valid. We can compute the derivative of $f(x)$ by differentiating each term of the defining series *before* we form the sum. Since this differentiation merely amounts to computing the derivatives of powers of x, we see that finding derivatives for functions defined by power series is simplicity itself. The formal statement of this differentiation rule is the following theorem that is proved in advanced calculus.

THEOREM 30-2

The function f defined by Equation 30-4 is differentiable at each point $x \in I$, and

$$f'(x) = \sum_{k=1}^{\infty} kc_k(x - a)^{k-1}.$$

The interval of convergence of this "derived series" also is I.

You will recall that we defined e^{At} as the sum of a power series and that we used Theorem 30-2 to show that $D_t e^{At} = e^{At}A$. Suppose we look at another example.

Example 30-3. In Exercise 29-4, we reminded you that

$$\frac{1}{1-x} = \sum_{k=0}^{\infty} x^k \text{ for } x \in (-1, 1).$$

Apply Theorem 30-2 to this equation.

Solution. According to Theorem 30-2,

$$D_x \left(\frac{1}{1-x}\right) = \sum_{k=0}^{\infty} D_x x^k = \sum_{k=1}^{\infty} k x^{k-1}.$$

Since $D_x \left(\dfrac{1}{1-x}\right) = \left(\dfrac{1}{1-x}\right)^2 = \left(\displaystyle\sum_{k=0}^{\infty} x^k\right)^2$ and $\displaystyle\sum_{k=1}^{\infty} k x^{k-1} = \sum_{k=0}^{\infty} (k+1) x^k,$

our calculations in this example agree with those of Example 30-2.

We can start with a power series and use it to define a function, or we can go the other way. We may be able to start with a function and then find a power series whose sums are values of the given function. If f is a function with derivatives of all orders at a point a, then the series $\displaystyle\sum_{k=0}^{\infty} \frac{f^{(k)}(a)}{k!} (x-a)^k$ is called **Taylor's Series** for $f(x)$ about the point a. For many functions (you can refer to your calculus book for the details) there is an interval whose center is a and in which

$$f(x) = \sum_{k=0}^{\infty} \frac{f^{(k)}(a)}{k!} (x-a)^k;$$

that is, the sum of Taylor's Series for $f(x)$ is $f(x)$.

Example 30-4. Discuss Taylor's Series for $\sin x$ about the origin.

Solution. We leave it to you to verify that if $f(x) = \sin x$, then

$$f^{(k)}(x) = \sin \left(x + \tfrac{1}{2} k\pi\right), \ k = 0, 1, 2, \ldots,$$

and so $f^{(k)}(0) = \sin \frac{1}{2}k\pi$. It follows that coefficients of terms with even indices are 0, and we have the familiar series

(30-6)
$$\sin x = \sum_{k=0}^{\infty} \frac{(-1)^k}{(2k+1)!} x^{2k+1}.$$

The nice thing about power series is that the only mathematical operations they require are addition, subtraction, multiplication, and division. Of course, we have to pay a price for the privilege of computing, say, sin x by just these elementary operations. We have to perform infinitely many of them to get the "exact" answer. But for practical purposes, we need not pay this price; we don't have to add *all* the terms of Taylor's Series in order to get a number that is adequate for any conceivable need.

It would pay you to go back to your calculus book and look up *Taylor's Formula*. Use it to show that for a given positive integer N,

$$\left| \sin x - \sum_{k=0}^{N} \frac{(-1)^k}{(2k+1)!} x^{2k+1} \right| \le \frac{|x|^{2N+3}}{(2N+3)!}.$$

Therefore, if we add terms in the series on the right-hand side of Equation 30-6 up to and including the one that contains x^9 ($N = 4$), our error will be no greater than $|x|^{11}/11!$. A table of trigonometric values need only contain values of the sine function that correspond to x in the interval $[0, 1.6]$, and so our error will be less than $(1.6)^{11}/11! < .000004$. Let us see how we can get the computer to print such a table for us.

We are going to let x vary from 0 to 1.6 in steps of .1, which explains the outer loop in the flow chart of Fig. 30-1. For each such x, we get an infinite series $\sum_{k=0}^{\infty} a_k$, where, according to Equation 30-6, $a_k = \frac{(-1)^k}{(2k+1)!} x^{2k+1}$. Thus, since $a_0 = x$, the first statement inside the main loop is $a = x$. Of course, the zeroth partial sum is this value, so the next statement is $s = a$. Now we insert another loop to calculate the partial sum S_n for $n = 1, 2, 3, 4$. In the nth swing through this loop, we compute the nth term of our series by means of the recursion formula

$$a_n = -a_{n-1}x^2/2n(2n+1)$$

and add it to the previous partial sum,

$$S_n = S_{n-1} + a_n.$$

In the computer program, these equations become $a = -a * x * x/(4 * n * n + 2 * n)$ and $s = s + a$. When we have calculated S_4, we write it and go on to the next value of x.

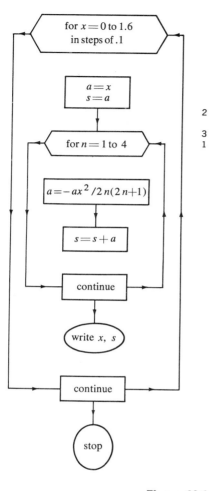

```
DO 1 I = 1, 17
X = .1*(I − 1)
A = X
S = A
DO 2 N = 1, 4
A = −A*X*X/(4*N*N+2*N)
S = S + A
2   CONTINUE
WRITE(6, 3) X, S
3   FORMAT(1X, F3.1, F12.4)
1   CONTINUE
STOP
END
```

Figure 30-1

EXERCISE 30

1. You know (or can look up in your calculus book) series in powers of x whose sums are e^x, $\cos x$, and $\sin x$. Use these series and Equations 30-2 and 30-3 to find series with the following sums.
   (a) $\frac{1}{2}(e^x + e^{-x})$ (d) $e^x \cos x$
   (b) $\frac{1}{2}(e^x - e^{-x})$ (e) $e^{x^2} + (e^x)^2$
   (c) $e^x \sin x$ (f) $(\sin x)(\cos x)$

2. Use the identity $\sin^2 x = \frac{1}{2}(1 - \cos 2x)$ to find Taylor's Series for $\sin^2 x$ about 0. Differentiate the result to find Taylor's Series for $\sin 2x$ about 0. How else could you find this series?

3. The equation $f(x) = \displaystyle\sum_{k=0}^{\infty} \frac{x^{2k+1}}{(2k+1)!}$ defines a function f.

   (a) Find the domain of f.
   (b) Find the range of f.
   (c) Show that f is an odd function.
   (d) Show that f is increasing.
   (e) Show that $y = f(x)$ satisfies the differential equation $y'' - y = 0$.
   (f) Compare $f'(x)$ and $\int_0^x f(t)dt$.
   (g) Write a computer program to print a table of values of f at the points of the set $\{0, .1, .2, \ldots , 1.0\}$.

4. Can we find a sequence $\{c_k\}$ such that the equation $|x| = \displaystyle\sum_{k=0}^{\infty} c_k x^k$ is valid in some interval $(-r, r)$?

5. Show that if $f(x) = \displaystyle\sum_{k=0}^{\infty} c_k(x - a)^k$, then the following equations are correct.

   (a) $f'(x) = \displaystyle\sum_{k=1}^{\infty} kc_k(x - a)^{k-1} = \sum_{k=0}^{\infty} (k + 1)c_{k+1}(x - a)^k$

   (b) $f''(x) = \displaystyle\sum_{k=2}^{\infty} k(k - 1)c_k(x - a)^{k-2} = \sum_{k=0}^{\infty} (k + 2)(k + 1)c_{k+2}(x - a)^k$

6. What is the difference between Taylor's *Formula* for $f(x)$ about the point a and Taylor's *Series* for $f(x)$ about a?

7. Let $\{p_n\}$ be the sequence of prime numbers; thus, $p_1 = 2$, $p_2 = 3$, and so on. Then the equation $f(x) = \displaystyle\sum_{k=1}^{\infty} \frac{p_k}{k!} x^k$ defines a function f.

   (a) If you are told that $\displaystyle\lim_{k \uparrow \infty} \frac{p_k}{kp_{k-1}} = 0$, what can you say about the domain of f?
   (b) What is the number $f^{(5)}(0)$?
   (c) Write a computer program to print a table of values of f at the points of the set $\{0, .2, .4, .6, .8, 1.0\}$.

8. Modify the computer program of Fig. 30-1 so that it prints a third column of "exact" (to 4 decimal places) values of the sine function.

9. (a) Using Taylor's Series for e^x about 0, write a computer program for finding the values of e^x at the points of the set $\{0, .1, .2, \ldots , 2.0\}$.
   (b) Use Taylor's Formula to get an idea of the accuracy of your result.
   (c) Modify your program so that it also prints values of e^{-x}.
   (d) Modify your program so that it also prints values of $\sinh x$.

10. Let $f(x) = \displaystyle\sum_{k=0}^{\infty} x^k \sum_{k=0}^{\infty} \frac{1}{k!} x^k$.
    (a) What is the domain of f?

(b) Express $f(x)$ as the sum of a single series.

(c) Use the series you found in part (b) and the computer to find the values of f at the points of the set $\{0, .1, .2, .3, .4, .5\}$.

(d) Can you express $f(x)$ *without* using series?

11. (a) Show that if $\overline{\lim_{k \uparrow \infty}} |c_k(x - a)^k|^{1/k} = L$, then $L = \overline{\lim_{k \uparrow \infty}} (|c_k|^{1/k}|x - a|)$.

(b) Show that if $\overline{\lim_{k \uparrow \infty}} |c_k|^{1/k} = 0$, then $L < 1$ for each $x \in (-\infty, \infty)$, and hence Series 30-1 converges for every choice of x.

(c) Show that if $\overline{\lim_{k \uparrow \infty}} |c_k|^{1/k} = \infty$, then $L = 0$ when $x = a$ and $L = \infty$ when $x \neq a$. Hence, we conclude that Series 30-1 converges if, and only if, $x = a$.

(d) Show that if $\overline{\lim_{k \uparrow \infty}} |c_k|^{1/k} = c$, where c is a positive number, then $L = c|x - a|$, and hence Series 30-1 converges if $|x - a| < 1/c$ and diverges if $|x - a| > 1/c$.

(e) Put the above results together and prove Theorem 30-1.

12. Use the results of the previous exercise to show that the series $\sum_{k=1}^{\infty} kc_k(x - a)^{k-1}$

and $\sum_{k=0}^{\infty} c_k(x - a)^k$ have the same radius of convergence.

31 USING POWER SERIES TO SOLVE AN INITIAL VALUE PROBLEM

Perhaps the best way to introduce the techniques of solving initial value problems with power series is by means of an example. So let us consider the homogeneous linear initial value problem

(31-1) $y'' + 3xy' + 3y = 0$ and $y = 2, y' = -1$ when $x = 0$.

(Notice that none of the solution techniques we developed in earlier chapters will help us solve this problem.) We are going to find a power series $\sum_{k=0}^{\infty} c_k x^k$

such that $y = \sum_{k=0}^{\infty} c_k x^k$ satisfies Problem 31-1, and our first step is to substitute in the given differential equation. Thus, since

$$y' = \sum_{k=0}^{\infty} kc_k x^{k-1} \text{ and } y'' = \sum_{k=0}^{\infty} k(k - 1)c_k x^{k-2},$$

our differential equation becomes

$$(31\text{-}2) \qquad \sum_{k=0}^{\infty} k(k-1)c_k x^{k-2} + \sum_{k=0}^{\infty} 3kc_k x^k + \sum_{k=0}^{\infty} 3c_k x^k = 0.$$

We are really looking for infinitely many numbers, the terms of the coefficient sequence $\{c_k\}$, and Equation 31-2 will furnish us with infinitely many equations in these infinitely many unknowns. We simply combine the three series on the left-hand side of this equation into a single power series. Since the sum of this latter power series is to be 0, it must be true that *all* its coefficients are 0. So when we equate each coefficient of the combined series to 0, we obtain the equations we must solve to find our desired coefficient sequence $\{c_k\}$.

Because x appears to different powers in the terms of the three series in Equation 31-2, we must make certain adjustments before we can combine them. Thus, in the first series we will change the index of summation from k to j and write it as

$$\sum_{k=0}^{\infty} k(k-1)c_k x^{k-2} = \sum_{j=2}^{\infty} j(j-1)c_j x^{j-2}.$$

(Why is it permissible to change the "lower limit" of the index of summation from 0 to 2?) In the second and third series, we make the substitution $k = j - 2$:

$$\sum_{k=0}^{\infty} 3kc_k x^k = \sum_{j=2}^{\infty} 3(j-2)c_{j-2} x^{j-2} \text{ and } \sum_{k=0}^{\infty} 3c_k x^k = \sum_{j=2}^{\infty} 3c_{j-2} x^{j-2}.$$

Then Equation 31-2 becomes

$$\sum_{j=2}^{\infty} j(j-1)c_j x^{j-2} + \sum_{j=2}^{\infty} 3(j-2)c_{j-2} x^{j-2} + \sum_{j=2}^{\infty} 3c_{j-2} x^{j-2} = 0,$$

or

$$(31\text{-}3) \qquad \sum_{j=2}^{\infty} [j(j-1)c_j + 3(j-1)c_{j-2}]x^{j-2} = 0.$$

Now we equate each coefficient of this final series to 0:

$$j(j-1)c_j + 3(j-1)c_{j-2} = 0, \, j = 2, 3, 4, \ldots .$$

Finally, we solve for c_j and so complete the derivation of our recursion formula for the coefficients of the solution series:

$$(31\text{-}4) \qquad\qquad c_j = -\frac{3}{j} c_{j-2}, \, j = 2, 3, 4, \ldots$$

This recursion formula tells us that $c_2 = -\frac{3}{2}c_0$, $c_3 = -\frac{3}{3}c_1 = -c_1$, and so on. It is clear that once we choose c_0 and c_1, all the other coefficients are determined. The values of the first two coefficients come from the initial conditions of Problem 31-1. We are given that $y = 2$ and $y' = -1$ when $x = 0$, and these conditions immediately tell us that we must take $c_0 = 2$ and $c_1 = -1$. Therefore, $c_2 = -3$, $c_3 = 1$, and so on. Thus, we have found that

$$y = 2 - x - 3x^2 + x^3 + \cdots\cdot$$

satisfies our initial value problem. We will now discuss our solution series in greater detail.

We find its radius of convergence by using the slightly modified ratio test that we mentioned in Exercise 29-7. Thus, if we think of our solution series as $\sum\limits_{k=0}^{\infty} a_k = \sum\limits_{k=0}^{\infty} c_k x^k$, then

$$\frac{|a_k|}{|a_{k-2}|} = \frac{|c_k|}{|c_{k-2}|} x^2.$$

Hence, from Equation 31-4, we see that

$$\lim_{k \uparrow \infty} \frac{|a_k|}{|a_{k-2}|} = \lim_{k \uparrow \infty} \frac{3}{k} x^2 = 0.$$

This number is certainly less than 1 for every x, and so the modified ratio test tells us that the interval of convergence of our solution series is $(-\infty, \infty)$.

We are shortly going to be more specific about the solution series of Problem 31-1 and find explicit formulas for *all* the coefficients, not just for the first four. However, if we want to use the computer to write a table of values of the solution, it is best to use Recursion Formula 31-4.

So let us write a computer program that uses the series $y = \sum\limits_{k=0}^{\infty} c_k x^k$ to calculate the values of the solution at the points of the set $\{0, .1, .2, \ldots, 1.0\}$. Thus, x is to vary from 0 to 1 in steps of .1, as the outer loop in the program of Fig. 31-1 shows. For each such x, we have a series of numbers $\sum\limits_{k=0}^{\infty} a_k$ whose

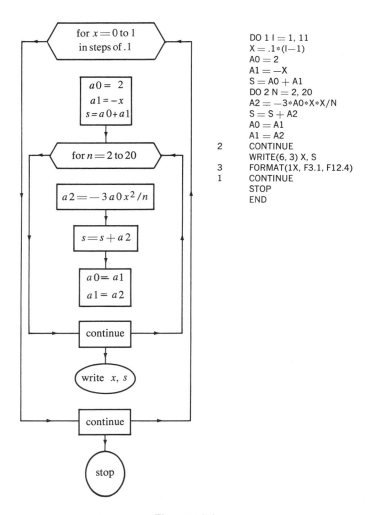

```
         DO 1 I = 1, 11
         X = .1*(I−1)
         A0 = 2
         A1 = −X
         S = A0 + A1
         DO 2 N = 2, 20
         A2 = −3*A0*X*X/N
         S = S + A2
         A0 = A1
         A1 = A2
      2  CONTINUE
         WRITE(6, 3) X, S
      3  FORMAT(1X, F3.1, F12.4)
      1  CONTINUE
         STOP
         END
```

Figure 31-1

sum we must find. Of course, we do not find the "whole" sum. We have to stop somewhere, and in our program we have chosen to stop with the 20th partial sum. In other words, we will consider S_{20} to be a satisfactory substitute for the true functional value.

The "natural" way to find S_{20} would be to set $S_1 = a_0 = 2$ and then successively calculate $S_1, S_2, \ldots, S_{20}$ by means of the formula

$$S_n = S_{n-1} + a_n,$$

and this is essentially what we will do. But there are a few problems here, because each term of our series is not calculated from its immediate predecessor, but from the term that comes *two* indices earlier. Thus, $a_n = c_n x^n$, and according to Equation 31-4, $c_n = -\dfrac{3}{n} c_{n-2}$. Therefore, $c_n x^n = -\dfrac{3}{n} c_{n-2} x^n = -\dfrac{3x^2}{n} c_{n-2} x^{n-2}$, and since $c_{n-2} x^{n-2} = a_{n-2}$, we see that

$$(31\text{-}5) \qquad\qquad a_n = -\frac{3x^2}{n} a_{n-2}.$$

In order to take this "two-step" equation into account, we start by writing explicitly the first two terms of the series, and our first calculated partial sum is $S_1 = a_0 + a_1$. In the inner loop of our program, $a2$ plays the role of a_n, and $a0$ plays the role of a_{n-2}. So the first statement calculates a_n and the next adds it to S_{n-1}. We use the symbol $a1$ to denote a_{n-1}. The statement $a0 = a1$ therefore means that a_{n-1} will play the role of a_{n-2} in the next swing through the inner loop, and the statement $a1 = a2$ indicates that a_n will become a_{n-1}.

In our present example, it is relatively easy to calculate explicit formulas for the terms of the coefficient sequence $\{c_j\}$, so let us do it. Formula 31-4 expresses c_j in terms of c_{j-2}; that is, it expresses c_2 in terms of c_0, c_4 in terms of c_2, and so on, and c_3 in terms of c_1, c_5 in terms of c_3, and so on. Therefore, it is reasonable to group the terms of the series into two classes, the terms with even indices and the terms with odd indices. In other words, we write the equation that defines the solution of our initial value problem as

$$(31\text{-}6) \qquad\qquad y = \sum_{k=0}^{\infty} (c_{2k} x^{2k} + c_{2k+1} x^{2k+1}).$$

To see how the coefficient c_{2k} is related to the coefficient c_{2k-2} that comes two indices earlier, we simply replace j with $2k$ in Equation 31-4:

$$c_{2k} = -\frac{3}{2k} c_{2k-2}.$$

Similarly, replacing j with $2k + 1$ yields

$$c_{2k+1} = -\frac{3}{2k+1} c_{2k-1}.$$

Thus, since $c_0 = 2$, we see that

$$c_2 = -\frac{3}{2} \cdot 2, \quad c_4 = -\frac{3}{4} c_2 = \frac{3^2}{2 \cdot 4} \cdot 2, \quad c_6 = -\frac{3}{6} c_4 = -\frac{3^3}{2 \cdot 4 \cdot 6} \cdot 2,$$

and so on. If one writes out sufficiently many of these terms, he is tempted to guess that

$$c_{2k} = \left(-\frac{3}{2}\right)^k \frac{2}{k!}.$$

We can use mathematical induction to verify this guess. Similarly, we find that the formula for the "odd" coefficients is

$$c_{2k+1} = -\frac{(-6)^k k!}{(2k+1)!}.$$

When we insert these explicit formulas into Equation 31-6, we obtain the equation

$$y = \sum_{k=0}^{\infty} \left[\left(-\frac{3}{2}\right)^k \frac{2}{k!} x^{2k} - \frac{(-6)^k k!}{(2k+1)!} x^{2k+1}\right].$$

In some ways, this explicit formula does not give us much information that we had not already found from the basic recursion formula for the coefficients. For example, the recursion formula allowed us to calculate the interval of convergence of the solution series, and it also enabled us to write a computer program for finding values of the solution. On the other hand, our explicit formulas do tell us that the coefficients do not get small very fast. For example, c_{21} is about .000034. Therefore, we want to use quite a few terms when we compute with our series; that is why we used twenty terms in the computer program of Fig. 31-1.

Let us remark that this entire procedure could perfectly well be carried out if our original differential equation is not homogeneous. For example, if the differential equation were $y'' + 3xy' + 3y = e^x$, then we would write $e^x = \sum_{j=2}^{\infty} \frac{1}{(j-2)!} x^{j-2}$, and Equation 31-3 would become

$$\sum_{j=2}^{\infty} [j(j-1)c_j + 3(j-1)c_{j-2}] x^{j-2} = \sum_{j=2}^{\infty} \frac{1}{(j-2)!} x^{j-2}.$$

Since two power series are equal only when their coefficients are equal, then

$$j(j-1)c_j + 3(j-1)c_{j-2} = \frac{1}{(j-2)!};$$

that is, the members of the coefficient sequence $\{c_j\}$ satisfy the recursion formula

(31-7)
$$c_j = \frac{1}{j!} - \frac{3}{j} c_{j-2}, \, j = 2, 3, \ldots$$

If our initial values are still $c_0 = 2$ and $c_1 = -1$, these equations give us a rule for calculating the remaining coefficients.

We should perhaps be a little more precise about the logic we use when we solve Problem 31-1 by series. We substituted $y = \sum\limits_{k=0}^{\infty} c_k x^k$ into the given differential equation and hence found Equations 31-4 for the coefficients. Thus, we have shown that these equations are *necessary* conditions that $y = \sum\limits_{k=0}^{\infty} c_k x^k$ satisfy the differential equation. They are also sufficient. That is, if we *start* with a series whose coefficients satisfy Equations 31-4, then the ratio test tells us that it converges for all x. Hence, the series defines a function in the interval $(-\infty, \infty)$. According to Theorem 30-2, we can differentiate this function, finding its derivatives by term-by-term differentiation of the series. When we substitute these derivatives into the left-hand side of the differential equation, we see from Equations 31-4 that the result is 0; that is, the series defines a solution of the differential equation.

Exactly this same procedure can be carried out in the case of a general initial value problem of the second order with a homogeneous linear differential equation:

(31-8) $y'' + p(x)y' + q(x)y = 0$ and $y = y_0, y' = y_1$ when $x = x_0$.

Here, we will assume that $p(x) = \sum\limits_{k=0}^{\infty} p_k(x - x_0)^k$ and $q(x) = \sum\limits_{k=0}^{\infty} q_k(x - x_0)^k$, these series converging in some interval $I = (x_0 - r, x_0 + r)$. If we substitute a series $\sum\limits_{k=0}^{\infty} c_k(x - x_0)^k$ for y in the given differential equation, we obtain an equation in which one side is an infinite series and the other side is 0. Therefore, each coefficient of the series is 0, and these infinitely many equations give us a means of calculating the coefficient sequence $\{c_k\}$. In general, we would find that c_k depends on $c_{k-1}, c_{k-2}, \ldots, c_0$, so we calculate the coefficients recursively, one after the other. The recursion formula does not give us c_0 and c_1. These numbers are the values of y and y' when $x = x_0$; that is, $c_0 = y_0$ and $c_1 = y_1$. The process is reversible. If we start with a series whose coefficients satisfy the recursion formula we just mentioned, then it is not hard to show (there is a proof in Reference [3]) that it converges at each point of the interval

I. Such a series defines a solution function for our differential equation; the coefficients were chosen so that it would. So we have the following theorem.

THEOREM 31-1

If Taylor's Series for $p(x)$ and $q(x)$ about x_0 converge to $p(x)$ and $q(x)$ in an interval I, and if w is the solution of Initial Value Problem 31-8, then Taylor's Series for $w(x)$ about x_0 converges to $w(x)$ in I.

In principle, the technique of solving Problem 31-8 by means of power series is straightforward, but if $p(x)$ and $q(x)$ are complicated, some of the details can become difficult. You should be warned that we chose as our example a problem in which the difficult details were minimized.

EXERCISE 31

1. Suppose that the function exp is defined as the solution of the initial value problem $y' - y = 0$ and $y = 1$ when $x = 0$. Express exp (x) as the sum of a series of powers of x.

2. (a) Suppose that the sine function is defined as the solution of the initial value problem $y'' + y = 0$ and $y = 0$, $y' = 1$ when $x = 0$. Express sin x as the sum of a series of powers of x.
   (b) Same as part (a), except change "sine" to "cosine" and make the necessary adjustments in the initial value problem.

3. (a) Find a recursion formula satisfied by the members of the sequence $\{c_k\}$ if
   $$y = \sum_{k=0}^{\infty} c_k x^k \text{ satisfies the initial value problem}$$

   $$y'' - 4y = 0 \text{ and } y = 1, y' = 0 \text{ when } x = 0.$$

   (b) Use the ratio test to check the radius of convergence of this series.
   (c) Write a computer program that uses your series to evaluate the solution at the points of the set $\{0, .2, .4, .6, .8, 1.0\}$.
   (d) Find an explicit formula for the coefficient c_k (that is, a formula that involves k but does not involve another coefficient c_j).
   (e) How would you use infinite series to solve the initial value problem

   $$y'' - 4y = x \text{ and } y = 1, y' = 0 \text{ when } x = 0?$$

   (f) Check your results in parts (c), (d), and (e) with the solutions found by our earlier techniques.

4. Show that the initial value problem $y'' - 2xy' + 10y = 0$ and $y = 0$, $y' = 15$ when $x = 0$ has a polynomial solution, and find it.

5. Use power series to solve the initial value problem

$$y'' + (x - 1)y' + 2y = 0 \text{ and } y = 3, y' = -2 \text{ when } x = 1.$$

6. Solve the initial value problem $y' = (2x + 1)y$ and $y = 1$ when $x = 0$ with and without using power series, and compare the results.

7. Use Formula 31-7 to find the first six terms of the series in powers of x whose sum satisfies the initial value problem

$$y'' + 3xy' + 3y = e^x \text{ and } y = 2, y' = -1 \text{ when } x = 0.$$

8. (a) Show that if $y = \displaystyle\sum_{k=0}^{\infty} c_k x^k$ satisfies the differential equation $y'' + e^x y = 0$,

then

$$\sum_{j=2}^{\infty} \left[j(j - 1)c_j + \sum_{i=0}^{j-2} \frac{c_{j-i-2}}{i!} \right] x^{j-2} = 0.$$

(b) From the equation of part (a), find a recursion formula that expresses c_j in terms of c's with smaller indices.

(c) Find c_2, c_3, and c_4 if $c_0 = 2$ and $c_1 = -3$.

(d) Write a computer program to calculate $\{c_2, c_3, \ldots, c_{20}\}$ if $c_0 = 2$ and $c_1 = -3$.

9. Discuss the problem of using power series to solve the pendulum equation

$$\theta'' + \frac{g}{r} \sin \theta = 0.$$

32 MORE EXAMPLES OF USING SERIES TO SOLVE DIFFERENTIAL EQUATIONS

We have the homogeneous linear differential equation

(32-1) $$y'' + p(x)y' + q(x)y = 0$$

completely under our control when we find two solutions u and v that are linearly independent in the basic interval I in which we are working. All other solutions can be expressed as linear combinations of these two. Sometimes it is easy to find two series whose sums are values of linearly independent solutions.

For suppose that u and v are the solutions such that, for some point $x_0 \in I$,

$$u(x_0) = 1, u'(x_0) = 0, v(x_0) = 0, \text{ and } v'(x_0) = 1.$$

These conditions obviously imply that neither $u(x)$ nor $v(x)$ can be a constant multiple of the other in the interval I; that is, that u and v are independent solutions. We obtain a power series whose sum is $u(x)$ by choosing the members of the sequence $\{c_k\}$ so that $y = \sum\limits_{k=0}^{\infty} c_k(x - x_0)^k$ satisfies the differential Equation 32-1, and $c_0 = 1$ and $c_1 = 0$. Similarly, to find a power series whose sum is $v(x)$, we choose $c_0 = 0$ and $c_1 = 1$.

For example, in Exercise 31-2 you followed this procedure to find power series whose sums are values of independent solutions of the differential equation $y'' + y = 0$. Now we will find power series whose sums are values of linearly independent solutions of the only slightly less innocent looking equation

(32-2) $$y'' + xy = 0.$$

We will first find the relation among the coefficients so that $y = \sum\limits_{k=0}^{\infty} c_k x^k$ satisfies the given differential equation. Here, $y'' = \sum\limits_{k=0}^{\infty} k(k-1)c_k x^{k-2}$, and when we substitute in the equation $y'' + xy = 0$, it becomes

$$\sum_{k=0}^{\infty} k(k-1)c_k x^{k-2} + \sum_{k=0}^{\infty} c_k x^{k+1} = 0.$$

Now we replace k with j in the first series and make the substitution $j = k + 3$ in the second series to obtain the equation

$$\sum_{j=2}^{\infty} j(j-1)c_j x^{j-2} + \sum_{j=3}^{\infty} c_{j-3} x^{j-2} = 0.$$

We cannot combine these series as they stand, because they do not have the same limits of summation. So we write the first series as $2c_2 + \sum\limits_{j=3}^{\infty} j(j-1)c_j x^{j-2}$ before we add it to the second:

$$2c_2 + \sum_{j=3}^{\infty} [j(j-1)c_j + c_{j-3}]x^{j-2} = 0.$$

Each coefficient of the series on the left-hand side of this last equation must be zero; that is,

(32-3) $$c_2 = 0$$

and

(32-4)
$$c_j = -c_{j-3}/j(j - 1), j = 3, 4, 5, \ldots$$

According to Formula 32-4, each term of the sequence $\{c_j\}$ is determined by the term that is three steps behind it, and so it is appropriate to divide the coefficient sequence into three subsequences, $\{c_{3k}\} = \{c_0, c_3, c_6, \ldots\}$, $\{c_{3k+1}\} = \{c_1, c_4, c_7, \ldots\}$, and $\{c_{3k+2}\} = \{c_2, c_5, c_8, \ldots\}$. We get recursion formulas for these subsequences by substituting $3k$, $3k + 1$, and $3k + 2$ for j in Equation 32-4:

(32-5)
$$c_{3k} = -c_{3k-3}/3k(3k - 1),$$

(32-6)
$$c_{3k+1} = -c_{3k-2}/(3k + 1)3k,$$

and

(32-7)
$$c_{3k+2} = -c_{3k-1}/(3k + 2)(3k + 1), k = 1, 2, 3, \ldots$$

Since (see Equation 32-3) $c_2 = 0$, Formula 32-7 tells us that $c_5 = 0$, $c_8 = 0$, $c_{11} = 0$, and so on. These equations hold, regardless of the choice of c_0 and c_1.

For our particular solution u, we choose $c_0 = 1$ and $c_1 = 0$. It follows from Formula 32-6 that $c_4 = 0$, $c_7 = 0$, $c_{10} = 0$, and so on. Therefore, all the non-zero coefficients of the power series whose sum is $u(x)$ are given by Equation 32-5 and the initial value $c_0 = 1$.

If v is the solution of Equation 32-2 that satisfies the initial conditions $y = 0$ and $y' = 1$, then $v(x) = \sum_{k=0}^{\infty} c_k x^k$, provided that $c_0 = 0$, $c_1 = 1$, and Equations 32-4 hold. Since $c_0 = 0$, Formula 32-5 tells us that each term of the sequence $\{c_{3k}\}$ is 0. Therefore, the non-zero coefficients of our power series whose sum is $v(x)$ are given by Formula 32-6 and the initial value $c_1 = 1$. For example, $c_4 = -c_1/4 \cdot 3 = -1/4 \cdot 3$ and $c_7 = -c_4/7 \cdot 6 = 1/7 \cdot 6 \cdot 4 \cdot 3$.

Example 32-1. Write a computer program to calculate the values of the solution u of the initial value problem $y'' + xy = 0$ and $y = 1$, $y' = 0$ when $x = 0$ at the points of the set $\{0, .1, .2, .3, .4, .5\}$.

Solution. In the computer program of Fig. 32-1, we departed slightly from the practice we followed in Fig. 31-1. Thus, since the value of our solution function when $x = 0$ is (by definition) 1, we simply write it down without going through the formality of using an infinite series to calculate it. Now we introduce a loop

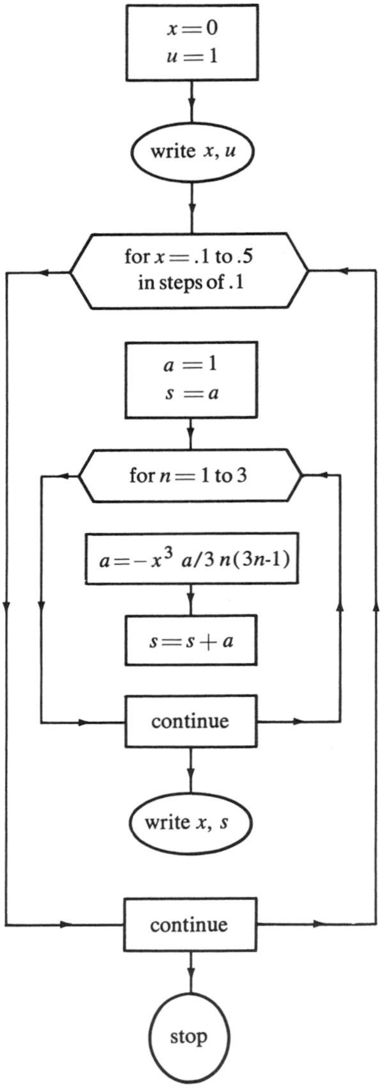


```
      X = 0
      U = 1
      WRITE(6, 1) X, U
1     FORMAT(1X, F3.1, F12.4)
      DO 2 I = 1, 5
      X = .1*I
      A = 1
      S = A
      DO 3 N = 1, 3
      A = -X**3*A/(3*N*(3*N-1))
      S = S + A
3     CONTINUE
      WRITE(6, 1) X, S
2     CONTINUE
      STOP
      END
```

Figure 32-1

in which x varies from .1 to .5 in steps of .1. For each such x, we have $u(x) = \sum_{k=0}^{\infty} c_{3k}x^{3k}$, and we think of this series as $\sum_{k=0}^{\infty} a_k$, where

$$a_0 = 1 \text{ and } a_k = -x^3 a_{k-1}/3k(3k-1).$$

These terms decrease very rapidly, so we will assume that S_3, the third partial sum of the series, is an adequate substitute for the number $u(x)$ that we are seeking. Therefore, we write down our first term, $a_0 = 1$, and our first partial sum, $S_0 = a_0$. Then we successively calculate S_n for $n = 1, 2,$ and 3, by calculating a_n and adding it to S_{n-1}. When S_3 has been calculated, we write it and go on to the next x.

Together with the given initial conditions, the recursion formulas for the coefficients of our series determine them completely. However, it is sometimes of interest to find explicit formulas for the coefficients.

Example 32-2.   Find an explicit formula for the coefficients of our series whose sum is $v(x)$.

Solution. The first coefficient is 1, and its successors are given by Formula 32-6. Therefore, $c_4 = -1/4 \cdot 3$, $c_7 = -c_4/7 \cdot 6 = 1/7 \cdot 6 \cdot 4 \cdot 3$, $c_{10} = -c_7/10 \cdot 9 = -1/10 \cdot 9 \cdot 7 \cdot 6 \cdot 4 \cdot 3$, and so on. From these few terms, it is easy to infer the general pattern. We leave it to you to show (by mathematical induction) that

(32-8) $c_{3k+1} = (-1)^k/3 \cdot 4 \cdot 6 \cdot 7 \cdot \cdots \cdot 3k(3k+1), \ k \geq 1.$

If the denominator of this fraction were the *sum* $3 + 4 + 6 + 7 + \cdots + 3k + (3k+1)$, you would naturally abbreviate it as $\sum_{i=1}^{k} [3i + (3i+1)]$. Since it is the *product* $3 \cdot 4 \cdot 6 \cdot 7 \cdot \cdots \cdot 3k(3k+1)$, we use the notation $\prod_{i=1}^{k} 3i(3i+1)$. Thus, just as the Greek letter Σ stands for "sum," so does the Greek letter Π stand for "product," and Equation 32-8 can therefore be compactly written as

$$c_{3k+1} = (-1)^k \Big/ \prod_{i=1}^{k} 3i(3i+1) \text{ for } k \geq 1.$$

It follows that

$$v(x) = x + \sum_{k=1}^{\infty} (-1)^k x^{3k+1} \Big/ \prod_{i=1}^{k} 3i(3i+1).$$

Whether this "explicit" formula tells us any more than our recursion formula did is perhaps a debatable question. It does indicate, for example, that the coefficients of the series decrease very rapidly as the index of the terms increases.

We haven't discussed our "standard example," the initial value problem

(32-9) $y' = 1 + y^2$ and $y = 0$ when $x = 0$

for some time, so let us return to it now. It provides us with an example of a nonlinear differential equation that can be solved easily by series methods.

Example 32-3.   Utilize the fact that $y = \text{Tan } x$ satisfies Problem 32-9 to find the coefficients of Taylor's Series for Tan x about 0.

Solution. We let $y = \sum\limits_{k=0}^{\infty} c_k x^k$ and substitute in the given differential equation:

$$\sum_{k=1}^{\infty} k c_k x^{k-1} = 1 + \sum_{k=0}^{\infty} c_k x^k \sum_{k=0}^{\infty} c_k x^k$$

$$= 1 + \sum_{k=0}^{\infty} \left(\sum_{i=0}^{k} c_i c_{k-i} \right) x^k \qquad \text{(Equation 30-3)}.$$

Now we let $k = j + 1$ in the series on the left-hand side of this equation and $k = j$ in the series on the right:

$$\sum_{j=0}^{\infty} (j + 1) c_{j+1} x^j = 1 + \sum_{j=0}^{\infty} \left(\sum_{i=0}^{j} c_i c_{j-i} \right) x^j.$$

When we equate coefficients of corresponding powers of x, we obtain the equations

$$c_1 = 1 + c_0^2$$

and

$$c_{j+1} = \frac{1}{j + 1} \sum_{i=0}^{j} c_i c_{j-i}, \, j = 1, 2, \ldots$$

Since we know that $c_0 = 0$, these formulas furnish us a way to calculate, one after another, the coefficients of Taylor's Series for Tan x about 0. You might look up the discussion of this subject in your calculus book. In Exercise 32-7, we translate this recursion formula into a computer program for finding these coefficients.

EXERCISE 32

1. It makes the calculations a little easier if you write the differential equation $y'' - \dfrac{1}{1 + x^2} y = 0$ in the form $(1 + x^2)y'' - y = 0$.

    (a) Find a recursion formula for the members of the sequence $\{c_k\}$ if $y = \sum\limits_{k=0}^{\infty} c_k x^k$ satisfies the differential equation.

(b) Find the interval of convergence of this series.

(c) Can you find a series whose sum is the value of a solution that is an even function? An odd function?

(d) Are the solutions you found in part (c) linearly independent?

2. Suppose that $u(x) = \sum_{k=0}^{\infty} a_k(x - x_0)^k$, $v(x) = \sum_{k=0}^{\infty} b_k(x - x_0)^k$, and $w(x) = \sum_{k=0}^{\infty} c_k(x - x_0)^k$, where u, v, and w are solutions of the initial value problems that consist of the differential equation $y'' + p(x)y' + q(x)y = 0$ and the respective initial conditions (1) $y = 1, y' = 0$ when $x = x_0$, (2) $y = 0, y' = 1$ when $x = x_0$, and (3) $y = y_0, y' = y_1$ when $x = x_0$. Show that, for each k, $c_k = y_0 a_k + y_1 b_k$.

3. In the text, we found power series whose sums were $u(x)$ and $v(x)$, where u and v were certain solutions of the differential equation $y'' + xy = 0$. What is the interval of convergence of these series?

4. In Example 32-3, we found a recursion formula for the coefficients of a power series whose sum is Tan x.

(a) Find, explicitly, c_1, c_2, c_3, c_4, and c_5.

(b) Show that the coefficients with *even* indices are all 0, and discuss this point.

(c) What is the interval of convergence of this power series?

5. Find power series whose sums are values of two linearly independent solutions of the differential equation $y'' - xy = 0$.

6. Let w be the solution of the initial value problem $y'' - 2yy' = 0$ and $y = 0$, $y' = 1$ when $x = 0$.

(a) Use the techniques of Example 32-3 to find Taylor's Series for $w(x)$ about 0.

(b) Use the techniques of Section 10 to solve this problem.

(c) In view of part (b), it might be interesting to compare the formulas for the coefficients that you found in part (a) with those we found in Example 32-3.

7. In Fig. 32-2, we show a computer program which calculates the coefficients of the series in Example 32-3. Discuss this program. Run it. Make a flow chart for it.

```
        DIMENSION C(20)
        C(1) = 1
        DO 1 J = 1, 19
        S = 0
        DO 2 I = 1, J
        N = J − I
        S = S + C(I)*C(N)
    2   CONTINUE
        C(J+1) = S/(J+1)
        K = J+1
        WRITE(6, 3) K, C(K)
    3   FORMAT(1X, I2, F20.4)
    1   CONTINUE
        STOP
        END
```

Figure 32-2

8. Write a computer program that calculates the values of the solution v of the initial value problem $y'' + xy = 0$ and $y = 0$, $y' = 1$ when $x = 0$ at the points of the set $\{0, .1, .2, .3, .4, .5\}$.

33 LEGENDRE POLYNOMIALS

We have been finding *infinite series* whose sums are values of solutions of given differential equations. Here, we will look at an important equation that arises in practice and which has *polynomial* functions ("finite series") as solutions.

In certain problems involving electric or gravitational potential in a region of spherical symmetry, we are presented with **Legendre's Equation** in the form

$$(33\text{-}1) \qquad -((1 - x^2)y')' = \lambda y, \qquad x \in (-1, 1).$$

Here, λ is a number, so we have a whole family of differential equations, one for each choice of λ. We will now show that, for certain choices of λ, Equation 33-1 has polynomial solutions. For example, if $\lambda = 0$, it is easy to verify that $y = 1$ satisfies Equation 33-1, and if $\lambda = 2$, $y = x$ satisfies the equation. We will also show, however, that for some choices of λ ($\lambda = 1$ is such a choice), Equation 33-1 does *not* have a polynomial solution. Notice that $y = 0$ satisfies Equation 33-1 for each choice of λ, but this polynomial solution is a "trivial" solution, and we hereby rule it out. When we say "solution" in this section, we mean "non-trivial solution."

Our search for a polynomial solution of Equation 33-1 amounts to this: Find a sequence $\{c_k\}$ in which only a finite number of terms are different from 0 and such that $y = \sum\limits_{k=0}^{\infty} c_k x^k$ satisfies Equation 33-1. Let us write this differential equation as

$$y'' - x^2 y'' - 2xy' + \lambda y = 0$$

and substitute our series expression for y:

$$\sum_{k=2}^{\infty} (k - 1)k c_k x^{k-2} - \sum_{k=0}^{\infty} (k - 1)k c_k x^k - \sum_{k=0}^{\infty} 2k c_k x^k + \sum_{k=0}^{\infty} \lambda c_k x^k = 0.$$

We set $j = k - 2$ in the first series and replace k with j in the other three, and then

$$\sum_{j=0}^{\infty} (j+1)(j+2)c_{j+2}x^j - \sum_{j=0}^{\infty} (j-1)jc_jx^j - \sum_{j=0}^{\infty} 2jc_jx^j + \sum_{j=0}^{\infty} \lambda c_jx^j = 0;$$

that is,

$$\sum_{j=0}^{\infty} [(j+1)(j+2)c_{j+2} - (j(j+1) - \lambda)c_j]x^j = 0.$$

Since each coefficient of this series must be 0, we have derived the recursion formula

(33-2) $$c_{j+2} = \frac{j(j+1) - \lambda}{(j+1)(j+2)} c_j, \quad j = 0, 1, 2, \ldots$$

Formula 33-2 will give us the conditions under which Equation 33-1 has a polynomial solution. We first suppose that there *is* a polynomial solution of degree n; that is, that our series $\sum_{k=0}^{\infty} c_k x^k$ stops with the term $c_n x^n$. Thus, the coefficient c_n is not 0, but each coefficient with a larger index is 0. In particular, $c_{n+2} = 0$, so if we replace j with n in Equation 33-2, then $0 = \frac{n(n+1) - \lambda}{(n+1)(n+2)} c_n$. Therefore, the only cases of Legendre's Equation that can have non-trivial polynomial solutions are those for which

(33-3) $$\lambda = n(n+1).$$

We might have $\lambda = 0$, $\lambda = 2$, $\lambda = 6$, $\lambda = 12$, and so on, but the equation has only the trivial polynomial solution if $\lambda = 1$, or 3, or π, and so on.

So far, we have shown only that Equation 33-3 is a *necessary* condition for Equation 33-1 to have polynomial solutions. We will now show that it is also sufficient. So suppose that $\lambda = n(n+1)$, and make this substitution in Equation 33-2:

(33-4) $$c_{j+2} = \frac{j(j+1) - n(n+1)}{(j+1)(j+2)} c_j = \frac{(j-n)(j+n+1)}{(j+1)(j+2)} c_j.$$

Equation 33-4 expresses each coefficient in terms of the one that comes two indices earlier. Thus, c_2 is a multiple of c_0, c_4 is a multiple of c_2 (and hence of c_0), and so on. It is immediately apparent that each coefficient with an even index is a multiple of c_0, and each coefficient with an odd index is a multiple of c_1. Therefore, if we choose $c_0 = 0$, the series $\sum_{k=0}^{\infty} c_k x^k$ will contain no even powers of x, whereas if we set $c_1 = 0$, it will have nothing *but* even powers. This observation shows us how to find polynomial solutions (if $\lambda = n(n+1)$).

First, let us suppose that n is an even number. By replacing j with n in Equation 33-4, we find that $c_{n+2} = 0$. Then we replace j with $n+2$, and we have $c_{n+4} = 0$. Next, we find that $c_{n+6} = 0$, and so on. Thus, all terms with even indices are 0 from index $n+2$ on. By choosing $c_1 = 0$, we make *all* the odd coefficients vanish, and so

$$y = c_0 + c_2 x^2 + c_4 x^4 + \cdots + c_n x^n$$

satisfies Equation 33-1. If n is odd, Equation 33-4 again shows that $c_{n+2} = c_{n+4} = c_{n+6} = \cdots = 0$. Thus, all terms with odd indices beyond n are 0. So we choose $c_0 = 0$ to remove *all* terms with even indices, and we see that

$$y = c_1 x + c_3 x^3 + c_5 x^5 + \cdots + c_n x^n$$

satisfies Equation 33-4. We can summarize these results as a theorem.

THEOREM 33-1

Equation 33-1 has a polynomial solution of degree n if, and only if, $\lambda = n(n+1)$. If n is even, the polynomial contains only even powers of x, whereas if n is odd, the polynomial contains only odd powers of x. The coefficients of the polynomial satisfy Recursion Formula 33-4.

Example 33-1.   Find a non-trivial solution of Equation 33-1 if $\lambda = 4 \cdot 5 = 20$.

Solution. Here, $n = 4$, so Theorem 33-1 tells us that a solution is defined by the equation

$$y = c_0 + c_2 x^2 + c_4 x^4,$$

where c_0, c_2, and c_4 satisfy the recursion formula

$$c_{j+2} = \frac{(j-4)(j+5)}{(j+1)(j+2)} c_j.$$

Therefore, if we take $c_0 = 1$, then $c_2 = -\frac{20}{2} \cdot 1 = -10$, and $c_4 = -\frac{14}{12}(-10) = \frac{35}{3}$. Finally, then, a polynomial solution is determined by the equation

$$y = 1 - 10x^2 + \frac{35}{3}x^4.$$

Of course, because the linear Equation 33-1 is also homogeneous, we can multiply a solution by any number and obtain another solution, so $y = 3 - 30x^2 + 35x^4$ also satisfies Equation 33-1, and so on. You can check this last statement by substituting in Equation 33-1 (with $\lambda = 20$).

We have observed that the linear Equation 33-1 is also homogeneous, so any constant multiple of a solution is again a solution. Equation 33-4 really determines only the *ratios* of the coefficients, not the coefficients themselves. If we specify any particular coefficient, for example, c_0 if n is even or c_1 if n is odd, then the other coefficients are determined. Actually, we exercise our freedom of choice at the other end of the polynomial and select as the coefficient of the highest power of x the rather surprising number

$$(33\text{-}5) \qquad\qquad c_n = \frac{(2n)!}{2^n (n!)^2}$$

(remember that $0! = 1$). With this particular choice of c_n, the polynomial whose coefficients we obtain from Equation 33-4 is the **Legendre polynomial** of degree n; it is usually denoted by $P_n(x)$.

Example 33-2. Find $P_4(x)$.

Solution. Since $y = P_4(x)$ satisfies Equation 33-1 with $\lambda = 4 \cdot 5$, $P_4(x)$ is simply a multiple of the polynomial we found in Example 33-1. Thus, there is a number m such that

$$P_4(x) = m(\tfrac{35}{3}x^4 - 10x^2 + 1).$$

According to Equation 33-5, the leading coefficient of this polynomial should be $\dfrac{8!}{16(4!)^2}$, and so m satisfies the equation

$$\frac{35}{3} m = \frac{8!}{16 \cdot 4! \cdot 4!} = \frac{35}{8}.$$

Thus, $m = \tfrac{3}{8}$, and

$$P_4(x) = \tfrac{35}{8}x^4 - \tfrac{15}{4}x^2 + \tfrac{3}{8}.$$

Table 33-1 lists the Legendre polynomials $P_0(x)$, $P_1(x)$, $P_2(x)$, $P_3(x)$, $P_4(x)$, and $P_5(x)$.

TABLE 33-1

$$
\begin{aligned}
P_0(x) &= 1 \\
P_1(x) &= x \\
P_2(x) &= \tfrac{3}{2}x^2 - \tfrac{1}{2} \\
P_3(x) &= \tfrac{5}{2}x^3 - \tfrac{3}{2}x \\
P_4(x) &= \tfrac{35}{8}x^4 - \tfrac{15}{4}x^2 + \tfrac{3}{8} \\
P_5(x) &= \tfrac{63}{8}x^5 - \tfrac{35}{4}x^3 + \tfrac{15}{8}x
\end{aligned}
$$

An interesting feature of $P_4(x)$ is that $P_4(1) = 1$. In fact, it is true that

(33-6) $P_n(1) = 1$

for every index n (check the polynomials listed in Table 33-1). The apparently arbitrary choice of c_n given in Equation 33-5 produces this result, but this fact is by no means obvious from our description of the Legendre polynomials. There are other descriptions of them, though, from which it is easy to deduce Equation 33-6. You would be amazed at the number of useful vantage points from which one can view the Legendre polynomials. Because they use Legendre polynomials a great deal, applied mathematicians do look at them from all possible angles.

We will not be able to go very deeply into the vast theory of the Legendre polynomials here, but we should at least mention their most important feature. The "standard form" of a homogeneous linear differential equation of the second order is $y'' + p(x)y' + q(x)y = 0$. If we write Equation 33-1 in this form, it becomes $y'' - 2x(1 - x^2)^{-1}y' + \lambda(1 - x^2)^{-1}y = 0$. Here, $p(x) = -2x(1 - x^2)^{-1}$ and $q(x) = \lambda(1 - x^2)^{-1}$, so both p and q are continuous in the open interval $(-1, 1)$, but they are not bounded in this interval. It is important to know when Equation 33-1 has bounded solutions in the interval $(-1, 1)$, and the facts are these. *Equation* 33-1 *has a non-trivial bounded solution in the interval* $(-1, 1)$ *if, and only if, there is a non-negative integer n such that* $\lambda = n(n + 1)$, *and then u is a bounded solution if, and only if, there is a number c such that* $u(x) = cP_n(x)$. In other words, Legendre polynomials, and constant multiples of them, give the only solutions of Equation 33-1 that are bounded in the interval $(-1, 1)$. We will have more to say on this point in Section 41.

You can find many other interesting facts about the Legendre polynomials in References [2] and [5]. We will now write a computer program for calculating the values of these polynomials at the points of the set $\{0, .1, .2, \ldots, 1.0\}$. We use the formula

(33-7) $P_n(x) = c_n x^n + c_{n-2} x^{n-2} + \cdots + c_{n-2m} x^{n-2m}$

$$= b(1)x^n + b(2)x^{n-2} + \cdots + b(m + 1)x^{n-2m}.$$

Here, $m = \text{int}(n/2)$, and the c's are given by Equations 33-4 and 33-5. Because of the peculiarities of Fortran notation, we have found it expedient to write $b(1)$ in place of c_n, $b(2)$ in place of c_{n-2}, and so on. Thus, in general, $b(i) = c_{n-2(i-1)} = c_{n-2i+2}$. To find the recursion formula that expresses $b(i + 1)$ in terms of $b(i)$, we simply replace j with $n - 2i$ in Equation 33-4 and rewrite the result as

(33-8) $b(i + 1) = -\dfrac{(n - 2i + 1)(n - 2i + 2)}{2i(2n - 2i + 1)} b(i).$

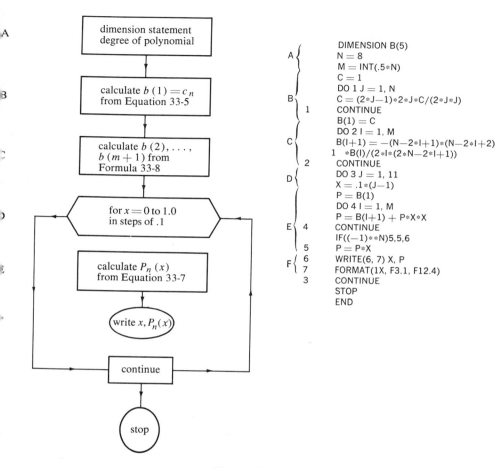

Figure 33-1

The flow chart of Fig. 33-1 is keyed to the computer program listed there to help you figure out what is going on. In this program, we have set $n = 8$; that is, we are calculating $P_8(x)$. To calculate other Legendre polynomials, we simply have to change the first two statements. For example, to calculate $P_7(x)$, the first two statements become dimension $b(4)$ and $n = 7$.

Notice that we only calculate values of $P_n(x)$ for $x \in [0, 1]$. But since $P_n(x)$ is odd or even, depending on n, it is easy to find the values of $P_n(x)$ for $x < 0$. If you run this program for various choices of n, you will see that $|P_n(x)| \leq 1$, and you will find that Equation 33-6 holds. Furthermore (if you keep n small), you will find illustrated the fact that $P_n(x)$ has exactly n zeros in $(-1, 1)$.

EXERCISE 33

1. (a) Explain why $P_n(-x) = (-1)^n P_n(x)$.
   (b) Show that the result of part (a) implies that $\int_{-1}^{1} P_n(x)P_m(x)dx = 0$ if $m + n$ is an odd number. (Actually, we will find in Section 41 that this equation is correct whenever $m \neq n$.)

2. Use Equations 33-4 and 33-5 to verify the entries for $P_2(x)$ and $P_3(x)$ in Table 33-1.

3. Find the following numbers.
   (a) $P_{12}'(0)$ (d) $P_{1493}^{(1776)}(0)$
   (b) $P_{13}^{(8)}(0)$ (e) $P_{1493}^{(1776)}(.5)$
   (c) $P_{1776}^{(1493)}(0)$

4. The details of the proof are somewhat complicated, but it can be shown [5] that for each integer n,

$$P_n(x) = \frac{1}{2^n n!} D_x^n (x^2 - 1)^n \qquad \text{(\textbf{Rodrigues' Formula}).}$$

   Verify this equation for $n = 5$. Use it to show that $P_n(1) = 1$.

5. Fairly complicated calculations [5] show that for each integer n,

$$\int_{-1}^{1} P_n(x)^2 dx = \frac{2}{2n + 1}.$$

   Verify this equation for $n = 3$.

6. Show that P_0 and P_1 are linearly independent solutions of Legendre's Equation in the interval $(-1, 1)$. Also, P_2 is a solution of Legendre's Equation, which is a homogeneous linear differential equation of the second order. Does it follow that $P_2(x)$ is a linear combination of $P_0(x)$ and $P_1(x)$?

7. (a) Start with the fact that $b(1) = c_n$, and use mathematical induction and Formula 33-8 to show that for each i,

$$b(i + 1) = (-1)^i \frac{(2n - 2i)!}{2^n i!(n - i)!(n - 2i)!}.$$

   (b) Now use Equation 33-7 to show that

$$P_n(x) = \sum_{i=0}^{\text{int }(n/2)} \frac{(-1)^i (2n - 2i)!}{2^n i!(n - i)!(n - 2i)!} x^{n-2i}$$

8. For what choices of μ does the differential equation $y'' + 2xy' + \mu y = 0$ have non-trivial polynomial solutions?

9. Using the fact that $P_n(1) = 1$, show how to find numbers $d_0, d_1, \ldots, d_n$ such that $P_n(x) = \sum_{k=0}^{n} d_k(x - 1)^k$.

10. Like any polynomial, $P_n(x)$ is a linear combination of powers of x, up to and including the nth power. Conversely, can you convince yourself that x^n can be expressed as a linear combination of $P_0(x)$, $P_1(x)$, $\ldots$, $P_n(x)$? For example, $x^2 = \frac{1}{3}P_0(x) + \frac{2}{3}P_2(x)$. Find the corresponding expression for x^3.

34 BESSEL FUNCTIONS OF THE FIRST KIND

Another important differential equation of applied mathematics is **Bessel's Equation,**

$$(34\text{-}1) \qquad\qquad x^2y'' + xy' + (x^2 - m^2)y = 0.$$

Here, m is a given number. Most often in applications, it is a non-negative integer, but there are times when we want to consider it as some other kind of number, even a complex number. So as not to get too far afield in this introductory course, let us suppose that $m \geq 0$ (it need not be an integer). We really have a whole family of differential equations, one for each choice of m. In most examples, one is interested in Bessel's Equation in the interval $(0, \infty)$, so let us restrict ourselves to this case.

Equation 34-1 is somewhat analogous to Euler's Equation $x^2y'' + axy' + by = 0$ that we mentioned in Exercise 24-9. In both cases, if we write the differential equation in the standard form $y'' + p(x)y' + q(x)y = 0$, we obtain coefficients $p(x)$ and $q(x)$ that "blow up" as $x \downarrow 0$. We found that solutions of Euler's Equation are given by equations of the form $y = x^r$, where r is a suitably chosen number. Now, we will find that we can pick an exponent r and a sequence $\{c_k\}$ such that $y = x^r \sum_{k=0}^{\infty} c_k x^k$ satisfies Equation 34-1 in the interval $(0, \infty)$. This trick is a standard one for handling "singular" differential equations. You can find out more about it by consulting more advanced books on differential equations, such as References [2] or [3].

To find the exponent r and the coefficient sequence $\{c_k\}$, we write $y = \sum_{k=0}^{\infty} c_k x^{k+r}$ and substitute in Equation 34-1:

$$x^2 \sum_{k=0}^{\infty} (k + r)(k + r - 1)c_k x^{k+r-2} + x \sum_{k=0}^{\infty} (k + r)c_k x^{k+r-1}$$

$$+ (x^2 - m^2) \sum_{k=0}^{\infty} c_k x^{k+r} = 0.$$

After some simplification and rearrangement, this equation becomes

$$\sum_{k=0}^{\infty} c_k x^{k+r+2} + \sum_{k=0}^{\infty} [(k+r)(k+r-1) + (k+r) - m^2] c_k x^{k+r} = 0.$$

Now let us make the substitution $j = k + 2$ in the first series, write j for k in the second, and observe that $(j+r)(j+r-1) + (j+r) = (j+r)^2$:

$$\sum_{j=2}^{\infty} c_{j-2} x^{j+r} + \sum_{j=0}^{\infty} [(j+r)^2 - m^2] c_j x^{j+r} = 0.$$

These series can be combined to yield the equation

$$(r^2 - m^2) c_0 x^r + [(1+r)^2 - m^2] c_1 x^{r+1} + \sum_{j=2}^{\infty} (c_{j-2} + [(j+r)^2 - m^2] c_j) x^{j+r} = 0.$$

When we equate the coefficients of the powers of x to 0, we obtain the equations

(34-2) $(r^2 - m^2) c_0 = 0,$

(34-3) $[(1+r)^2 - m^2] c_1 = 0,$

and

(34-4) $c_{j-2} + [(j+r)^2 - m^2] c_j = 0, \, j = 2, 3, 4, \ldots$

If the number r and the coefficients $\{c_j\}$ satisfy these equations, then

(34-5) $y = c_0 x^r + c_1 x^{r+1} + c_2 x^{r+2} + \cdots = x^r (c_0 + c_1 x + c_2 x^2 + \cdots)$

satisfies Equation 34-1, so now we must solve Equations 34-2 to 34-4.

    To satisfy Equation 34-2, we *could* pick $c_0 = 0$. But that choice would merely start the series in Equation 34-5 with the term $c_1 x^{r+1}$, which doesn't get us anywhere because r has not yet been determined. Therefore, we will satisfy Equation 34-2 by equating the factor $r^2 - m^2$ to 0. We have two choices, $r = m$ and $r = -m$, and we disregard the second possibility. In so doing, we may be restricting our attention to solutions of Equation 34-1 that are bounded near $x = 0$. If you need to know about unbounded solutions of Bessel's Equation, you can consult References [2] or [5].

    Now that Equation 34-2 is satisfied, we turn to Equation 34-3, which, since $r = m$, now reads $(2m + 1) c_1 = 0$. Because we are supposing that $m \geq 0$, we must have $c_1 = 0$. The remaining coefficients are determined from Equation 34-4. This formula expresses each coefficient in terms of the one that is two indices back. Since $c_1 = 0$, all coefficients with odd subscripts are 0. Thus, we only need to calculate terms with even subscripts, and so we will set $j = 2k$ in Equation 34-4 (and put $r = m$) and write it as

$$(34\text{-}6) \qquad c_{2k} = -\frac{c_{2k-2}}{4k(m + k)}, \; k = 1, 2, 3, \ldots$$

Formula 34-6 tells us that $c_2 = -c_0/4(m + 1)$, $c_4 = -c_2/4 \cdot 2(m + 2) = c_0/2^4 \cdot 1 \cdot 2(m + 1)(m + 2)$, and so on. It is clear that all the coefficients are multiples of c_0, so we see that for each choice of c_0,

$$(34\text{-}7) \quad y = c_0 x^m \left[1 - \frac{1}{2^2(m + 1)} x^2 + \frac{1}{2^4 \cdot 1 \cdot 2(m + 1)(m + 2)} x^4 - \cdots \right]$$

satisfies Equation 34-1. Furthermore, since $m \geq 0$, the solution defined by this equation is bounded near 0; in fact, if $m > 0$, the solution takes the value 0 when $x = 0$.

By replacing c_0 with specific numbers in Equation 34-7, we obtain specific solutions of Bessel's Equation. The choice

$$(34\text{-}8) \qquad\qquad c_0 = \frac{1}{2^m m!}$$

yields the **Bessel Function of the First Kind** of index m. This function is named J_m. (If m is not an integer, we have to extend our concept of $m!$ a little before we can use Equation 34-8. Rather than make this extension here, let us suppose that m is a non-negative integer from now on.) We are not going to discuss Bessel functions of the second kind, or the third kind, or any other kind. There are many different Bessel functions, with varying properties. Each is useful for certain things. The major distinguishing property of Bessel functions of the first kind of index $m \geq 0$ is that they (and of course constant multiples of them) are the only solutions of Equation 34-1 that are bounded near $x = 0$.

We have defined $J_m(x)$ as the sum of the series in Equation 34-5, where $r = m$, the coefficients with odd indices are 0, c_0 is given by Equation 34-8, and the remaining coefficients are calculated from Formula 34-6. In Exercise 34-3, we are going to ask you to show that this series converges for all x, but, of course, it is only practical to use it when x is close to 0.

Example 34-1. Write a table of values of J_1 at the points of the set $\{3, 3.1, 3.2, \ldots, 4.0\}$.

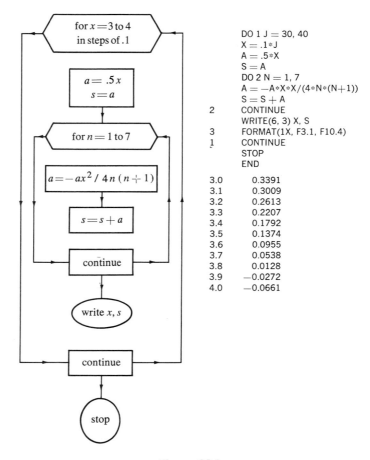

Figure 34-1

Solution. The forms of the flow chart and computer program shown in Fig. 34-1 are familiar. In the outer loop, we let x vary from 3 to 4 in steps of .1. For each such x, we think of our series as $\sum_{k=0}^{\infty} a_k$. Here, $m = 1$, so $c_0 = .5$, and hence $a_0 = .5x$. We are going to regard S_7 as a satisfactory approximation to the sum of our series (the value of $J_1(x)$), and the inner loop is therefore designed to calculate S_n for $n = 1, 2, \ldots , 7$. According to Equation 34-6 with $m = 1$, the nth term of the series is obtained by multiplying its predecessor by $-x^2/4n(1 + n)$, and, of course, $S_n = S_{n-1} + a_n$. When we find S_7, we write it and go on to the next value of x. Right after our program, we have listed its output.

As Example 34-1 illustrates, we don't need an explicit formula for c_{2k} to calculate $J_m(x)$; Recursion Formula 34-6 is enough. This formula is so simple, however, that it is easy to express c_{2k} directly in terms of k. Thus, from Equations 34-8 and 34-6,

$$c_2 = -\frac{1}{4 \cdot 1(m+1)}\frac{1}{2^m m!} = -\frac{1}{2^{m+2} \cdot 1 \cdot (m+1)!}.$$

Then,

$$c_4 = -\frac{c_2}{4 \cdot 2 \cdot (m+2)} = \frac{1}{2^{m+4} 2!(m+2)!},$$

$$c_6 = -\frac{c_4}{4 \cdot 3 \cdot (m+3)} = \frac{1}{2^{m+6} 3!(m+3)!},$$

and so on. It is therefore quite clear (if you doubt it, write out a few more terms) that

(34-9) $$c_{2k} = \frac{(-1)^k}{2^{m+2k} k!(m+k)!}.$$

Since $J_m(x) = x^m(c_0 + c_2 x^2 + c_4 x^4 + \cdots) = \sum_{k=0}^{\infty} c_{2k} x^{m+2k}$, finally,

(34-10) $$J_m(x) = \sum_{k=0}^{\infty} \frac{(-1)^k}{k!(m+k)!}\left(\frac{x}{2}\right)^{m+2k} = \left(\frac{x}{2}\right)^m \sum_{k=0}^{\infty} \frac{(-1)^k}{k!(m+k)!}\left(\frac{x}{2}\right)^{2k}.$$

Example 34-2. Find $\lim\limits_{x \downarrow 0} \dfrac{J_5'(x)}{J_4(x)}$.

Solution. We have

$$J_5(x) = \frac{1}{5!}\left(\frac{x}{2}\right)^5 - \frac{1}{6!}\left(\frac{x}{2}\right)^7 + \cdots, \text{ and } J_4(x) = \frac{1}{4!}\left(\frac{x}{2}\right)^4 - \frac{1}{5!}\left(\frac{x}{2}\right)^6 + \cdots.$$

Therefore,

$$\frac{J_5'(x)}{J_4(x)} = \frac{\dfrac{1}{2\cdot 4!}\left(\dfrac{x}{2}\right)^4 - \dfrac{7}{2\cdot 6!}\left(\dfrac{x}{2}\right)^6 + \cdots}{\dfrac{1}{4!}\left(\dfrac{x}{2}\right)^4 - \dfrac{1}{5!}\left(\dfrac{x}{2}\right)^6 + \cdots}.$$

Now divide the numerator and denominator of this fraction by $\left(\dfrac{x}{2}\right)^4$ and let $x \downarrow 0$, and you will see that $\lim\limits_{x \downarrow 0} J_5'(x)/J_4(x) = \frac{1}{2}$.

Example 34-3.   Show that $J_0'(x) = -J_1(x)$.

Solution. Since $J_0(x) = \displaystyle\sum_{k=0}^{\infty} \frac{(-1)^k}{k!k!} \left(\frac{x}{2}\right)^{2k}$, we have

$$J_0'(x) = \sum_{k=1}^{\infty} \frac{(-1)^k}{k!k!} \frac{2k}{2} \left(\frac{x}{2}\right)^{2k-1} = -\sum_{k=1}^{\infty} \frac{(-1)^{k-1}}{(k-1)!k!} \left(\frac{x}{2}\right)^{2k-1}.$$

In this last sum, make the substitution $j = k - 1$, and obtain the equation

$$J_0'(x) = -\sum_{j=0}^{\infty} \frac{(-1)^j}{j!(1+j)!} \left(\frac{x}{2}\right)^{2j+1} = -J_1(x).$$

EXERCISE 34

1. Show that, for each m, $J_m(-x) = (-1)^m J_m(x)$.

2. Find $\displaystyle\lim_{x \downarrow 0} J_m'(x)/J_{m-1}(x)$.

3. Use the ratio test to show that our series whose sum is $J_m(x)$ converges for all x.

4. Use mathematical induction to verify Formula 34-9.

5. Find $\displaystyle\lim_{x \downarrow 0} J_6(x)/P_6(x)$.

6. What is $\displaystyle\lim_{x \downarrow 0} J_5(x)$? Have we done anything in this section that would help us find $\displaystyle\lim_{x \uparrow \infty} J_5(x)$?

7. (a) Write and run a computer program that computes the values of J_0 at the points of the set $\{2.0, 2.1, 2.2, \ldots, 3.0\}$.
   (b) Find an approximate solution of the equation $J_0(x) = 0$.
   (c) Go to the library and find a table of values of J_0, and check your table against it.

8. Use Rolle's Theorem and the identity we derived in Example 34-3 to show that between every two solutions of the equation $J_0(x) = 0$ there is a solution of the equation $J_1(x) = 0$.

9. (a) Show that for each positive integer m, $D_x(x^m J_m(x)) = x^m J_{m-1}(x)$.
   (b) Show that for each non-negative integer m,

$$D_x(x^{-m} J_m(x)) = -x^{-m} J_{m+1}(x).$$

   (c) Use the results of parts (a) and (b), together with Rolle's Theorem, to show that between two consecutive solutions of the equation $J_m(x) = 0$ there is precisely one solution of the equation $J_{m+1}(x) = 0$.

10. By carrying out the differentiations indicated in the equations of parts (a) and (b) of Exercise 34-9, and then eliminating $J_m'(x)$, derive the identity

$$J_{m-1}(x) + J_{m+1}(x) = \frac{2m}{x} J_m(x).$$

From this identity, we see that we could use tables of values of J_0 and J_1 to compute a table of values of J_2, then use it again to compute a table of values of J_3, and so on.

11. Use the equations we developed in parts (a) and (b) of Exercise 34-9 (with particular values of m) to show that $D_x \frac{1}{2}x^2[J_0(x)^2 + J_1(x)^2] = xJ_0(x)^2$, and thus derive the integration formula

$$\int xJ_0(x)^2 dx = \tfrac{1}{2}x^2[J_0(x)^2 + J_1(x)^2].$$

35 SOME ADDITIONAL FACTS ABOUT BESSEL FUNCTIONS OF THE FIRST KIND

Because we just spend a day or two studying Bessel functions, and consequently can only scratch the surface of the immense body of knowledge about them which has grown up over the years, you are likely to be a little afraid of them. You realize that you do not understand them as well as you understand such functions as the trigonometric or logarithmic functions, and so you don't feel at ease with them. Of course, if you could spend as much time studying Bessel functions as you have on the trigonometric functions, you might take a different view of the matter. At any rate, with the power series we developed in the last section, and a high speed computer, you can now make tables of values of J_m for various choices of m. In that respect, J_m and the sine function are on an equal footing. In this section, we will discuss a few more properties of Bessel functions of the first kind.

We defined the Bessel function J_m by means of an infinite series. The next example suggests a way to define J_m as the solution of a type of initial value problem that we haven't discussed before.

Example 35-1. Show that the sine function is the unique solution of the initial value problem

$$y'' + y = 0 \text{ and } \lim_{x \downarrow 0} x^{-1}y = 1.$$

Solution. We know that each solution of the differential equation $y'' + y = 0$ is defined by an equation of the form $y = c \cos x + d \sin x$. If

$$\lim_{x \downarrow 0} x^{-1}(c \cos x + d \sin x) = 1,$$

it is clear that we must have $c = 0$ and $d = 1$, so $y = \sin x$ satisfies our problem, and nothing else does.

Although Bessel's Equation has a singularity at the origin, and consequently is more difficult to work with than the simple equation $y'' + y = 0$, it is nevertheless true that the Bessel function of the first kind J_m is the unique solution of the initial value problem

$$(35\text{-}1) \qquad x^2 y'' + xy' + (x^2 - m^2)y = 0 \text{ and } \lim_{x \downarrow 0} x^{-m}y = \frac{1}{2^m m!}.$$

So, if it suits our convenience, we can think of Problem 35-1 as a defining initial value problem for J_m.

Example 35-2. Show that $J_0(x) = \dfrac{1}{\pi} \displaystyle\int_0^{\pi} \cos(x \sin t)dt.$

Solution. We will show that

$$(35\text{-}2) \qquad\qquad\qquad y = \frac{1}{\pi} \int_0^{\pi} \cos(x \sin t)dt$$

satisfies Problem 35-1 with $m = 0$. It is plain that

$$\lim_{x \downarrow 0} x^0 y = \frac{1}{\pi} \lim_{x \downarrow 0} \int_0^{\pi} \cos(x \sin t)dt = \frac{1}{\pi} \int_0^{\pi} 1 \cdot dt = 1 = \frac{1}{2^0 0!},$$

so the initial condition is satisfied. Furthermore,

$$y' = -\frac{1}{\pi} \int_0^{\pi} \sin t \sin(x \sin t)dt$$

and

$$(35\text{-}3) \qquad\qquad\qquad y'' = -\frac{1}{\pi} \int_0^{\pi} \sin^2 t \cos(x \sin t)dt.$$

Now integrate the expression for y' by parts:

$$y' = \frac{1}{\pi} \left[\cos t \sin(x \sin t) \Big|_0^{\pi} - \int_0^{\pi} x \cos^2 t \cos(x \sin t)dt \right].$$

Thus,

$$(35\text{-}4) \qquad\qquad\qquad y' = -\frac{1}{\pi} \int_0^{\pi} x \cos^2 t \cos(x \sin t)dt.$$

If we multiply Equation 35-3 by x^2, Equation 35-4 by x, and Equation 35-2 by x^2, and add, we see that

$$x^2 y'' + xy' + x^2 y = \frac{1}{\pi} \int_0^\pi [-x^2 \sin^2 t - x^2 \cos^2 t + x^2] \cos (x \sin t)dt = 0;$$

that is, y satisfies the differential equation of Problem 35-1, and our solution is complete.

Our series expression for $J_m(x)$ that we discussed in the last section is especially useful when x is small, so now we will look at the behavior of $J_m(x)$ when x is large. Suppose that we make the substitution $y = x^{-1/2}z$ in Bessel's Equation. Since $y' = x^{-1/2}z' - \frac{1}{2}x^{-3/2}z$ and $y'' = x^{-1/2}z'' - x^{-3/2}z' + \frac{3}{4}x^{-5/2}z$, the equation becomes

$$x^2(x^{-1/2}z'' - x^{-3/2}z' + \tfrac{3}{4}x^{-5/2}z) + x(x^{-1/2}z' - \tfrac{1}{2}x^{-3/2}z) + (x^2 - m^2)x^{-1/2}z = 0.$$

With a little algebra, this equation can be written as

$$(35\text{-}5) \qquad\qquad z'' + \left[1 + \frac{1 - 4m^2}{4x^2}\right] z = 0.$$

For large x, Equation 35-5 is approximately $z'' + z = 0$, an old friend. We know that each solution of this latter equation is given by an equation of the form $z = A \cos (x - \delta)$, where A and δ are determined by initial values. Therefore, we suspect that for large x a solution of Equation 35-5 is given, at least approximately, by an equation of this form. Now we multiply by $x^{-1/2}$ to obtain an approximate solution of Bessel's Equation. In particular, it seems reasonable to suppose that there are numbers A and δ such that for large x,

$$J_m(x) \sim Ax^{-1/2} \cos (x - \delta).$$

This statement is true, and it is not too hard to verify. It *is* rather difficult to find the specific numbers A and δ. The trouble is that we defined J_m as the solution of Bessel's Equation that satisfies a certain condition as $x \downarrow 0$, and now we are working with *large* x. It can, however, be shown [2] that

$$(35\text{-}6) \qquad\qquad J_m(x) \sim \sqrt{\frac{2}{\pi x}} \cos (x - \tfrac{1}{2}m\pi - \tfrac{1}{4}\pi).$$

Here, by the symbol $\sim$ we mean that $\lim_{x \uparrow \infty} x \left[J_m(x) - \sqrt{\frac{2}{\pi x}} \cos \left(x - \frac{1}{2} m\pi - \right.\right.$

$\frac{1}{4}\pi\big)\Big] = 0$. In other words, when x is large, $J_m(x)$ and $\sqrt{\dfrac{2}{\pi x}}\cos\Big(x - \dfrac{1}{2}m\pi - $

$\frac{1}{4}\pi\Big)$ are so close together that even when we multiply their difference by x, the resulting number is small.

Approximation 35-6 states that for large x, the graph of the Bessel function J_m is nearly a "damped cosine curve with amplitude $\sqrt{2/\pi x}$." Figure 35-1

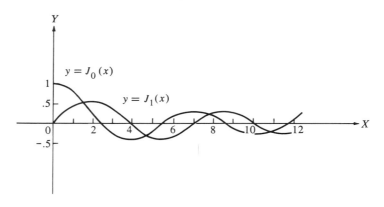

Figure 35-1

shows the graphs of J_0 and J_1. Notice, too, that Approximation 35-6 suggests (and it is true) that for each m there is an infinite sequence of positive numbers $\{z_{mn}\}$ such that $J_m(z_{mn}) = 0$, $n = 1, 2, 3, \ldots$, and these numbers are about π units apart when n is large. (Of course, the negatives of these solutions also satisfy the equation $J_m(x) = 0$, but as we said earlier, we are usually only interested in working with J_m in the interval $(0, \infty)$.) These positive zeros of J_m play an important role in certain applications of mathematics, and we will be using them in Section 41.

The next example does two things; it illustrates functional notation, and it provides us with a bit of information that we will need in Section 41.

Example 35-3. Show that $y = J_m(\sqrt{\lambda}\,x)$ satisfies the differential equation

(35-7) $$-(xy')' + \frac{m^2}{x}y = \lambda xy.$$

Solution. From the equation $y = J_m(\sqrt{\lambda}\,x)$ we obtain $y' = \sqrt{\lambda}\,J_m'(\sqrt{\lambda}\,x)$ and $y'' = \lambda J_m''(\sqrt{\lambda}\,x)$. Now J_m is a solution of Bessel's Equation of index m; that is, for any number t,

$$t^2 J_m''(t) + t J_m'(t) + (t^2 - m^2)J_m(t) = 0.$$

If we replace t with $\sqrt{\lambda}\, x$, this equation becomes

$$\lambda x^2 J_m''(\sqrt{\lambda}\, x) + \sqrt{\lambda}\, x J_m'(\sqrt{\lambda}\, x) + (\lambda x^2 - m^2) J_m(\sqrt{\lambda}\, x) = 0.$$

Now we replace $\lambda J_m''(\sqrt{\lambda}\, x)$ with y'', $\sqrt{\lambda}\, J_m'(\sqrt{\lambda}\, x)$ with y', and $J_m(\sqrt{\lambda}\, x)$ with y, and we have $x^2 y'' + xy' + (\lambda x^2 - m^2)y = 0$, which, as you can easily check is, simply another form of Equation 35-7.

EXERCISE 35

1. What is $\lim\limits_{x \uparrow \infty} J_m(x)$?

2. Is there a number z such that $J_5(z) = J_5'(z) = 0$?

3. Find two linearly independent solutions of Bessel's Equation of index $\frac{1}{2}$. (Hint: See Equation 35-5.)

4. Show that the cosine function is the solution of the initial value problem

$$y'' + y = 0 \quad \text{and} \quad \lim_{x \downarrow 0} x^{-2}(1 - y) = \tfrac{1}{2}.$$

5. As in Example 35-3, use the fact that the sine function is a solution of the equation $y'' + y = 0$ to show that $y = \sin \sqrt{\lambda}\, x$ satisfies the differential equation $-y'' = \lambda y$.

6. For reasons that we need not go into here, $\frac{1}{2}!$ is defined as $\frac{1}{2}\sqrt{\pi}$. Use Equation 35-5 to find $J_{1/2}(x)$. Does your result agree with Formula 35-6?

7. (a) Apply a change of variable of integration in our integral formula for $J_0(x)$ to show that $J_0(x) = \dfrac{2}{\pi} \displaystyle\int_0^1 \dfrac{\cos ux}{\sqrt{1 - u^2}}\, du.$

   (b) Find $J_0(0)$ from this equation.

   (c) Show that $|J_0(x)| \leq 1$ for all x.

8. Assume that we know that $(\frac{1}{3})! \approx .893$, so that $J_{1/3}(x)$ is defined as the solution of Problem 35-1 with $m = \frac{1}{3}$. Show that $y = x^{1/2} J_{1/3}(\frac{2}{3}x^{3/2})$ satisfies the differential equation $y'' + xy = 0$. Have you seen this equation before?

9. Use Formula 35-6 to approximate $J_1(\pi)$, and compare the result with the value you get from the table in Fig. 34-1.

10. A more general version of the integral formula in Example 35-2 is

$$J_m(x) = \frac{1}{\pi} \int_0^\pi \cos(x \sin t - mt)\, dt.$$

   (a) Verify this formula for $m = 1$ and $m = 2$. Can you verify it for an arbitrary non-negative integer m?

   (b) Show that $|J_m(x)| \leq 1$ for all x.

   (c) In fact, show that $|J_m^{(n)}(x)| \leq 1$ for each non-negative integer n and all x.

REVIEW EXERCISE, CHAPTER 5

Use the following exercises to test yourself on the material in this chapter.

1. Since $e^{2x} = (e^x)^2$, we can find Taylor's Series for e^{2x} about 0 either by replacing x with $2x$ in Taylor's Series for e^x or by squaring this latter series. Show that we get the same answer in either case.

2. Show that $\int_{-1}^{1} P_n(x)dx = 0$ for $n = 1, 2, \ldots$ (In Section 41, we will give a much more general set of equations, of which these are special cases.)

3. Express $J_4(x)$ in terms of $J_0(x)$ and $J_1(x)$. (Hint: You will find the formula you need in one of the exercises of this chapter.)

4. Show that the differential equation $(1 - x^2)y'' - xy' + \gamma y = 0$ has a polynomial solution if γ is the square of an integer.

5. For each number x, the equation $f(z) = (1 - 2xz + z^2)^{-1/2}$ defines a function in a neighborhood of the point $z = 0$. The coefficients of Taylor's Series for $f(z)$ about 0 depend on x, of course, and it can be shown [5] that

$$(1 - 2xz + z^2)^{-1/2} = \sum_{k=0}^{\infty} P_k(x)z^k.$$

Show that the first few coefficients of Taylor's Series for $f(z)$ about 0 really are Legendre polynomials.

6. Solve the initial value problem $y'' + 2y' + 2y = 0$ and $y = 0$, $y' = 1$ when $x = 0$ with and without using power series, and compare your answers.

7. Show that $J_0(x) = \frac{1}{\pi}\int_0^{\pi} \cos(x \cos t)dt$, and compare with our similar formula of Example 35-2.

8. Find a series in powers of x whose sum defines an *even* function that is a solution of the differential equation $y'' + x^2y = 0$.

9. In Exercise 12-10, we introduced Picard's Method of successive approximations. Apply this method to solve our standard initial value problem $y' = 1 + y^2$ and $y = 0$ when $x = 0$. Compare the result with what we found in Example 32-3.

10. (a) Show that if $x = \cos\theta$, then $D_\theta y = -\sin\theta\, D_x y$, and

$$D_\theta^2 y = D_\theta(-\sin\theta\, D_x y) = -\cos\theta\, D_x y + \sin^2\theta\, D_x^2 y.$$

(b) Hence, show that the substitution $x = \cos\theta$ changes the differential equation $\sin\theta\, D_\theta^2 y + \cos\theta\, D_\theta y + \lambda\sin\theta y = 0$ into Legendre's Equation.

CHAPTER *6*

BOUNDARY VALUE PROBLEMS

AND FOURIER SERIES

The subject of boundary value problems furnishes us with our final topic in differential equations. Such problems are especially important because, on the one hand, they arise in "practical" applications of differential equations, and on the other, their study leads in a natural way to the subject of linear operators in general. Thus, differential boundary value problems serve as a bridge connecting very practical matters with very abstract ones.

245

36 MATRICES AS LINEAR OPERATORS

We have already called your attention to the linearity of the differential operator D_x. Thus, if u and v are differentiable functions, and m and n are numbers, then

(36-1) $D_x(mu(x) + nv(x)) = mD_xu(x) + nD_xv(x).$

The derivative of a linear combination is the same linear combination of the derivatives. If p and q are continuous functions in some interval $[a, b]$, then the equation

(36-2) $L_xy = y'' + p(x)y' + q(x)y$

defines a somewhat more general **linear differential operator** L_x, one of the second order. For example, if $L_xy = y'' + 2xy' + (\sin x)y$, then

$$L_x(3x^2 + 2e^x) = 3L_xx^2 + 2L_xe^x$$
$$= 3(2 + 2x \cdot 2x + x^2 \sin x) + 2(e^x + 2xe^x + e^x \sin x)$$
$$= 6 + 12x^2 + 3x^2 \sin x + 2e^x + 4xe^x + 2e^x \sin x.$$

It is with operators like this that we will be dealing in this chapter.

Linear *differential* operators comprise only a small fraction of the class of linear operators, and we can get some insight into the way they behave by first studying a somewhat simpler type of linear operator. So we will devote this preliminary section to a consideration of *matrices* as linear operators. Suppose, for example, that we have a 2 by 2 matrix of real numbers

$$A = \begin{bmatrix} a & b \\ c & d \end{bmatrix}.$$

Then if $\mathbf{x} = (x, y)$ is an element of R^2, so is $A\mathbf{x}$. Thus, we can think of A as an *operator* that *maps* each element of R^2 into an element of R^2. Furthermore, A is a linear operator. In other words, if $\mathbf{v} = (v, w)$ is another element of R^2, and m and n are scalars, then

$$A(m\mathbf{v} + n\mathbf{x}) = mA\mathbf{v} + nA\mathbf{x},$$

an equation that is obviously analogous to Equation 36-1.

For each given $\mathbf{x} \in R^2$, there is a corresponding vector $\mathbf{r} = A\mathbf{x}$. Now let us look at this problem from the other direction. Suppose that $\mathbf{r}$ is given; can we find $\mathbf{x}$ such that $A\mathbf{x} = \mathbf{r}$? The solution of this equation is $A^{-1}\mathbf{r}$, *if* A^{-1} exists, so we are interested in those matrices that have inverses. Similarly, one of our main goals in this chapter will be to develop inverses of differential operators.

Our other major effort will be in the direction of *diagonalizing* an operator. As you recall from Section 21, it is "usually" possible to find an invertible matrix P such that

$$(36\text{-}3) \qquad\qquad P^{-1}AP = L,$$

where L is a diagonal matrix. We are going to transfer this idea to differential operators in Section 39. The problem of diagonalizing a "general" linear operator is a formidable one, and we will not attempt it. Instead, we will restrict our attention to certain *symmetric* operators. So let us now look at symmetric matrices to get an idea of what to expect from our symmetric differential operators.

A 2 by 2 **symmetric** matrix with real components has the form

$$A = \begin{bmatrix} a & b \\ b & c \end{bmatrix}.$$

The symmetry is with respect to the main diagonal. Thus, a 3 by 3 symmetric matrix looks like this:

$$\begin{bmatrix} a & b & c \\ b & d & e \\ c & e & f \end{bmatrix},$$

and so on. The basic property of symmetric matrices is illustrated in the following example.

Example 36-1. If $\mathbf{u} = (1, -2)$, $\mathbf{v} = (3, -1)$, and $A = \begin{bmatrix} 3 & 2 \\ 2 & 0 \end{bmatrix}$, show that

$$(36\text{-}4) \qquad\qquad A\mathbf{u} \cdot \mathbf{v} = \mathbf{u} \cdot A\mathbf{v}.$$

Solution. We are to show that if we apply the operator A to the vector $\mathbf{u}$ and dot the resulting vector with $\mathbf{v}$, we get the same result that we do when we apply A to $\mathbf{v}$ and dot the result with $\mathbf{u}$. So let us perform the necessary calculations. We have

$$A\mathbf{u} = \begin{bmatrix} 3 & 2 \\ 2 & 0 \end{bmatrix} \begin{pmatrix} 1 \\ -2 \end{pmatrix} = \begin{pmatrix} -1 \\ 2 \end{pmatrix},$$

and hence $A\mathbf{u} \cdot \mathbf{v} = -1 \cdot 3 + 2(-1) = -5$.

Also,

$$Av = \begin{bmatrix} 3 & 2 \\ 2 & 0 \end{bmatrix} \begin{pmatrix} 3 \\ -1 \end{pmatrix} = \begin{pmatrix} 7 \\ 6 \end{pmatrix},$$

and hence $u \cdot Av = 1 \cdot 7 + (-2) \cdot 6 = -5$.

In Example 36-1, we verified Equation 36-4 by replacing A, $\mathbf{u}$, and $\mathbf{v}$ with a specific numerical matrix and specific vectors. If we had used an arbitrary symmetric matrix, and vectors whose components were arbitrary letters, we would see that Equation 36-4 is true in general; that is, a symmetric matrix operator can be applied to either member of a dot product. Thus, we have the following theorem.

THEOREM 36-1

If A is a symmetric matrix of real numbers and $\mathbf{u}$ and $\mathbf{v}$ are vectors with real components, then Equation 36-4 is valid.

Now we will explain why a symmetric matrix of real numbers is real diagonable. As we see from Equation 36-3, the criterion for diagonability is that there exist an *invertible* matrix P whose columns are characteristic vectors of A, and A will then be *real* diagonable if these characteristic vectors have real components. Hence, the characteristic values of A must be real numbers. Let us show that they are.

THEOREM 36-2

The characteristic values of a symmetric matrix A are real numbers.

Proof. We will show that if $\lambda = \sigma + i\tau$ is a characteristic value of A, then $\tau = 0$. Suppose that $\mathbf{u} = \mathbf{p} + i\mathbf{q}$ is a corresponding characteristic vector. In Section 21 (Equations 21-9) we found that

$$A\mathbf{p} = \sigma\mathbf{p} - \tau\mathbf{q} \text{ and } A\mathbf{q} = \tau\mathbf{p} + \sigma\mathbf{q}.$$

We dot the first of these equations with $\mathbf{q}$ and the second with $\mathbf{p}$:

$$A\mathbf{p} \cdot \mathbf{q} = \sigma\mathbf{p} \cdot \mathbf{q} - \tau\mathbf{q} \cdot \mathbf{q} \text{ and } \mathbf{p} \cdot A\mathbf{q} = \tau\mathbf{p} \cdot \mathbf{p} + \sigma\mathbf{p} \cdot \mathbf{q}.$$

Therefore, the basic symmetry equation $A\mathbf{p} \cdot \mathbf{q} = \mathbf{p} \cdot A\mathbf{q}$ tells us that

$$\sigma\mathbf{p} \cdot \mathbf{q} - \tau\mathbf{q} \cdot \mathbf{q} = \tau\mathbf{p} \cdot \mathbf{p} + \sigma\mathbf{p} \cdot \mathbf{q},$$

an equation that immediately reduces to $\tau(\mathbf{p} \cdot \mathbf{p} + \mathbf{q} \cdot \mathbf{q}) = 0$; that is,

$$\tau(|\mathbf{p}|^2 + |\mathbf{q}|^2) = 0.$$

The characteristic vector $\mathbf{p} + i\mathbf{q}$ is not the vector $\mathbf{0}$ (*no* characteristic vector is $\mathbf{0}$), and so $\tau = 0$.

It will take us some time to show that there is an invertible matrix whose columns are characteristic vectors of our symmetric matrix A. The key fact is that a symmetric matrix has a set of n *orthogonal* characteristic vectors (that is, the dot product of two of them is 0). This statement is based on the following theorem.

THEOREM 36-3

If $\mathbf{u}_1$ and $\mathbf{u}_2$ are characteristic vectors of a real symmetric matrix A that correspond to different characteristic values λ_1 and λ_2, then $\mathbf{u}_1 \cdot \mathbf{u}_2 = 0$.

Proof. We are supposing that

$$A\mathbf{u}_1 = \lambda_1\mathbf{u}_1 \text{ and } A\mathbf{u}_2 = \lambda_2\mathbf{u}_2.$$

If we dot the first of these equations with $\mathbf{u}_2$ and the second with $\mathbf{u}_1$ and subtract, we obtain the equation

$$A\mathbf{u}_1 \cdot \mathbf{u}_2 - \mathbf{u}_1 \cdot A\mathbf{u}_2 = (\lambda_1 - \lambda_2)\mathbf{u}_1 \cdot \mathbf{u}_2.$$

Equation 36-4 tells us that the left-hand side of this equation is 0, and since we are assuming that $\lambda_1 \neq \lambda_2$, it follows that $\mathbf{u}_1 \cdot \mathbf{u}_2 = 0$.

Example 36-2. Find the characteristic values and corresponding characteristic vectors of the symmetric matrix A of Example 36-1.

Solution. The characteristic equation of our matrix is

$$\det(\lambda I - A) = \begin{vmatrix} \lambda - 3 & -2 \\ -2 & \lambda \end{vmatrix} = (\lambda - 3)\lambda - 4 = (\lambda - 4)(\lambda + 1) = 0.$$

Its solutions are the numbers $\lambda_1 = -1$ and $\lambda_2 = 4$. To find a characteristic vector $\mathbf{u}_1$ corresponding to -1, we must solve the equation $A\mathbf{u}_1 = -\mathbf{u}_1$, or $(A + I)\mathbf{u}_1 = \mathbf{0}$. In component form, this equation reads

$$\begin{bmatrix} 4 & 2 \\ 2 & 1 \end{bmatrix}\begin{pmatrix} u_1 \\ v_1 \end{pmatrix} = \begin{pmatrix} 0 \\ 0 \end{pmatrix}.$$

It is therefore clear that we can take $\mathbf{u}_1 = (u_1, v_1) = (1, -2)$. The equation that we must solve to find a vector $\mathbf{u}_2$ such that $A\mathbf{u}_2 = 4\mathbf{u}_2$ is $(A - 4I)\mathbf{u}_2 = 0$; that is,

$$\begin{bmatrix} -1 & 2 \\ 2 & -4 \end{bmatrix} \begin{pmatrix} u_2 \\ v_2 \end{pmatrix} = \begin{pmatrix} 0 \\ 0 \end{pmatrix}.$$

Clearly, $\mathbf{u}_2 = (u_2, v_2) = (2, 1)$ satisfies it. Now notice that

$$\mathbf{u}_1 \cdot \mathbf{u}_2 = 1 \cdot 2 + (-2) \cdot 1 = 0,$$

in agreement with Theorem 36-3.

Theorem 36-3 states that characteristic vectors corresponding to *different* characteristic values must be orthogonal. What if a given n by n matrix does not have n different characteristic values? For example, what if a 2 by 2 symmetric matrix A has only one characteristic value λ? Then we have to *choose* some of our characteristic vectors so as to obtain an orthogonal set. The important point is that such a choice is always possible. Thus, it is not hard to show that a 2 by 2 symmetric matrix with only one characteristic value must have the simple form $A = \begin{bmatrix} \lambda & 0 \\ 0 & \lambda \end{bmatrix}$. It is easy to find orthogonal characteristic vectors for this matrix; we could choose $\mathbf{u}_1 = (1, 0)$ and $\mathbf{u}_2 = (0, 1)$, for instance. In higher dimensions, the details are more difficult, but the result is the same.

THEOREM 36-4

An n by n symmetric matrix of real numbers has a set $\{\mathbf{u}_1, \mathbf{u}_2, \ldots, \mathbf{u}_n\}$ of n characteristic vectors such that $\mathbf{u}_i \cdot \mathbf{u}_j = 0$ if $i \neq j$.

We need to introduce one more concept before we show that every symmetric matrix is diagonable. If $\mathbf{u}$ is a characteristic vector of a matrix A, then so is $p\mathbf{u}$, where p is any non-zero number. Thus, the vectors $(2, 1)$, $(4, 2)$, $(-2, -1)$, and so on, are all characteristic vectors, corresponding to the characteristic value 4, of the matrix A of Example 36-1. If we multiply a given characteristic vector $\mathbf{u}$ by the reciprocal of its length, $1/|\mathbf{u}|$, the resulting characteristic vector is, of course, 1 unit long. This process is called *normalization*, and since it is (in concept) so simple, we often just suppose that our characteristic vectors have been normalized; that is, that they are chosen so as to be 1 unit long.

Example 36-3. Normalize the characteristic vectors we found in Example 36-2.

Solution. The length of the vector $\mathbf{u}_1 = (1, -2)$ is the number $|\mathbf{u}_1| = \sqrt{1 + 4} = \sqrt{5}$, so the corresponding normalized characteristic vector is $(1/\sqrt{5}, -2/\sqrt{5})$.

Similarly, $|\mathbf{u}_2| = \sqrt{4+1} = \sqrt{5}$, and so the corresponding normalized characteristic vector is $(2/\sqrt{5}, 1/\sqrt{5})$.

We are finally in a position to write down an invertible matrix P whose columns are characteristic vectors of a given symmetric matrix A. As usual, we treat only the 2 by 2 case explicitly. Suppose that $\mathbf{u}_1$ and $\mathbf{u}_2$ are normalized orthogonal characteristic vectors of A, and let P be the matrix whose columns are $\mathbf{u}_1$ and $\mathbf{u}_2$ ($P = [\mathbf{u}_1 \quad \mathbf{u}_2]$). To show that P is invertible, we will simply display its inverse. Thus, let Q be the matrix whose *rows* are $\mathbf{u}_1$ and $\mathbf{u}_2$ $\left(Q = \begin{bmatrix} \mathbf{u}_1 \\ \mathbf{u}_2 \end{bmatrix}\right)$. If you analyze the definition of matrix multiplication, you will see that

$$QP = \begin{bmatrix} \mathbf{u}_1 \cdot \mathbf{u}_1 & \mathbf{u}_2 \cdot \mathbf{u}_1 \\ \mathbf{u}_1 \cdot \mathbf{u}_2 & \mathbf{u}_2 \cdot \mathbf{u}_2 \end{bmatrix}.$$

But we have chosen our vectors so that $\mathbf{u}_1 \cdot \mathbf{u}_1 = \mathbf{u}_2 \cdot \mathbf{u}_2 = 1$ and $\mathbf{u}_1 \cdot \mathbf{u}_2 = 0$. Therefore, $QP = I$; that is, $Q = P^{-1}$. In general, if $\{\mathbf{u}_1, \ldots, \mathbf{u}_n\}$ is a set of normalized orthogonal characteristic vectors of an n by n symmetric matrix A, then the matrix $P = [\mathbf{u}_1 \cdots \mathbf{u}_n]$ is invertible (its inverse is simply the matrix whose *rows* are the given characteristic vectors). So the diagonability of A follows immediately from the existence of n orthogonal characteristic vectors.

Example 36-4. Find an invertible matrix P whose columns are characteristic vectors of the matrix A of Example 36-1.

Solution. We can use the normalized characteristic vectors we found in Example 36-3 to construct the matrix

$$P = \begin{bmatrix} 1/\sqrt{5} & 2/\sqrt{5} \\ -2/\sqrt{5} & 1/\sqrt{5} \end{bmatrix} = \frac{1}{\sqrt{5}} \begin{bmatrix} 1 & 2 \\ -2 & 1 \end{bmatrix}.$$

Notice that $P^{-1} = \dfrac{1}{\sqrt{5}} \begin{bmatrix} 1 & -2 \\ 2 & 1 \end{bmatrix}$.

We have said that a matrix A is diagonable if, and only if, there is an invertible matrix $P = [\mathbf{u}_1 \quad \mathbf{u}_2]$ whose columns are characteristic vectors of A. For our work with differential operators, we will want to word this diagonability condition a little differently. Since P is invertible, there exists a matrix P^{-1} such that $PP^{-1} = I$. Hence, for each vector $\mathbf{w} \in R^2$, we have $\mathbf{w} = PP^{-1}\mathbf{w} = P\mathbf{x}$, where we have written $\mathbf{x}$ in place of $P^{-1}\mathbf{w}$. When we defined the product of a vector by a matrix (Equation 18-8), we pointed out that the product vector is a linear combination of the columns of the matrix. Thus, if $\mathbf{x} = (x, y)$, then the equation $\mathbf{w} = P\mathbf{x}$ states that

(36-5) $$\mathbf{w} = x\mathbf{u}_1 + y\mathbf{u}_2.$$

In other words, *each vector in R^2 can be expressed as a linear combination of two characteristic vectors of A*. Of course, the same result holds for $n > 2$; for each n by n diagonable matrix, there are sets of n characteristic vectors that "generate" R^n.

   If A is a symmetric matrix, we can assume that the columns of the diagonalizing matrix P are orthogonal, and then the formulas by which we calculate the coefficients x and y in Equation 36-5 are both simple and important. To find the formula for x, we merely dot both sides of the equation with $\mathbf{u}_1$:

$$\mathbf{w} \cdot \mathbf{u}_1 = x\mathbf{u}_1 \cdot \mathbf{u}_1 + y\mathbf{u}_2 \cdot \mathbf{u}_1.$$

Since $\mathbf{u}_1$ and $\mathbf{u}_2$ are orthogonal, $\mathbf{u}_2 \cdot \mathbf{u}_1 = 0$, so $\mathbf{w} \cdot \mathbf{u}_1 = x\mathbf{u}_1 \cdot \mathbf{u}_1 = x|\mathbf{u}_1|^2$; that is, $x = \mathbf{w} \cdot \mathbf{u}_1/|\mathbf{u}_1|^2$. Similarly, of course, $y = \mathbf{w} \cdot \mathbf{u}_2/|\mathbf{u}_2|^2$. If $\mathbf{u}_1$ and $\mathbf{u}_2$ were normalized characteristic vectors (that is, $|\mathbf{u}_1| = |\mathbf{u}_2| = 1$), then x and y would simply be the numbers $\mathbf{w} \cdot \mathbf{u}_1$ and $\mathbf{w} \cdot \mathbf{u}_2$. We can thus state the following theorem, which we will later carry over to differential operators.

THEOREM 36-5

If A is a symmetric n by n matrix of real numbers, then every vector $\mathbf{w} \in R^n$ can be expressed as a linear combination of n orthogonal characteristic vectors $\{\mathbf{u}_1, \ldots, \mathbf{u}_n\}$ of A. In this combination, the coefficient of the characteristic vector $\mathbf{u}_i$ is the number $\mathbf{w} \cdot \mathbf{u}_i/|\mathbf{u}_i|^2$.

Example 36-5. Express the vector $\mathbf{w} = (3, -5)$ as a linear combination of characteristic vectors of the matrix of Example 36-1.

Solution. According to Theorem 36-5,

$$\mathbf{w} = \frac{\mathbf{w} \cdot \mathbf{u}_1}{|\mathbf{u}_1|^2}\mathbf{u}_1 + \frac{\mathbf{w} \cdot \mathbf{u}_2}{|\mathbf{u}_2|^2}\mathbf{u}_2,$$

where $\mathbf{u}_1 = (1, -2)$ and $\mathbf{u}_2 = (2, 1)$, as we found in Example 36-2. Thus, $\mathbf{w} \cdot \mathbf{u}_1/|\mathbf{u}_1|^2 = \frac{13}{5}$ and $\mathbf{w} \cdot \mathbf{u}_2/|\mathbf{u}_2|^2 = \frac{1}{5}$, and so

$$(3, -5) = \tfrac{13}{5}(1, -2) + \tfrac{1}{5}(2, 1),$$

an obviously correct equation.

We have not gone very deeply into the theory of symmetric matrices, to say nothing of the theory of symmetric linear operators in general. But perhaps you have got some idea of the key role that Equation 36-4 plays in showing that symmetric operators have real characteristic values and orthogonal characteristic vectors. Symmetric operators have been studied at all levels of generality, and they find their way into all sorts of applications of mathematics.

EXERCISE 36

1. Solve the equation $A\mathbf{x} = (3, 3)$ for each of the following choices of A. How does Theorem 18-1 apply?

   (a) $A = \begin{bmatrix} 2 & 1 \\ 1 & 1 \end{bmatrix}$ (b) $A = \begin{bmatrix} 1 & -1 \\ 1 & -1 \end{bmatrix}$ (c) $A = \begin{bmatrix} 1 & 1 \\ -1 & -1 \end{bmatrix}$

2. Verify Equation 36-4 if A is an arbitrary symmetric 2 by 2 matrix of real numbers, $A = \begin{bmatrix} a & b \\ b & c \end{bmatrix}$, and $\mathbf{u}$ and $\mathbf{v}$ are arbitrary elements of R^2.

3. (a) Show that the vectors $\mathbf{u}_1 = (3, 4)$ and $\mathbf{u}_2 = (4, -3)$ are orthogonal.
   (b) Normalize $\mathbf{u}_1$ and $\mathbf{u}_2$.
   (c) Express $\mathbf{w} = (1, 1)$ as a linear combination of $\mathbf{u}_1$ and $\mathbf{u}_2$, and show that your result agrees with the last sentence of Theorem 36-5.

4. Let $S = \begin{bmatrix} 1 & 1 \\ 1 & 1 \end{bmatrix}$.

   (a) Find the characteristic values of S.
   (b) Find corresponding normalized characteristic vectors.
   (c) Express the vector $\mathbf{w} = (3, -2)$ as a linear combination of these characteristic vectors.
   (d) Find a matrix P such that $P^{-1}SP$ is diagonal.

5. Let $A = \begin{bmatrix} 7 & 3 \\ 3 & -1 \end{bmatrix}$.

   (a) Find the characteristic values of A.
   (b) Find corresponding characteristic vectors $\mathbf{u}_1$ and $\mathbf{u}_2$.
   (c) Express the vector $\mathbf{w} = (3, -2)$ as a linear combination of $\mathbf{u}_1$ and $\mathbf{u}_2$.

6. Is the sum of two symmetric matrices necessarily symmetric? A product? If A is symmetric, does it necessarily follow that e^{At} is symmetric?

7. The characteristic values of the symmetric matrix $A = \begin{bmatrix} a & b \\ b & c \end{bmatrix}$ are the solutions of the characteristic equation $\det(\lambda I - A) = 0$. Use the quadratic formulas to show that if the elements of A are real numbers, then characteristic values of A are real.

8. Write a computer program for which the input consists of the three different elements of a 2 by 2 symmetric matrix A and the output consists of the characteristic values of A. Can you also output characteristic vectors?

9. Let λ_1 be the smaller and λ_2 be the larger characteristic value of the symmetric matrix $S = \begin{bmatrix} 2 & 1 \\ 1 & 2 \end{bmatrix}$. Show that if $\mathbf{x}$ is any element of R^2, then

$$\lambda_1 |\mathbf{x}|^2 \leq S\mathbf{x} \cdot \mathbf{x} \leq \lambda_2 |\mathbf{x}|^2.$$

(This useful inequality holds for *all* symmetric matrices, of any order.)

10. Suppose that $\mathbf{u}_1$ and $\mathbf{u}_2$ are orthogonal (but not necessarily normalized) characteristic vectors of a symmetric matrix. Show that $P = [\mathbf{u}_1 \quad \mathbf{u}_2]$ is invertible.

11. Explain why the operator L_x defined by Equation 36-2 is linear.

37 THE INVERSE OF A DIFFERENTIAL OPERATOR: INITIAL CONDITIONS

Now we will begin to transfer some of the things we know about matrix operators to linear differential operators of the second order. In this section and the next, we will discuss the inverses of such operators, and after that we turn to the very interesting study of the characteristic values and characteristic "vectors" of a symmetric linear differential operator.

Let us preface our discussion of differential operators by disposing of a notational fine point. Throughout this book, we have been using the differential operator D_x, which we apply to *functional values*. Thus, cos x is a value of the cosine function, and $D_x \cos x = -\sin x$. Associated with D_x in an obvious way is a differential operator D that applies to *functions*. Thus, $D \cos = -\sin$. Since many mathematicians think that our distinction between D and D_x is too fine to bother with, we will not harp on it here. We will, however, use an analogous notation as we talk about other differential operators in the sections ahead. We will apply the differential operator L_x to the *functional value* $u(x)$, and the corresponding differential operator L to the *function* u. If this hairsplitting bothers you, ignore it and devote your full attention to the main ideas.

Suppose that p and q are continuous functions in some interval (a, b), and let $L_x y = y'' + p(x)y' + q(x)y$. If r is a given continuous function, then the differential equation

(37-1) $L_x y = r(x)$

is analogous to the algebraic equation $A\mathbf{x} = \mathbf{r}$ that we mentioned in the last section. If our differential operator L had an inverse, Equation 37-1 would be satisfied by $y = L^{-1}r(x)$.

But L does not have an inverse, and it is easy to see why not. We simply have to think about what we mean by the inverse of an operator (or a function). From what we said about inverses in Section 3, we know that the condition for L to be invertible is that Equation 37-1 have *exactly one* solution for each choice of r in the range of L. Our difficulty is that this equation has too many solutions. For example, the simple differential equation $y'' = 6x$ is satisfied by $y = x^3$, $y = x^3 + 3x - 1$, $y = x^3 - 1492x + 1776$, and so on. The situation is analogous to the one we face when we try to find inverses of the trigonometric functions. For example, the equation $\sin x = \frac{1}{2}$ is satisfied by $x = \frac{1}{6}\pi$, $x = \frac{5}{6}\pi$, $x = \frac{13}{6}\pi$, and so on. So we proceed now just as we did for the trigonometric functions; we *restrict the domain* of L.

Thus, we are naturally led to the question, "What is the domain of our operator?" This question is really the most basic (and difficult) one that arises in the study of differential operators and their inverses. It becomes especially crucial when we study boundary value problems. The answers we give to this question for the operators we deal with in this chapter, though perhaps sufficient for an introductory course, tell far less than the whole story.

The domain of a differential operator L is a set of functions. Since we will be calculating second derivatives, we want to be sure to consider only functions that *have* second derivatives, of course. For example, we cannot apply the operator D_x^2 to $|x|$ if our basic interval (a, b) contains the point 0. We will therefore take as the domain of L the set of all functions whose second derived functions are continuous at each point of (a, b). It is customary to use the symbol $C''(a, b)$ to denote this class of functions. For example, if abs is the absolute value function, then abs $\in C''(0, 1)$, but abs $\notin C''(-1, 1)$.

By restricting the domain of L, we mean choosing a subset M of $C''(a, b)$ and defining a new operator L_0 whose domain is M and such that for a given function $u \in M$, we have $L_{0x}u(x) = L_xu(x)$ for each $x \in (a, b)$. We want to make this choice of M so that L_0 has an inverse; that is, so that the equation $L_{0}y = r(x)$ has a *unique* solution. Written out, the equation $L_xy = r(x)$ is $y'' + p(x)y' + q(x)y = r(x)$, and we studied such second order equations in Chapter Four. There, we found that if we select a point x_0 in our basic interval (a, b), and two numbers y_0 and y_1, and adjoin the *initial conditions* $y = y_0$, $y' = y_1$ when $x = x_0$ to our differential equation, we obtain a problem that has only one solution. So that is what we will do here. We will select an arbitrary point x_0 in (a, b) and take as y_0 and y_1 the number 0. Then we define M to consist of those members of $C''(a, b)$ whose value at x_0 is 0 and whose first derived function also has the value 0 at x_0. Thus,

$$M = \{u: u \in C''(a, b), u(x_0) = u'(x_0) = 0\}.$$

Figure 37-1 shows the graph of a typical member u of M. We chose y_0 and y_1 to be 0 so that M would be a *linear space*; that is, linear combinations of members

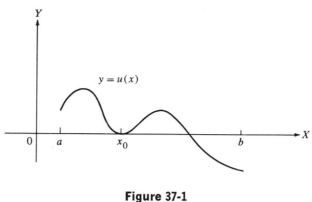

Figure 37-1

of M are also in M. This fact is important, since we want our restriction of L to M to be a linear operator.

With this choice of M as the domain of L_0, the single equation $L_{0x}y = r(x)$ is equivalent to the initial value problem

(37-2) $\qquad\qquad L_x y = r(x)$ and $y = 0, y' = 0$ when $x = x_0$.

(In exactly the same way, the single equation $\operatorname{Sin} x = \frac{1}{2}$ is equivalent to the *two* relations $\sin x = \frac{1}{2}$ and $x \in [-\frac{1}{2}\pi, \frac{1}{2}\pi]$.) This initial value problem, we know, has a unique solution, so we have indeed produced an operator with an inverse.

Let us remark that because L_0 is a *linear* operator, it would only have been possible for the equation $L_{0x}y = r(x)$ to have two solutions if the homogeneous equation $L_{0x}y = 0$ had a non-trivial solution. For suppose that u_1 and u_2 were two solutions of the equation $L_{0x}y = r(x)$. Then $L_{0x}(u_1(x) - u_2(x)) = r(x) - r(x) = 0$; that is, $y = u_1(x) - u_2(x)$ satisfies the homogeneous equation. If for some x this difference were not 0, the homogeneous equation would have a non-trivial solution. As was the case with matrices (Theorem 18-1), the invertibility of our linear operator L_0 really hinges upon the question of whether or not the homogeneous equation $L_{0x}y = 0$ has only the trivial solution, the constant function with value 0.

Not only does our previous theory of linear differential equations of the second order tell us that L_0 has an inverse, it even tells us what that inverse is. For except for a slight change of letters, Problem 37-2 is identical with Problem 23-8, and Equation 23-7 gives the solution of that problem. Thus, we already know that if u and v are linearly independent solutions of the equation $L_x y = 0$, and $W(u(x), v(x))$ is their Wronskian, then $y = \displaystyle\int_{x_0}^{x} \dfrac{u(t)v(x) - u(x)v(t)}{W(u(t), v(t))} r(t)\,dt$ satisfies

Problem 37-2. Therefore, we can write

(37-3)
$$L_0^{-1}r(x) = \int_{x_0}^{x} \frac{u(t)v(x) - u(x)v(t)}{W(u(t), v(t))} r(t)dt.$$

Example 37-1. Find L_0^{-1} if $L_x y = y'' - 3y'$ and $x_0 = 0$.

Solution. Two linearly independent solutions of the equation $y'' - 3y' = 0$ are defined by the equations $u(x) = 1$ and $v(x) = e^{3x}$. Therefore,

$$W(u(x), v(x)) = \begin{vmatrix} 1 & e^{3x} \\ 0 & 3e^{3x} \end{vmatrix} = 3e^{3x},$$

and so Equation 37-3 becomes

$$L_0^{-1}r(x) = \int_0^x \frac{e^{3x} - e^{3t}}{3e^{3t}} r(t)dt = \frac{1}{3}\int_0^x (e^{3(x-t)} - 1)r(t)dt.$$

The inverse of the *differential* operator L_0 is the *integral* operator L_0^{-1} defined by Equation 37-3. If we write

$$K(x, t) = \frac{u(t)v(x) - u(x)v(t)}{W(u(t), v(t))},$$

then that equation can be abbreviated as

(37-4)
$$L_0^{-1}r(x) = \int_{x_0}^{x} K(x, t)r(t)dt.$$

We call $K(x, t)$ the **kernel** of the integral operator L_0^{-1}.

Example 37-2.   Find $L_0^{-1}r(x)$ if L_0 is the operator of Example 37-1 and $r(x) = 2x$.

Solution. In Example 37-1, we found that the kernel of L_0^{-1} is $\frac{1}{3}(e^{3(x-t)} - 1)$. Therefore, since $r(x) = 2x$ and $x_0 = 0$, Equation 37-4 becomes

$$L_0^{-1}r(x) = \frac{1}{3}\int_0^x (e^{3(x-t)} - 1)2t\,dt = [-\tfrac{2}{9}te^{3(x-t)} - \tfrac{2}{27}e^{3(x-t)} - \tfrac{1}{3}t^2]\Big|_0^x$$

$$= -\tfrac{2}{9}x - \tfrac{2}{27} - \tfrac{1}{3}x^2 + \tfrac{2}{27}e^{3x}.$$

The material we have presented in this section is not new. The language may be unfamiliar, but the ideas are not. After all, the equation $L_0 y = r(x)$ is equivalent to Initial Value Problem 37-2, and we studied such problems at considerable length in Chapter Four. Our goal in this section is to set the stage for the study of the inverse of a linear differential operator that we obtain from L by restricting its domain to a different class of functions than we used here. We will make that study in the next section. By wording some of our results of Chapter Four in the language of operators and their inverses, we are able to introduce new concepts, such as integral operators and their kernels, that will play key roles in the next section. There, we will be dealing with really new material.

EXERCISE 37

1. Suppose that $L_xy = y''$ and $x_0 = 0$.
   (a) What is the general formula for $L_0^{-1}r(x)$?
   (b) What is the formula for $L_0^{-1}r(x)$ if $r(x) = 6x$?
   (c) Answer the questions in parts (a) and (b) if $x_0 = 1$.

2. Suppose that $L_xy = y'' + y$ and $x_0 = 0$.
   (a) What is $K(x, t)$?
   (b) What is $L_0^{-1}r(x)$ if $r(x) = x$?

3. Suppose that $L_xy = y'' - y$ and $x_0 = 0$.
   (a) What is $K(x, t)$?
   (b) What is $L_0^{-1}r(x)$ if $r(x) = e^x$?

4. Suppose that $L_xy = y'' - 4x^{-1}y' + 6x^{-2}y$ and that $x_0 = 1$.
   (a) Notice that the equation $L_xy = 0$ is Euler's Equation (Exercise 24-9), and so you can find two linearly independent solutions by setting $y = x^r$ and determining r. Do it.
   (b) What is $K(x, t)$?
   (c) What is $L_0^{-1}r(x)$ if $r(x) = 12x^4$?

5. We know that $y = L_0^{-1}r(x)$ satisfies the initial value problem $L_xy = r(x)$ and $y = 0$, $y' = 0$ when $x = x_0$. Show that it is possible to choose numbers c and d such that $y = cu(x) + dv(x) + L_0^{-1}r(x)$ satisfies the initial value problem $L_xy = r(x)$ and $y = y_0$, $y' = y_1$ when $x = x_0$, where y_0 and y_1 *need not* be 0. (We are assuming that u and v are linearly independent solutions of the homogeneous differential equation $L_xy = 0$.)

6. Let $K(x, t)$ be the kernel defined in the text, and show that if x_0 and x_1 are two points of our basic interval (a, b), then $y = \int_{x_0}^{x_1} K(x, t)r(t)dt$ satisfies the equation $L_xy = 0$ for each continuous function r.

7. Is L_0^{-1} a *linear* operator? What is $(L_0^{-1})^{-1}$?

8. Let L_0 be the operator of Exercise 37-1, and suppose that $u(x) = L_0^{-1}r(x)$, where $r(x) = \sqrt{1 + x^3}$. Write a computer program to print the values of u at the points of the set $\{0, 1, 2, 3, 4, 5\}$.

9. Suppose that L is the linear differential operator of the first order defined by the equation $L_xy = y' + p(x)y$, where p is a given function that is continuous in the interval (a, b). How might we restrict the domain of L to construct an

operator L_0 that has an inverse? Express this inverse operator as an integral operator.

10. Show that, given our hypotheses on its domain and the continuity of its coefficients, the range of the operator L defined by the equation $L_x y = y'' + p(x)y' + q(x)y$ is the set of functions continuous in the interval (a, b). What is the range of L_0?

38 THE INVERSE OF A DIFFERENTIAL OPERATOR: BOUNDARY CONDITIONS

In the last section, we restricted the domain of a linear differential operator L, where $L_x y = y'' + p(x)v' + q(x)y$, to a class of functions that satisfied two *initial conditions* and thus obtained an operator L_0 that had an inverse. Now we are going to restrict the domain of L to a class of functions that satisfy two *boundary conditions*, and again we will obtain an operator with an inverse. We pointed out that the material in the last section was simply a rewording of some of the things we studied earlier; the material in this section is new.

Since we are going to be considering its boundary points, we will think of the basic interval in which we are now working as the closed interval $[a, b]$ (rather than the open interval (a, b) we talked about in the last section). And we will suppose that our coefficient functions p and q are continuous in this closed interval. As before, we will take as the domain of L the set of functions with continuous second derived functions in the basic interval. Of course, when we talk about derivatives of a function at the left and right endpoints, we mean derivatives from the right and from the left. We denote this class of functions by $C''[a, b]$.

Thus, our operator L is practically indistinguishable from the operator we dealt with in the last section. In particular, it does not have an inverse. To obtain an invertible operator L_0, we will restrict the domain of L to the set M of members of $C''[a, b]$ that take the value 0 at the endpoints a and b. In other words, a function u belongs to M if, and only if, u'' is continuous in $[a, b]$, and $u(a) = u(b) = 0$. The graph of a typical member of M is shown in Fig. 38-1. Notice that M is a linear space; linear combinations of members of M belong to M. Hence, the restriction L_0 of L to M is again a linear operator. Our choice of boundary conditions is only one of many possibilities; we will see others later. With this choice, the equation $L_{0x} y = r(x)$ is equivalent to the **boundary value problem**

(38-1) $L_x y = r(x)$ and $y = 0$ when $x = a$, $y = 0$ when $x = b$.

Have we now produced an operator with an inverse? The answer is "maybe."

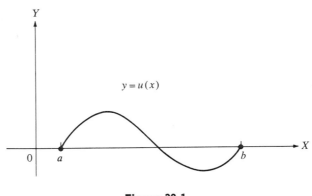

$$y = u(x)$$

Figure 38-1

As we saw in the last section, in order for our linear operator L_0 to have an inverse, it must be true that the only solution of the homogeneous equation $L_{0x}y = 0$ is the trivial solution. For an initial value problem, this condition follows from our general uniqueness theorem, but for a boundary value problem, we will have to make it an explicit hypothesis. Thus, *we will assume that the only solution of the boundary value problem $L_xy = 0$ and $y = 0$ when $x = a$, $y = 0$ when $x = b$ is the constant function with value 0.*

Then L_0 has an inverse, and we will now develop a formula for it. Like the inverse of the differential operator of the last section, L_0^{-1} is an integral operator. There is a kernel G such that for each r in the range of L_0,

$$(38\text{-}2) \qquad\qquad y = \int_a^b G(x, t) r(t) dt$$

satisfies the equation $L_{0x}y = r(x)$ (equivalently, Boundary Value Problem 38-1). The function G is called **Green's Function** for our operator L_0, and we construct it as follows.

Let u be the solution of the equation $L_xy = 0$ such that $u(a) = 0$ and $u'(a) = 1$, and let v be the solution of the equation $L_xy = 0$ such that $v(b) = 0$ and $v'(b) = 1$. (The existence of these functions follows from our earlier theory of initial value problems.) The solution u cannot be a constant multiple of v (nor can v be a constant multiple of u), for otherwise $y = u(x)$ would satisfy the boundary condition $y = 0$ when $x = b$, as well as the condition $y = 0$ when $x = a$, and hence the equation $L_{0x}y = 0$ would have a non-trivial solution. Thus, the Wronskian $W(u(x), v(x))$ is not equal to 0 at any point of the interval $[a, b]$. Now we define G by means of the following equations:

$$(38\text{-}3) \qquad G(x, t) = \begin{cases} u(t)v(x)/W(u(t), v(t)) & \text{if } a \leq t \leq x \\ u(x)v(t)/W(u(t), v(t)) & \text{if } x \leq t \leq b. \end{cases}$$

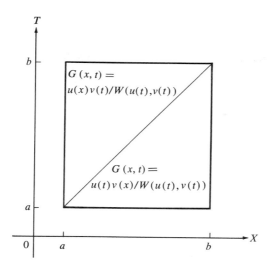

Figure 38-2

The domain of G is the square in the XT-plane whose corners are (a, a), (a, b), (b, b), and (b, a). Figure 38-2 illustrates the definition of G. We should emphasize that G is Green's Function *for* L_0. It depends on the boundary conditions we impose as well as the operator L. If we had restricted the domain of L to obtain a different invertible operator, Green's Function would have been different, too.

It is simply a matter of verification to see that y, as given by Equation 38-2, satisfies Problem 38-1. We use Equations 38-3 to write Equation 38-2 as

$$y = \int_a^x G(x, t)r(t)\,dt + \int_x^b G(x, t)r(t)\,dt$$

$$= v(x) \int_a^x \frac{u(t)r(t)}{W(u(t), v(t))}\,dt + u(x) \int_x^b \frac{v(t)r(t)}{W(u(t), v(t))}\,dt.$$

Since $u(a) = 0$ and $v(b) = 0$, it follows immediately that $y = 0$ when $x = a$ and when $x = b$; the boundary conditions are satisfied. Now we will show that $L_x y = r(x)$. We have

$$y' = v'(x) \int_a^x \frac{u(t)r(t)}{W(u(t), v(t))}\,dt + v(x)\frac{u(x)r(x)}{W(u(x), v(x))}$$

$$+ u'(x) \int_x^b \frac{v(t)r(t)}{W(u(t), v(t))}\,dt - u(x)\frac{v(x)r(x)}{W(u(x), v(x))}$$

$$= v'(x) \int_a^x \frac{u(t)r(t)}{W(u(t), v(t))}\,dt + u'(x) \int_x^b \frac{v(t)r(t)}{W(u(t), v(t))}\,dt.$$

Then,

$$y'' = v''(x) \int_a^x \frac{u(t)r(t)}{W(u(t), v(t))}\, dt + v'(x) \frac{u(x)r(x)}{W(u(x), v(x))}$$

$$+ u''(x) \int_x^b \frac{v(t)r(t)}{W(u(t), v(t))}\, dt - u'(x) \frac{v(x)r(x)}{W(u(x), v(x))}$$

$$= v''(x) \int_a^x \frac{u(t)r(t)}{W(u(t), v(t))}\, dt + u''(x) \int_x^b \frac{v(t)r(t)}{W(u(t), v(t))}\, dt + 1 \cdot r(x).$$

Therefore,

$$L_x y = y'' + p(x)y' + q(x)y$$

$$= (Lv(x)) \int_a^x \frac{u(t)r(t)}{W(u(t), v(t))}\, dt + (Lu(x)) \int_x^b \frac{v(t)r(t)}{W(u(t), v(t))}\, dt + r(x).$$

Since $Lv(x) = Lu(x) = 0$, we finally see that $L_x y = r(x)$. Thus $L_{0x} y = r(x)$, so we have shown that

$$L_0^{-1} r(x) = \int_a^b G(x, t) r(t)\, dt.$$

Example 38-1.　Find $G(x, t)$ for the operator L_0 if $L_x y = y''$ and $[a, b] = [0, 1]$.

Solution. To find this kernel, we use Equations 38-3, where u and v are solutions of the initial value problems

$$u \longrightarrow \quad y'' = 0 \text{ and } y = 0, y' = 1 \text{ when } x = 0$$

and

$$v \longrightarrow \quad y'' = 0 \text{ and } y = 0, y' = 1 \text{ when } x = 1,$$

respectively. It is easy to see that $u(x) = x$ and $v(x) = x - 1$. Hence,

$$W(u(x), v(x)) = \begin{vmatrix} x & x - 1 \\ 1 & 1 \end{vmatrix} = 1,$$

and so

(38-4)
$$G(x, t) = \begin{cases} t(x - 1) & \text{if } 0 \le t \le x \\ x(t - 1) & \text{if } x \le t \le 1. \end{cases}$$

Example 38-2.　Solve the boundary value problem

$$y'' = 6x \text{ and } y = 0 \text{ when } x = 0, y = 0 \text{ when } x = 1.$$

Solution. We calculated Green's Function for the operator L_0 of this problem in the last example, and so we know that the solution of the given boundary value problem is given by the equation

$$y = \int_0^1 G(x, t)6t\,dt$$

$$= \int_0^x G(x, t)6t\,dt + \int_x^1 G(x, t)6t\,dt$$

$$= (x - 1)\int_0^x 6t^2\,dt + x\int_x^1 (t - 1)6t\,dt$$

$$= (x - 1)2t^3 \Big|_0^x + x(2t^3 - 3t^2)\Big|_x^1$$

$$= (x - 1)2x^3 - x - 2x^4 + 3x^3 = x^3 - x.$$

You can easily check this result.

Incidentally, our construction of Green's Function for the particular operator L_0 we have been dealing with in this section suggests a relatively simple criterion for determining whether or not L_0 has an inverse. Let u be the solution of the initial value problem $L_x y = 0$ and $y = 0$, $y' = 1$ when $x = a$. Then if w is any other solution of the equation $L_x y = 0$ such that $w(a) = 0$, it must be true that $w(x)$ is a constant multiple of $u(x)$. For, $W(u(a), w(a)) = u(a)w'(a) - w(a)u'(a) = 0 \cdot w'(a) - 0 \cdot 1 = 0$, and hence $W(u(x), w(x)) = 0$ for each $x \in [a, b]$. It follows, therefore, that the boundary value problem $L_x y = 0$ and $y = 0$ when $x = a$, $y = 0$ when $x = b$ has a non-trivial solution only when u itself is such a solution. That is, L_0 *has an inverse if, and only if,* $u(b) \neq 0$.

Example 38-3. Let $L_x y = y'' + y$. Show that if $[a, b] = [0, \pi]$, then L_0 is not invertible, whereas if $[a, b] = [0, 1]$, then L_0 is invertible.

Solution. If $u(x) = \sin x$, then $Lu(x) = 0$, $u(0) = 0$, and $u'(0) = 1$. Therefore, if we are working in an interval $[0, b]$, L_0 has an inverse if, and only if, $u(b) \neq 0$. In our first case, $b = \pi$, so $u(b) = \sin \pi = 0$. In the second case, $b = 1$, so $u(b) = \sin 1 \neq 0$.

The main point we wanted to make in the last two sections is that the inverse of a differential operator turns out to be an integral operator, hardly a surprising result. What may be surprising is that integral operators are, in many ways, "nicer" than differential operators. For example, if we think of Equation 38-2 as *defining* an integral operator, then we see that its domain includes all integrable functions. Partly for this reason, a good deal of work with boundary value problems is cast in terms of integral operators, rather than differential operators. It would take us too far afield to do more than allude to this point, however.

EXERCISE 38

1. Suppose that $L_x y = y''$ and $[a, b] = [-1, 1]$.
   (a) Find $G(x, t)$.
   (b) Solve the equation $L_{0x} y = 2x$.

2. Find $G(x, t)$ if $L_x y = y'' + y'$ and $[a, b] = [0, 1]$.

3. Suppose that $L_x y = y'' + \pi^2 y$.
   (a) If $[a, b] = [0, 1]$, show that the operator L_0 *does not* have an inverse.
   (b) If $[a, b] = [0, \frac{1}{2}]$, show that the operator L_0 *does* have an inverse.
   (c) Find L_0^{-1} for the operator of part (b).

4. (a) Let G be Green's Function for our operator L_0 (as defined by Equations 38-3). Show that if c and d are given numbers, and r is a given function, then

$$y = \frac{d}{u(b)} u(x) + \frac{c}{v(a)} v(x) + \int_a^b G(x, t) r(t) dt$$

   satisfies the boundary value problem

$$L_x y = r(x) \text{ and } y = c \text{ when } x = a, \ y = d \text{ when } x = b.$$

   (b) Solve the boundary value problem

$$y'' = 2x \text{ and } y = 2 \text{ when } x = 0, \ y = -1 \text{ when } x = 1.$$

5. Let L_0 be the operator of Example 38-1, and suppose that $w(x) = L_0^{-1} r(x)$, where $r(x) = \sqrt{1 + x^3}$. Write a computer program to print values of w at the points of the set $\{0, .1, .2, .3, .4, .5\}$.

6. (a) Show that the *two* Equations 38-4 can be combined into the single equation

$$G(x, t) = xt - \tfrac{1}{2}[x + t - |x - t|].$$

   (b) Is G continuous?

7. (a) Show that the *two* Equations 38-3 can be replaced by the single equation

$$G(x, t) = \frac{u(\tfrac{1}{2}[x + t - |x - t|]) v(\tfrac{1}{2}[x + t + |x - t|])}{W(u(t), v(t))}.$$

   (b) Is G continuous?

8. If G is Green's Function for the operator L_0 of Example 38-1, show that $G(t, x) = G(x, t)$. Show that if $L_x y = y'' + q(x)y$ (that is, $p(x) = 0$), then Green's Function for L_0 (as defined by Equations 38-3) also has the property that $G(t, x) = G(x, t)$. (Hint: $D_t W(u(t), v(t)) = 0$.)

9. For the function G defined by Equations 38-3, show that

$$\lim_{t \uparrow x} G_1(x, t) - \lim_{t \downarrow x} G_1(x, t) = 1.$$

(Remember: The derived function G_1 is defined by the equation $G_1(x, t) = \dfrac{\partial G(x, t)}{\partial x}$.) Is G_1 continuous?

10. Let $L_x y = y''$ and $[a, b] = [0, 1]$. But now suppose that M consists of those functions in the set $C''[0, 1]$ that satisfy the boundary conditions $y = 0$ when $x = 0$ and $y' = 0$ when $x = 1$, and let L_1 be the restriction of L to this class.

   (a) Can you show that L_1^{-1} exists; that is, that the only solution of the boundary value problem $y'' = 0$ and $y = 0$ when $x = 0$, $y' = 0$ when $x = 1$ is the trivial solution?

   (b) Verify that $L_1^{-1} r(x) = \int_0^1 G(x, t) r(t) dt$, where $G(x, t) = \frac{1}{2}[|x - t| - x - t]$.

39 THE OPERATOR $-D^2$ AND FOURIER SINE SERIES

We have just discussed analogues, for differential operators, of the inverse of a matrix. Now we turn to the problem of finding characteristic values and characteristic "vectors" of a differential operator. To be concrete, we will be very specific in this section and consider as our operator L_0 the restriction of the operator $L = -D^2$ to those functions of the class $C''[0, \pi]$ that take the value 0 at 0 and at π. Thus, the domain of L_0 is the set $\{u: u \in C''[0, \pi], u(0) = u(\pi) = 0\}$, and Fig. 39-1 shows the graph of one of its members. (Our artificial-appearing choice of π as one of the endpoints of the basic interval makes some of our formulas simpler than they would be with some other choice of endpoint.)

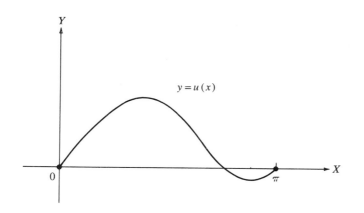

Figure 39-1

Just as for matrices, a **characteristic value** of L_0 is a number λ such that the equation

(39-1) $$L_{0x}y = \lambda y$$

has a non-trivial solution. Such a solution, of course, is a **characteristic function** that corresponds to λ. Since $L_{0x}y = -y''$, and the domain of L_0 consists of functions that satisfy our boundary conditions, we see that we are to find a number λ such that the boundary value problem

(39-2) $\quad y'' + \lambda y = 0$ and $y = 0$ when $x = 0$, $y = 0$ when $x = \pi$

has a non-trivial solution. Because it is based on a simple linear differential equation with constant coefficients, this characteristic value problem is easy to solve. But before we solve it, we will look at Problem 39-1 from a more general viewpoint.

When it comes time to talk about their characteristic values and characteristic vectors, we find that *symmetric* matrices are especially nice to work with. This statement applies to linear operators in general, and we have therefore selected a symmetric differential operator L_0 to discuss in this section. Thus, the fundamental symmetry equation (Equation 36-4)

(39-3) $$L_0 u \cdot v = u \cdot L_0 v$$

holds for any two functions u and v in the domain of our operator L_0.

Naturally, we cannot verify Equation 39-3 until we explain what it means. It says that the dot product of one pair of functions equals the dot product of another pair, so our first order of business is to define the **dot product** of two functions. As with vectors, the dot product of two functions is a *number*, and (for the purposes of this section, anyway) we will say that if the functions f and g are continuous in $[0, \pi]$, then

$$f \cdot g = \int_0^\pi f(x)g(x)dx.$$

For example, if $f(x) = e^{\sin x}$ and $g(x) = \cos x$, then

$$f \cdot g = \int_0^\pi e^{\sin x} \cos x \, dx = e^{\sin x} \Big|_0^\pi = e^0 - e^0 = 0.$$

To indicate that our definition is a "reasonable" one, we can show that the basic properties of a dot product (those listed in Equations 18-6) are satisfied. Thus, if f, g, and h are arbitrary continuous functions, and r is a scalar, then it is a matter of the most elementary calculus to verify the equations

$$f \cdot g = g \cdot f,$$

(39-4) $$(f + g) \cdot h = f \cdot h + g \cdot h,$$

$$(rf) \cdot g = r(f \cdot g).$$

By analogy with the vector case, we say that f and g are **orthogonal** if $f \cdot g = 0$; that is, if $\int_0^\pi f(x)g(x)dx = 0$. Similarly, the **norm** of a function f is the number $|f| = \sqrt{f \cdot f} = \left(\int_0^\pi f(x)^2 dx\right)^{1/2}$.

Now that we know what it says, we can set about verifying the fundamental symmetry equation, Equation 39-3. We must show that

$$\int_0^\pi (L_0 u(x))v(x)dx = \int_0^\pi u(x)L_0 v(x)dx$$

for any two functions u and v in the domain of L_0. Since $L_0 u(x) = -u''(x)$, and $L_0 v(x) = -v''(x)$, we are therefore to show that

(39-5) $$\int_0^\pi -u''(x)v(x)dx = \int_0^\pi u(x)(-v''(x))dx$$

for two functions u and v such that

(39-6) $$u(0) = u(\pi) = v(0) = v(\pi) = 0.$$

The key to our proof is the identity

$$u''(x)v(x) - u(x)v''(x) = D_x[u'(x)v(x) - u(x)v'(x)],$$

which you can verify at a glance. When we integrate both sides of this identity from 0 to π, we obtain the equation

$$\int_0^\pi [u''(x)v(x) - u(x)v''(x)]dx = u'(x)v(x) - u(x)v'(x) \Big|_0^\pi$$

$$= u'(\pi)v(\pi) - u(\pi)v'(\pi) - u'(0)v(0) + u(0)v'(0).$$

Since u and v belong to the domain of L_0 (Equations 39-6), this number is 0, and so we have verified Equation 39-5.

The symmetry of L_0 implies that characteristic values of L_0 are real numbers, and characteristic functions that correspond to different characteristic values are orthogonal. We proved these statements for matrix operators in Section 36, and the same proofs apply to any symmetric operator. You probably wondered why we chose to study the operator $-D^2$, rather than D^2. Paradoxically, attaching the minus sign gives us an operator with *positive* characteristic values.

Example 39-1. Show that the characteristic values of L_0 are positive.

Solution. Let λ be a characteristic value of L_0 and u be a corresponding characteristic function. Because L_0 is symmetric, we know that λ is real, and hence u can be chosen to be real-valued. The characteristic function u is a solution of the equation $L_{0x}y = \lambda y$, so

$$-u''(x) = \lambda u(x).$$

We multiply both sides of this equation by $u(x)$,

$$-u''(x)u(x) = \lambda u(x)^2,$$

and integrate from 0 to π:

$$(39\text{-}7) \qquad -\int_0^\pi u''(x)u(x)dx = \lambda \int_0^\pi u(x)^2 dx.$$

On the left-hand side, we integrate by parts, using the fact that $u(0) = u(\pi) = 0$:

$$-\int_0^\pi u''(x)u(x)dx = -u'(x)u(x)\Big|_0^\pi + \int_0^\pi u'(x)^2 dx$$

$$= 0 + \int_0^\pi u'(x)^2 dx.$$

Therefore, Equation 39-7 can be written as

$$\int_0^\pi u'(x)^2 dx = \lambda \int_0^\pi u(x)^2 dx.$$

It follows that $\lambda > 0$, as we were to show.

Now that we have discussed the characteristic values and characteristic functions of L_0 in general terms, let us see what these numbers and functions really are. A characteristic value λ is a number chosen so that the operator $L_0 - \lambda I$ does not have an inverse. (Here, of course, the identity operator I is such that $If = f$ for each function f.) In the remarks preceding Example 38-3, we suggested a criterion for the non-invertibility of this operator. Thus, suppose we select a function u such that $(L - \lambda I)u(x) = 0, u(0) = 0$, and $u'(0) \neq 0$. Then $L_0 - \lambda I$ fails to be invertible if, and only if, $u(\pi) = 0$. Since $(L - \lambda I)u(x) = 0$ is merely another way of writing the equation $u''(x) + \lambda u(x) = 0$, we see that we can take $u(x) = \sin \sqrt{\lambda} x$. Therefore, $L_0 - \lambda I$ does not have an inverse (that is, λ is a characteristic value of L_0) if, and only if,

$$\sin \sqrt{\lambda}\, \pi = 0.$$

Since this equation gives us the characteristic values of L_0, we might call it the *characteristic equation* of that operator. Its positive solutions are the numbers $\lambda_1 = 1$, $\lambda_2 = 4$, $\lambda_3 = 9$, and so on. So, if we denote by λ_n the nth characteristic value of L_0, we have shown that

(39-8) $$\lambda_n = n^2.$$

We chose λ_n so that the equation $u_n(x) = \sin \sqrt{\lambda_n}\, x$ defines a function that belongs to the domain of L_0 and is such that $(L - \lambda_n I)u_n(x) = 0$. In other words, $L_0 u_n(x) = \lambda_n u_n(x)$. But this equation simply says that u_n is a characteristic function that corresponds to the characteristic value λ_n. Thus, we see that characteristic functions of our operator are given by the formula

(39-9) $$u_n(x) = \sin nx.$$

(Notice that a scalar multiple of a characteristic function is again a characteristic function, just as was the case with vectors.)

Example 39-2. Since L_0 is a symmetric operator, our theory tells us that characteristic functions that correspond to different characteristic values of L_0 are orthogonal. Verify this fact by a direct computation with actual characteristic functions.

Solution. We are to show that if $m \neq n$, then $u_m \cdot u_n = 0$; that is,

$$\int_0^\pi u_m(x)u_n(x)\,dx = \int_0^\pi \sin mx \sin nx\,dx = 0.$$

By using the trigonometric identity

$$\sin A \sin B = \tfrac{1}{2}[\cos(A - B) - \cos(A + B)],$$

we can write

$$\int_0^\pi \sin mx \sin nx\,dx = \frac{1}{2}\int_0^\pi [\cos(m - n)x - \cos(m + n)x]\,dx$$

$$= \frac{1}{2}\left[\frac{\sin(m - n)x}{m - n} - \frac{\sin(m + n)x}{m + n} \right]\Bigg|_0^\pi = 0.$$

A given n by n symmetric matrix A is diagonable, or equivalently, each vector of R^n can be written as a linear combination of characteristic vectors of A.

It is certainly not obvious, but the analogous statement holds for our operator L_0. That is, every function in the domain of L_0 can be expressed as a linear combination of characteristic functions of L_0. Of course, since L_0 has infinitely many characteristic functions, these "linear combinations" are really infinite series. Thus, suppose that f is any function in the domain of L_0 ($f \in C''[0, \pi]$ and $f(0) = f(\pi) = 0$). Then there is a sequence $\{b_n\}$ of numbers such that for each $x \in [0, \pi]$,

$$(39\text{-}10) \qquad\qquad f(x) = \sum_{n=1}^{\infty} b_n \sin nx.$$

The coefficient sequence $\{b_n\}$ is generated by the same formula that we used for matrices (Theorem 36-5); that is, $b_n = f \cdot u_n / |u_n|^2$. Here,

$$f \cdot u_n = \int_0^\pi f(x) \sin nx\, dx \text{ and } |u_n|^2 = \int_0^\pi \sin^2 nx\, dx = \tfrac{1}{2}\pi,$$

so our formula for b_n reads

$$(39\text{-}11) \qquad\qquad b_n = \frac{2}{\pi} \int_0^\pi f(x) \sin nx\, dx.$$

The infinite series on the right-hand side of Equation 39-10, with the coefficients given by Equation 39-11, is called the **Fourier sine series** for $f(x)$.

The proof that Equation 39-10 holds for an arbitrary function f in the domain of L_0 (that is, that the Fourier sine series for $f(x)$ converges to $f(x)$ for each $x \in [0, \pi]$) can be made to consist of two parts. We first show that the series converges, and then we convince ourselves that its sum is $f(x)$. Thus, let us apply integration by parts to the integral in Equation 39-11:

$$b_n = \frac{2}{\pi} \left[\frac{-f(x) \cos nx}{n} \Big|_0^\pi + \frac{1}{n} \int_0^\pi f'(x) \cos nx\, dx \right].$$

Since $f(\pi) = f(0) = 0$, this equation reduces to $b_n = \dfrac{2}{n\pi} \displaystyle\int_0^\pi f'(x) \cos nx\, dx$, and we apply integration by parts again:

$$b_n = \frac{2}{n\pi} \left[\frac{f'(x) \sin nx}{n} \Big|_0^\pi - \frac{1}{n} \int_0^\pi f''(x) \sin nx\, dx \right] = -\frac{2}{n^2\pi} \int_0^\pi f''(x) \sin nx\, dx.$$

We are assuming that f'' is continuous in the interval $[0, \pi]$, so there is a number

M such that $|f''(x)| \leq M$ for each $x \in [0, \pi]$. Therefore,

$$|b_n| \leq \frac{2}{n^2\pi} \int_0^\pi M|\sin nx|dx = \frac{4M}{n^2\pi}.$$

But this inequality implies that our Fourier series $\sum\limits_{n=1}^{\infty} b_n \sin nx$ converges.
For since $|\sin nx| \leq 1$, we have shown that each of its terms is not greater in
absolute value than the corresponding term of the convergent series $\dfrac{4M}{\pi} \sum\limits_{n=1}^{\infty} \dfrac{1}{n^2}$.
The comparison test now tells us that the Fourier sine series converges.

It was quite easy to show that for each $x \in [0, \pi]$ the Fourier sine series
for $f(x)$ converges. Suppose we call its sum $g(x)$. It is a subtler matter to show
that, in fact, $g(x) = f(x)$, and we will only indicate how it might be done. We
first show that $\int_0^\pi [f(x) - g(x)] \sin nx \, dx = 0$ for $n = 1, 2, \ldots$. In other
words, we show that the difference function $f - g$ is orthogonal to each characteristic function. Next we have to convince ourselves that our set of characteristic functions is *complete;* that is, the only function that is orthogonal to all
of them is the constant function with value 0. Then, of course, we see that
$g(x) = f(x)$. We won't attempt to show that our sequence $\{u_n\}$ is indeed complete. For a discussion of this point, and for other facts about Fourier series that
we are omitting, you may consult References [2] and [5]. Chapter Eight of
Reference [7] has an especially good discussion of Fourier series.

Example 39-3. Let $f(x) = x(\pi - x)$ for each $x \in [0, \pi]$. Find the Fourier
sine series for $f(x)$, and discuss its convergence.

Solution. This function f is in the domain of L_0, and so its Fourier sine series will
converge to $f(x)$ for each $x \in [0, \pi]$. We calculate the coefficients of the series by
means of Equation 39-11:

$$b_n = \frac{2}{\pi} \int_0^\pi x(\pi - x) \sin nx\, dx$$

$$= \frac{2}{\pi} \left[\frac{-x(\pi - x)\cos nx}{n} \Big|_0^\pi + \frac{1}{n} \int_0^\pi (\pi - 2x) \cos nx\, dx \right]$$

$$= \frac{2}{\pi n} \left[\frac{(\pi - 2x)\sin nx}{n} \Big|_0^\pi + \frac{2}{n} \int_0^\pi \sin nx\, dx \right]$$

$$= -\frac{4}{\pi n^3} \cos nx \Big|_0^\pi = \frac{4}{\pi n^3} (1 - \cos n\pi).$$

Thus, $b_1 = 8/\pi$, $b_2 = 0$, $b_3 = 8/\pi3^3$, $b_4 = 0$, . . . , and so

$$(39\text{-}12) \qquad x(\pi - x) = \frac{8}{\pi} \left[\sin x + \frac{1}{3^3} \sin 3x + \frac{1}{5^3} \sin 5x + \cdots \right].$$

Example 39-4. Determine experimentally how well the series in Equation 39-12 converges.

Solution. Suppose we multiply both sides of Equation 39-12 by $\pi/8$ and use the resulting series to calculate $\pi x(\pi - x)/8$ for each $x \in \{0, 1, 2, 3\}$. The computer program shown in Fig. 39-2 adds seven terms of this series. We print three columns, a column of x values, a column of partial sums of the series, and a column of true values. A glance at the output should make you a believer in Fourier series.

```
          DO 1 I = 1, 4
          X = I − 1
          S = 0
          DO 2 K = 1, 7
          R = 2*K − 1
          S = S + SIN(R*X)/(R*R*R)
    2     CONTINUE
          Y = 3.14159*X*(3.14159 − X)/8
          WRITE(6, 3) X, S, Y
    3     FORMAT(1X, F3.1, 2F8.4)
    1     CONTINUE
          STOP
          END
```

```
    0.0    0.0000      0.0000
    1.0    0.8409      0.8410
    2.0    0.8968      0.8966
    3.0    0.1665      0.1668
```

Figure 39-2

It is a remarkable fact that our function f need not even be in the domain of L_0 for Equation 39-10 to hold. We can weaken the condition that f'' be continuous or that $f(0) = 0$ or $f(\pi) = 0$. Of course, if we weaken the conditions on f too much, we may not get all the convergence we hope for. A full discussion of these points is totally out of the question here, but you should at least be told that Equation 39-10 is "practically true" for a function like the one whose graph appears in Fig. 39-3. This function is discontinuous at the points a and b, and $f(0) = 1$, not 0. Nevertheless, the Fourier sine series for $f(x)$ converges for each $x \in [0, \pi]$, and its sum—except at the "bad spots" 0, a, and b—is $f(x)$. It is obvious that the series does not converge to $f(0)$ when $x = 0$. After all, each term is 0, so the sum must be 0. At the points a and b, the story is a little different.

At these "bad spots," the series converges to the *average value* of f, and to say precisely what we mean by the "average value" of f at a point, we will introduce some notation. We denote by $f(x^-)$ the limit from the left of f at x.

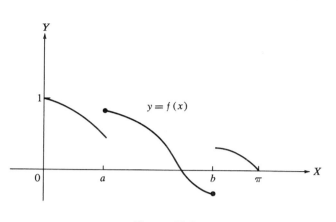

Figure 39-3

Thus, $f(x^-) = \lim\limits_{z \uparrow x} f(z)$. Similarly, $f(x^+) = \lim\limits_{z \downarrow x} f(z)$. Then the *average value* of f at x is defined as the average of these limits; that is, the number $\frac{1}{2}[f(x^-) + f(x^+)]$. So when we say that our Fourier sine series converges to the average value of f at the point a, we mean that its sum is $\frac{1}{2}[f(a^-) + f(a^+)]$. Similarly, the sum of the Fourier sine series when $x = b$ is $\frac{1}{2}[f(b^-) + f(b^+)]$. Actually, our series converges to $\frac{1}{2}[f(x^-) + f(x^+)]$ at *each* point x of $(0, \pi)$. For if f is continuous at x, the average value of f is the true value of f; that is, $\frac{1}{2}[f(x^-) + f(x^+)] = f(x)$.

The following theorem is not the most general possible statement about the convergence of Fourier series, but it is more than adequate for most practical applications.

THEOREM 39-1

Suppose that f and f' are continuous in the interval $(0, \pi)$, except for a finite number of points. At these exceptional points, we assume that the limits of f and f' from the right and from the left exist, and we also assume that f and f' have limits from the right at 0 and from the left at π. Then the Fourier sine series for $f(x)$ converges for each $x \in (0, \pi)$, and its sum is

$$\tfrac{1}{2}[f(x^-) + f(x^+)].$$

As we remarked above, at a point of continuity, the average value of f is the actual value, so the Fourier series converges to the value of f, except at a finite number of points. At these points, f is allowed to have a "jump discontinuity," and the sum of the Fourier series is the average of the "values of f at the two sides of the jump."

Example 39-5. Let $f(x) = 1$ for each $x \in (0, \pi)$. Find the Fourier sine series for $f(x)$, and discuss its convergence.

Solution. According to Equation 39-11, the Fourier sine coefficients of our function f are given by the formula

$$b_n = \frac{2}{\pi} \int_0^\pi 1 \cdot \sin nx\,dx = -\frac{2}{n\pi} \cos nx \Big|_0^\pi = \frac{2}{n\pi} [1 - (-1)^n].$$

Therefore, $b_1 = 4/\pi$, $b_2 = 0$, $b_3 = 4/3\pi$, $b_4 = 0$, $b_5 = 4/5\pi$, and so on. Since f is continuous at each point of the open interval $(0, \pi)$, Theorem 39-1 tells us that for each x in that interval,

(39-13) $$1 = \frac{4}{\pi} \left[\sin x + \frac{1}{3} \sin 3x + \frac{1}{5} \sin 5x + \cdots \right].$$

For example, if we set $x = \frac{1}{2}\pi$, we obtain the interesting equation

(39-14) $$\pi = 4(1 - \tfrac{1}{3} + \tfrac{1}{5} - \tfrac{1}{7} + \cdots).$$

EXERCISE 39

1. Find $f \cdot g$ for the functions defined by the following equations.
   (a) $f(x) = \cos x$, $g(x) = \sin x$ (c) $f(x) = e^{x^2}$, $g(x) = 2x$
   (b) $f(x) = x^p$, $g(x) = x^q$ (d) $g(x) = f'(x)$

2. How "long," according to our definition of the norm of a function, are the functions defined by the following equations?
   (a) $f(x) = |x - \frac{1}{2}\pi|$ (b) $f(x) = \cos 2x$

3. Which of the functions defined by the following equations belong to the domain of L_0? Which belong to the class of functions mentioned in Theorem 39-1?
   (a) $f(x) = e^{x^2} \sin x$ (c) $f(x) = \text{int } (3 \sin 3x)$

   (b) $f(x) = \sin (xe^{x^2})$ (d) $f(x) = x \sin \dfrac{1}{x}$

4. Explain why Equations 39-4 are correct.

5. Since $|\cos \theta| \le 1$ for any angle θ, it follows from Equation 18-5 that if x_1 and x_2 are any two vectors in R^2, then $|x_1 \cdot x_2| \le |x_1| |x_2|$. It is not hard to show that this inequality, known as **Schwarz's Inequality,** holds for *any* dot product, in particular, for the one we introduced in this section. Express the inequality $|f \cdot g| \le |f| |g|$ in terms of integral signs, and verify that it holds for the functions of Exercise 39-1.

6. Find the Fourier sine series for each of the functions defined by the following equations, and discuss its convergence.
   (a) $f(x) = 2$ (d) $f(x) = mx + b$
   (b) $f(x) = \text{int } (2x/\pi)$ (e) $f(x) = |\cos x|$
   (c) $f(x) = x$ (f) $f(x) = -\text{int } (\cos x)$

7. Suppose that f is a function with the properties described in Theorem 39-1 and that $\sum\limits_{n=1}^{\infty} b_n \sin nx$ is the Fourier sine series for $f(x)$. Does this series converge if x is a point outside the interval $[0, \pi]$; for example, does the series converge if $x = 1492$?

8. Use the computer to calculate partial sums (say, of five terms) of the series in Equation 39-13 for x in the set $\{0, 1, 2, 3\}$.

9. Use the computer to add "many" terms of the series in Equation 39-14. As you see, it converges very slowly.

10. Set $x = \frac{1}{2}\pi$ in Equation 39-12 to obtain an interesting series whose sum is π^3. Use the computer to add up a few terms of this series to see how fast it converges.

11. Fourier series are used in the analysis of vibrating strings (for example, violin strings). Suppose that $f(x) = .1 - \dfrac{1}{5\pi}|x - .5\pi|$, and sketch the graph of the equation $y = f(x)$ for $x \in [0, \pi]$. Why do you think this equation is called the equation of the "plucked string"? Find the Fourier sine series for $f(x)$.

12. The characteristic value problem

$$y'' + \lambda y = 0 \text{ and } y = 0 \text{ when } x = 0, \, y + y' = 0 \text{ when } x = \pi$$

is obtained from Problem 39-2 by changing one boundary condition. Discuss the problem of finding its characteristic values and characteristic functions.

40　FOURIER SERIES

　　　　No matter what similarities they may have, two functions (or two operators) are different if their domains are different. In this section, we are going to restrict the operator $-D^2$ to a domain different from the domain of our operator L_0, and hence the resulting operator will be a different operator. We will name it L_P for reasons that will soon be apparent. A minor difference between the operators L_0 and L_P is that L_0 operates on functions defined on the interval $[0, \pi]$, while for L_P we extend this interval to $[-\pi, \pi]$. The really important difference, though, is the boundary conditions that we require members of the domains of the two operators to satisfy. A function u of the class $C''[-\pi, \pi]$ belongs to the domain of L_P if

$$u(-\pi) = u(\pi) \text{ and } u'(-\pi) = u'(\pi).$$

Figure 40-1 shows the graph of a typical function u in the domain of L_P. If we shift this graph 2π units to the right and to the left, function values and

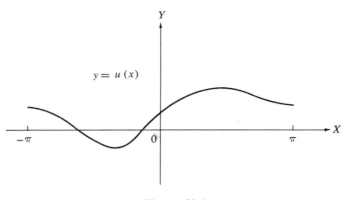

Figure 40-1

derivatives "match up" at $-\pi$ and π, and we can continue this shifting process, thus obtaining the graph of a function whose domain is the whole real line. This function is *periodic*, and its first derived function is periodic. Therefore, we say that our operator L_P is determined by **periodic boundary conditions.**

Our basic interval is now $[-\pi, \pi]$, so we use a slightly different dot product than the one we used in the last section. If f and g are continuous functions, we will write

$$f \cdot g = \int_{-\pi}^{\pi} f(x)g(x)dx.$$

Therefore, the condition that L_P be a symmetric operator ($L_P u \cdot v = u \cdot L_P v$) is that, for each pair u, v of functions in its domain,

$$\int_{-\pi}^{\pi} -u''(x)v(x)dx = \int_{-\pi}^{\pi} u(x)(-v''(x))dx.$$

The verification of this equation follows practically the same steps that we used to verify the analogous Equation 39-5, so we will leave it to you.

When the equation $L_{P}y = \lambda y$ is written as a boundary value problem, it becomes

$$y'' + \lambda y = 0$$

(40-1)

and y and y' have the same values at both ends of the interval $[-\pi, \pi]$.

Because L_P is symmetric, we can assume that λ is a real number, and the argument carried out in Example 39-1 shows us that λ cannot be negative. So we only need to consider the differential equation $y'' + \lambda y = 0$ for $\lambda \geq 0$. The equations $u(x) = \cos \sqrt{\lambda}\, x$ and $v(x) = \sin \sqrt{\lambda}\, x$ define two linearly independent solutions of this differential equation, and therefore a solution of Problem 40-1 must be given by an equation of the form $y = c \cos \sqrt{\lambda}\, x + d \sin \sqrt{\lambda}\, x$. Simple calculations, whose details we omit, now show that if y has the same value at $-\pi$ and at π, then $d \sin \sqrt{\lambda}\, \pi = 0$, whereas if y' has the same value at $-\pi$ and at π, then $c \sin \sqrt{\lambda}\, \pi = 0$. *Both c and d cannot be equal to 0*, for then we would be dealing with the trivial solution. Therefore, as with L_0, characteristic values of L_P are solutions of the equation

$$\sin \sqrt{\lambda}\, \pi = 0.$$

Even though we end up with the same characteristic equation that we found for L_0, the characteristic values and characteristic functions of L_P are not the same. For example, $\lambda_0 = 0$ is now a characteristic value. We can take as a corresponding characteristic function the constant function with value 1 (check it and see). As with L_0, the remaining characteristic values of L_P are members of the sequence $\{\lambda_n\} = \{n^2\}$, with $n \geq 1$. But to each of these numbers there correspond *two* independent characteristic functions; we can take them to be the functions that are defined by the equations

$$y = \cos nx \quad \text{and} \quad y = \sin nx.$$

Notice that the symmetry of L_P insures that characteristic functions that correspond to *different* characteristic values are orthogonal (Theorem 36-3). We *chose* our characteristic functions so that those corresponding to the same characteristic value are orthogonal. Thus,

$$\int_{-\pi}^{\pi} \cos nx \sin nx\, dx = \frac{1}{2} \int_{-\pi}^{\pi} \sin 2nx\, dx \qquad (\text{since } \sin 2A = 2 \cos A \sin A)$$

$$= -\frac{1}{4n} \cos 2nx \Big|_{-\pi}^{\pi} = 0.$$

As before, values of functions in the domain of L_P can be expressed as "infinite combinations" of values of characteristic functions. If f is in the domain of L_P, then there are sequences of coefficients $\{a_n\}$ and $\{b_n\}$ such that

(40-2) $$f(x) = a_0 + \sum_{n=1}^{\infty} (a_n \cos nx + b_n \sin nx).$$

These coefficients are given by the "standard formula" that we derived in Theorem 36-5; that is, the coefficient of the characteristic function u is the number $f \cdot u / |u|^2$. In this section, $|u|^2 = \int_{-\pi}^{\pi} u(x)^2 dx$, and so the squares of the lengths of our characteristic functions of L_P are the numbers

$$\int_{-\pi}^{\pi} 1^2 dx = 2\pi, \ \int_{-\pi}^{\pi} \cos^2 nx\, dx = \pi, \text{ and } \int_{-\pi}^{\pi} \sin^2 nx\, dx = \pi.$$

The dot products of f with these characteristic functions are the numbers

$$\int_{-\pi}^{\pi} f(x) \cdot 1\, dx, \ \int_{-\pi}^{\pi} f(x) \cos nx\, dx, \text{ and } \int_{-\pi}^{\pi} f(x) \sin nx\, dx.$$

Therefore, the members of the sequences $\{a_n\}$ and $\{b_n\}$ of coefficients of the series in Equation 40-2 are given by the equations

(40-3)
$$a_0 = \frac{1}{2\pi} \int_{-\pi}^{\pi} f(x)\, dx,$$

$$a_n = \frac{1}{\pi} \int_{-\pi}^{\pi} f(x) \cos nx\, dx,$$

$$\text{(for } n \geq 1\text{)}$$

$$b_n = \frac{1}{\pi} \int_{-\pi}^{\pi} f(x) \sin nx\, dx.$$

With the coefficients determined by Equations 40-3, the series on the right-hand side of Equation 40-2 is the **Fourier series** for $f(x)$.

As is the case with Fourier sine series, Fourier series can be applied to a broader class of functions than merely the domain of L_P. The following theorem is analogous to Theorem 39-1.

THEOREM 40-1

Suppose that f and f' have limits from the right and from the left at each point $x \in (-\pi, \pi)$, and also have limits from the right at $-\pi$ and from the left at π. Furthermore, suppose that the equations $f(x^-) = f(x^+) = f(x)$ and $f'(x^-) = f'(x^+) = f'(x)$ fail to hold at only a *finite* number of points in the interval $(-\pi, \pi)$. Then the Fourier series for $f(x)$ converges for each $x \in [-\pi, \pi]$, and its sum is

$$\tfrac{1}{2}[f(x^-) + f(x^+)] \text{ if } x \in (-\pi, \pi) \text{ and } \tfrac{1}{2}[f(-\pi^+) + f(\pi^-)] \text{ if } |x| = \pi.$$

Example 40-1. Let $f(x) = \text{int}(x/\pi)$ for each $x \in [-\pi, \pi]$. Find the Fourier series for $f(x)$, and discuss its convergence.

Solution. Since $\text{int}(x/\pi) = 0$ for $x \in (0, \pi)$, and $\text{int}(x/\pi) = -1$ for $x \in (-\pi, 0)$, Formulas 40-3 for the Fourier coefficients reduce to

$$a_0 = -\frac{1}{2\pi} \int_{-\pi}^{0} 1\, dx = -\frac{1}{2},$$

$$a_n = -\frac{1}{\pi} \int_{-\pi}^{0} \cos nx\, dx = 0,$$

$$b_n = -\frac{1}{\pi} \int_{-\pi}^{0} \sin nx\, dx = \frac{\cos nx}{n\pi}\Big|_{-\pi}^{0} = \frac{1 - (-1)^n}{n\pi}.$$

Thus, $b_1 = 2/\pi$, $b_2 = 0$, $b_3 = 2/3\pi$, $b_4 = 0$, $b_5 = 2/5\pi$, and so on. Hence, if $x \in (-\pi, 0) \cup (0, \pi)$, then

$$\text{int}\,(x/\pi) = -\frac{1}{2} + \frac{2}{\pi}\left(\sin x + \frac{1}{3}\sin 3x + \frac{1}{5}\sin 5x + \cdots\right).$$

Notice that when $x = 0$, this series reduces to (and hence converges to) $-\frac{1}{2}$, which is the number $\frac{1}{2}[f(0^+) + f(0^-)]$. Similarly, when $x = -\pi$ or $x = \pi$, the sum of the series is $-\frac{1}{2}$, which is the number $\frac{1}{2}[f(-\pi^+) + f(\pi^-)]$.

The characteristic functions of our operator L_P are periodic with period 2π. As a result, the Fourier series of a function that satisfies the hypotheses of Theorem 40-1 converges for each real number x (not just for values in the interval $[-\pi, \pi]$), and its sum is the "periodic repetition" of its sum in the interval $[-\pi, \pi]$.

Example 40-2. Sketch the graph of the sum of the series you obtained in the last example for x in the interval $[-2\pi, 3\pi]$.

Solution. Our series converges to the average value of f (where $f(x) = \text{int}(x/\pi)$) in the open interval $(-\pi, \pi)$ and to $-\frac{1}{2}$ at the endpoints. So we sketch the graph of the sum in the closed interval $[-\pi, \pi]$ and then extend it periodically to get the answer to our question. The result appears in Fig. 40-2.

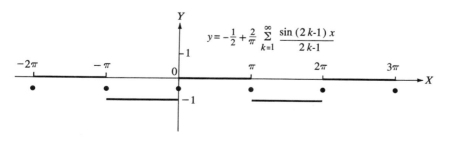

Figure 40-2

Fourier series are sums of values of odd and even functions—the sine function and the cosine function. Consequently, it is worth our while to consider odd and even functions in connection with Fourier series. An *even* function F is characterized by the equation $F(-x) = F(x)$, whereas an *odd* function G has the property $G(-x) = -G(x)$. For example, the equations $y = x^2$, $y = \cos 12x$, and $y = 7$ define even functions, and the equations $y = x$, $y = \sin 3x$, and $y = x|x|$ define odd functions. Figure 40-3 shows the graphs of a typical even function and

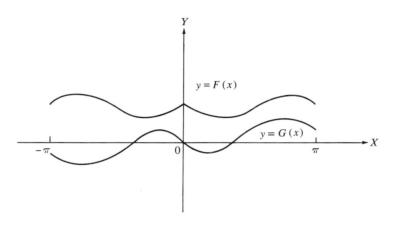

Figure 40-3

a typical odd function in the interval $[-\pi, \pi]$. The following equations are obvious from a glance at Fig. 40-3 and from the geometric interpretation of the integral as an area: *If F is even and G is odd, then*

(40-4) $$\int_{-\pi}^{\pi} F(x)\,dx = 2\int_{0}^{\pi} F(x)\,dx \text{ and } \int_{-\pi}^{\pi} G(x)\,dx = 0.$$

In Fig. 40-4, we list the results of combining even and odd functions algebraically.
    Now suppose that f is an even function in the interval $[-\pi, \pi]$. Then the equation $y = f(x) \cos nx$ defines an even function (the product of two even

even + even = even

odd + odd = odd

even × odd = odd

even × even = even

odd × odd = even

Figure 40-4

functions), and the equation $y = f(x) \sin nx$ defines an odd function. So if we apply Equations 40-4 to Equations 40-3, we obtain much simpler formulas for the Fourier coefficients of f. We see that *the Fourier coefficients of an even function f are given by the equations*

(40-5) $$a_0 = \frac{1}{\pi} \int_0^\pi f(x)dx, \quad a_n = \frac{2}{\pi} \int_0^\pi f(x) \cos nxdx, \text{ and } b_n = 0.$$

Similarly, *if f is an odd function, its Fourier coefficients are given by the equations*

(40-6) $$b_n = \frac{2}{\pi} \int_0^\pi f(x) \sin nxdx, \quad a_n = 0.$$

Example 40-3. Let $f(x) = x^2$ for each $x \in [-\pi, \pi]$. Find the Fourier series for $f(x)$ and discuss its convergence.

Solution. Since our function f is even, we use Equations 40-5 to obtain its Fourier coefficients. We have $b_n = 0$,

$$a_0 = \frac{1}{\pi} \int_0^\pi x^2 dx = \frac{1}{\pi} \frac{\pi^3}{3} = \frac{\pi^2}{3},$$

and, for $n > 0$,

$$a_n = \frac{2}{\pi} \int_0^\pi x^2 \cos nxdx$$

$$= \frac{2}{\pi} \left[\frac{x^2 \sin nx}{n} \Big|_0^\pi - \frac{2}{n} \int_0^\pi x \sin nx \, dx \right]$$

$$= \frac{4}{n\pi} \left[\frac{x \cos nx}{n} \Big|_0^\pi - \frac{1}{n} \int_0^\pi \cos nx \, dx \right]$$

$$= \frac{4}{n^2} \cos n\pi = 4 \frac{(-1)^n}{n^2}.$$

Theorem 40-1 tells us that the Fourier series for $f(x)$ converges to $f(x)$ at each point of continuity in the interval $(-\pi, \pi)$. Since our function is continuous at every point, the series converges to $f(x)$. At the endpoints, the series converges to the average of the limiting values of f at the endpoints, and here, too, the average value is the actual value. Hence, for each $x \in [-\pi, \pi]$,

$$x^2 = \frac{\pi^2}{3} - 4 \left[\cos x - \frac{\cos 2x}{2^2} + \frac{\cos 3x}{3^2} - \frac{\cos 4x}{4^2} + \cdots \right].$$

For example, if we set $x = \pi$, we obtain the equation

$$\pi^2 = \frac{\pi^2}{3} - 4\left[-1 - \frac{1}{2^2} - \frac{1}{3^2} - \frac{1}{4^2} - \cdots\right];$$

that is,

(40-7)
$$\frac{\pi^2}{6} = 1 + \frac{1}{2^2} + \frac{1}{3^2} + \frac{1}{4^2} + \cdots$$

Finally, let us see how we can avoid our dependence on π. Suppose we are given a function f that satisfies the hypotheses of Theorem 40-1 in the interval $[-r, r]$, where r is some positive number, not necessarily π. Can we find a Fourier series whose sum is $f(x)$ at points of this interval? The answer is yes; it is a simple matter to do it by "stretching the domain" of f. We are supposing that the domain of f is the interval $[-r, r]$, so if we define a new function by means of the equation $y = f\left(\frac{r}{\pi} t\right)$, the domain of this new function will be $[-\pi, \pi]$. Therefore, we can use our present theory to represent its values as sums of a Fourier series. Thus,

(40-8)
$$f\left(\frac{r}{\pi} t\right) = a_0 + \sum_{n=1}^{\infty} (a_n \cos nt + b_n \sin nt),$$

for each t at which our new function is continuous. Here, of course,

$$a_0 = \frac{1}{2\pi} \int_{-\pi}^{\pi} f\left(\frac{r}{\pi} t\right) dt, \quad a_n = \frac{1}{\pi} \int_{-\pi}^{\pi} f\left(\frac{r}{\pi} t\right) \cos nt\, dt,$$

$$\text{and } b_n = \frac{1}{\pi} \int_{-\pi}^{\pi} f\left(\frac{r}{\pi} t\right) \sin nt\, dt.$$

Now we make the inverse substitution $x = \frac{r}{\pi} t$, and Equation 40-8 becomes

(40-9)
$$f(x) = a_0 + \sum_{n=1}^{\infty} \left(a_n \cos \frac{n\pi}{r} x + b_n \sin \frac{n\pi}{r} x\right).$$

We also make this substitution in the integrals that determine the coefficients. Thus, $x = -r$ when $t = -\pi$, $x = r$ when $t = \pi$, $dt = \frac{\pi}{r} dx$, and our formulas for the coefficients become

$$(40\text{-}10) \quad a_0 = \frac{1}{2r} \int_{-r}^{r} f(x)dx, \quad a_n = \frac{1}{r} \int_{-r}^{r} f(x) \cos \frac{n\pi}{r} x dx,$$

$$b_n = \frac{1}{r} \int_{-r}^{r} f(x) \sin \frac{n\pi}{r} x dx.$$

Example 40-4. Figure 40-5 shows the graph of a certain function f in the interval $[-1, 1]$. Find its Fourier series.

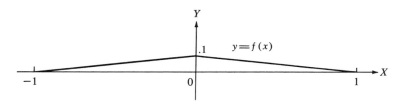

Figure 40-5

Solution. Our function f is even, so its coefficients are given by the obvious modifications of Equations 40-5. Since $f(x) = -.1(x - 1)$ for $x \in [0, 1]$, then

$$a_0 = \int_0^1 -.1(x - 1)dx = -\frac{.1(x - 1)^2}{2} \Big|_0^1 = .05.$$

Also,

$$a_n = -.2 \int_0^1 (x - 1) \cos n\pi x dx = -.2 \left[\frac{(x - 1) \sin n\pi x}{n\pi} \Big|_0^1 - \frac{1}{n\pi} \int_0^1 \sin n\pi x dx \right]$$

$$= -.2 \frac{\cos n\pi x}{n^2\pi^2} \Big|_0^1 = .2 \frac{(1 - (-1)^n)}{n^2\pi^2}.$$

Therefore,

$$(40\text{-}11) \quad f(x) = .05 + \frac{.4}{\pi^2} \left[\frac{\cos \pi x}{1^2} + \frac{\cos 3\pi x}{3^2} + \frac{\cos 5\pi x}{5^2} + \cdots \right].$$

EXERCISE 40

1. Let f be a function for which f'' is continuous. Show that the equation $y = f(\sin x)$ defines a function in the domain of L_P.

2. Suppose that $f(x) = \sin x \cos x$ and that $g(x) = 3 \cos x - 2 \cos 3x$. In terms of the dot product of this section, show that $f \cdot g = 0$.

3. Find the Fourier series for $f(x)$ in each of the following cases, and discuss its convergence in the interval $[-\pi, \pi]$. (Do not be alarmed by the queer formulas; just sketch a graph of f, and you will see how simple these functions are.)

   (a) $f(x) = |x|$ (d) $f(x) = |\sin x|$
   (b) $f(x) = x + |x|$ (e) $f(x) = 1 + \text{int }(\cos x)$
   (c) $f(x) = x|x|$ (f) $f(x) = .1 \cdot (\pi - |x|)/\pi$

4. If $|x| = a_0 + \sum\limits_{n=1}^{\infty} (a_n \cos nx + b_n \sin nx)$ for $x \in (-\pi, \pi)$, find the following coefficients.

   (a) a_0 (b) a_{1776} (c) b_{1492}

5. If $\{a_n\}$ and $\{b_n\}$ are the sequences of Fourier coefficients of a function f, and $\{A_n\}$ and $\{B_n\}$ are the sequences of Fourier coefficients of a function g, what are the coefficients of the Fourier series for $3f(x) - 5g(x)$?

6. Use Equation 40-11 to show that $\frac{1}{8}\pi^2 = 1 + 3^{-2} + 5^{-2} + \cdots$.

7. Sketch the graph of the sum of the series in Equation 40-11 for x in the interval $[-3, 3]$.

8. Verify the statements in Fig. 40-4.

9. Verify that L_P is a symmetric operator.

10. Run off a few partial sums of the series in Equation 40-7 on the computer to get an idea of how fast it converges. Which series converges faster, $\sum\limits_{n=1}^{\infty} n^{-2}$ or

$$\sum\limits_{n=1}^{\infty} 2^{-n}?$$

11. Using basic integration theorems, write out a formal proof of Equations 40-4.

12. Explain why the domain of L_P is a linear space; that is, linear combinations of its elements are also elements.

41   TWO SINGULAR CHARACTERISTIC VALUE PROBLEMS

Since our study of regular characteristic value problems is far from complete, it may seem out of place to devote a section to the much more difficult subject of singular problems. This class of problems is so important, however, that you should at least have a chance to see two of its best known members.

Our first singular characteristic value problem bears the name of **Legendre.** Legendre's differential operator L is defined by the equation

$$L_x y = -((1 - x^2)y')',$$

and we apply it to functions defined in the interval $(-1, 1)$. In this interval, L is a differential operator of the second order, so we naturally choose as its domain the class $C''(-1, 1)$ of functions with continuous second derived functions in $(-1, 1)$.

Now we will restrict the domain of L to a class of functions that "behave properly" at the boundary points -1 and 1 of our basic interval and thus obtain a new operator L_L. In our present situation, "proper behavior" of a function simply means belonging to the class $C''[-1, 1]$ of functions with continuous second derived functions in the *closed* interval $[-1, 1]$. So we choose as the domain of L_L the set $C''[-1, 1]$. Thus, the equation $u(x) = (1 - x)^2$ defines a function in the domain of L_L, but the equation $v(x) = (1 - x)^{1/2}$ does not (although v *is* in the domain of L).

The reason that Legendre's characteristic value problem is called *singular* becomes apparent when we consider the equation $L_{Lx}y = \lambda y$. Here, we have to solve the differential equation

(41-1) $$-((1 - x^2)y')' = \lambda y.$$

When we write this equation in the "standard form" for a homogeneous linear differential equation $(y'' + p(x)y' + q(x)y = 0)$ it becomes

$$y'' - \frac{2x}{1 - x^2}y' + \frac{\lambda}{1 - x^2}y = 0.$$

Obviously, the coefficient functions are not continuous in the closed interval $[-1, 1]$; the endpoints are *singular points*.

We might therefore expect trouble at the endpoints, and, in general, we would get it. Thus, suppose that λ is an arbitrary number. Since the coefficients of the homogeneous linear differential Equation 41-1 are continuous in the open interval $(-1, 1)$, the domain of a solution w will certainly contain this interval. But the chances are that w cannot be extended to the *closed* interval $[-1, 1]$. For example, it might be true that $\lim_{x \downarrow -1} w(x) = \infty$, and then w would not be a member of $C''[-1, 1]$. Only for certain choices of λ are solutions "continuable" to the whole interval $[-1, 1]$, and these choices are the characteristic values of our problem. Before we indicate what these characteristic values are, let us show that L_L is a symmetric operator.

Although the proof is the same as the one we used for our previous differential operators, we will run through it again, because it helps to illustrate the importance of choosing $C''[-1, 1]$ as the domain of L_L. We must show that two functions u and v of this class satisfy the fundamental symmetry relation $L_L u \cdot v = u \cdot L_L v$. Since we are working in the interval $[-1, 1]$, we will naturally define the dot product of two continuous functions f and g by means of the equation $f \cdot g = \int_{-1}^{1} f(x)g(x)dx$. Therefore, we must show that

$$(41\text{-}2) \quad -\int_{-1}^{1} ((1 - x^2)u'(x))'v(x)dx = -\int_{-1}^{1} u(x)((1 - x^2)v'(x))'dx.$$

From the rules for differentiating sums and products, we see that

$$[(1 - x^2)u'(x)v(x) - u(x)(1 - x^2)v'(x)]'$$
$$= ((1 - x^2)u'(x))'v(x) - u(x)((1 - x^2)v'(x))',$$

and hence

$$\int_{-1}^{1} [((1 - x^2)u'(x))'v(x) - u(x)((1 - x^2)v'(x))']dx$$
$$= (1 - x^2)u'(x)v(x) - u(x)(1 - x^2)v'(x) \Big|_{-1}^{1} = 0 \cdot u'(1)v(1)$$
$$- u(1) \cdot 0 \cdot v'(1) - 0 \cdot u'(-1)v(-1) + u(-1) \cdot 0 \cdot v'(-1) = 0.$$

This last equation is equivalent to Equation 41-2, so the symmetry of L_L is established. Notice that we did not need to know *what* the numbers $u(1)$, $v(1)$, and so on, are. But we did need to know that these numbers exist (more precisely, that $u(1^-)$, $v(1^-)$, and so on, exist).

Because it is symmetric, the characteristic values of our operator L_L are real numbers, and characteristic functions that correspond to different characteristic values are orthogonal. We even know what the characteristic values and characteristic functions are. In Section 33, we saw that if we replace λ with $n(n + 1)$, where n is a non-negative integer, then Equation 41-1 is satisfied by $y = P_n(x)$, the Legendre polynomial of degree n. Obviously, $P_n \in C''[-1, 1]$, and so at least some of the characteristic values for the Legendre problem are given by the formula

$$\lambda_n = n(n + 1), \, n = 0, 1, 2, \dots,$$

and corresponding characteristic functions are defined by the equation

$$u_n(x) = P_n(x).$$

Of course, we haven't proved that these are *all* the characteristic values and characteristic functions, but they are.

Example 41-1.   Verify directly that $u_2 \cdot u_4 = 0$.

Solution. We must show that

$$\int_{-1}^{1} P_2(x)P_4(x)dx = 0.$$

From Table 33-1, we find that

$$P_2(x) = \tfrac{3}{2}x^2 - \tfrac{1}{2} \text{ and } P_4(x) = \tfrac{35}{8}x^4 - \tfrac{15}{4}x^2 + \tfrac{3}{8}.$$

Therefore, since both polynomials are even,

$$\int_{-1}^{1} P_2(x)P_4(x)dx = 2\int_0^1 (\tfrac{3}{2}x^2 - \tfrac{1}{2})(\tfrac{35}{8}x^4 - \tfrac{15}{4}x^2 + \tfrac{3}{8})dx$$

$$= \tfrac{1}{8}\int_0^1 (3x^2 - 1)(35x^4 - 30x^2 + 3)dx = \tfrac{1}{8}\int_0^1 (105x^6 - 125x^4 + 39x^2 - 3)dx$$

$$\tfrac{1}{8}(15x^7 - 25x^5 + 13x^3 - 3x)\Big|_0^1 = \tfrac{1}{8}(15 - 25 + 13 - 3) = 0.$$

As we found in our non-singular problems, the values of an arbitrary function f in the domain of L_L can be expressed as an infinite combination of values of characteristic functions. That is, there is a sequence $\{c_n\}$ of coefficients such that

(41-3) $$f(x) = \sum_{n=0}^{\infty} c_n P_n(x).$$

The general formula $c_n = f \cdot u_n / |u_n|^2$ (Theorem 36-5) becomes in the present case

(41-4) $$c_n = \int_{-1}^{1} f(x)P_n(x)dx \Big/ \int_{-1}^{1} P_n(x)^2 dx.$$

In Exercise 33-5, we stated that $\displaystyle\int_{-1}^{1} P_n(x)^2 dx = \frac{2}{2n+1}$, and therefore Formula 41-4 simplifies to

(41-5) $$c_n = \frac{2n+1}{2} \int_{-1}^{1} f(x)P_n(x)dx.$$

As was true with Fourier series, Equation 41-3 holds for a somewhat broader class of functions than the domain of our operator L_L, but we won't go into that question here.

Example 41-2. In Exercise 33-10, we asked you to convince yourself that for each integer $n \geq 0$, x^n can be expressed as a linear combination of the polynomials in the set $\{P_0(x), P_1(x), \ldots, P_n(x)\}$. Find this combination for x^5.

Solution. The answer to the problem will be

$$x^5 = c_0 P_0(x) + c_1 P_1(x) + c_2 P_2(x) + c_3 P_3(x) + c_4 P_4(x) + c_5 P_5(x),$$

where (according to Equation 41-5)

$$c_n = \frac{2n+1}{2} \int_{-1}^{1} x^5 P_n(x)dx.$$

Notice that P_0, P_2, and P_4 are even, and that P_1, P_3, and P_5 are odd, while $y = x^5$ defines an odd function. Therefore, c_0, c_2, and c_4 are 0, and (see Table 33-1 for the explicit Legendre polynomials we are using)

$$c_1 = 3 \int_0^1 x^5 P_1(x)dx = 3 \int_0^1 x^6 dx = \tfrac{3}{7},$$

$$c_3 = 7 \int_0^1 x^5 P_3(x)dx = \tfrac{7}{2} \int_0^1 (5x^8 - 3x^6)dx = \tfrac{7}{2}(\tfrac{5}{9} - \tfrac{3}{7}) = \tfrac{4}{9},$$

$$c_5 = 11 \int_0^1 x^5 P_5(x)dx = \tfrac{11}{8} \int_0^1 (63x^{10} - 70x^8 + 15x^6)dx$$

$$= \tfrac{11}{8}(\tfrac{63}{11} - \tfrac{70}{9} + \tfrac{15}{7}) = \tfrac{8}{63}.$$

Thus, finally,

$$x^5 = \tfrac{8}{63}P_5(x) + \tfrac{4}{9}P_3(x) + \tfrac{3}{7}P_1(x),$$

an equation that is easy to check.

The other singular characteristic value problem we want to take up is **Bessel's.** We will suppose throughout our discussion that m is a given positive integer or 0 and that Bessel's differential operator L is defined by the equation

$$L_x y = -(xy')' + \frac{m^2}{x} y.$$

To be definite, let us suppose that $[0, 1]$ is our basic interval. Thus, our differential operator is "singular" at the left endpoint of this interval, but the right endpoint is a regular point. We therefore think of its domain as the class $C''(0, 1]$. Now we restrict the domain of L to a class of functions that "behave properly" at the singular point 0 and that satisfy a boundary condition at the regular point 1. Specifically, a function u belongs to the domain of our Bessel operator L_B if it satisfies the boundary condition $u(1) = 0$, if $u \in C''[0, 1]$, and if $\lim_{x \downarrow 0} m^2 u(x)/x$ exists.

Our present characteristic value problem is slightly different from our earlier ones. Instead of solving the equation $L_{Bx}y = \lambda y$ for a characteristic value λ, we try to find a number λ such that the equation

(41-6) $$L_{Bx}y = \lambda xy$$

has a non-trivial solution. Because of the x on the right-hand side of this equation, we here define the dot product of two continuous functions f and g by the equation

$$f \cdot g = \int_0^1 xf(x)g(x)\,dx.$$

From the easily verified symmetry equation $\int_0^1 u(x)L_B v(x)\,dx = \int_0^1 L_B u(x)v(x)\,dx$, it follows that characteristic values are real numbers, and characteristic functions corresponding to different characteristic values are orthogonal. Furthermore, as with the operator L_0 that we studied in Section 39, characteristic values of L_B are positive.

Although it certainly looks as if we are pulling operators, inner products, and so on, out of a bottomless hat, the fact is that these problems actually arise in practice. Problem 41-6 comes up when we study potential theory in a cylindrically symmetric region (along a straight wire, for example), and the Legendre problem arises when the region is spherically symmetric (around a point charge, for instance). Bessel originally ran into his equation when he was working on a problem in astronomy.

The differential equation of Problem 41-6 is

$$-(xy')' + \frac{m^2}{x}y = \lambda xy,$$

and in Example 35-3 we showed that this equation is satisfied by $y = J_m(\sqrt{\lambda}\,x)$, where J_m is the Bessel function of the first kind of index m. For any positive number λ, this equation defines a function of the class $C''[0, 1]$, and $\lim\limits_{x \downarrow 0} m^2 y/x$ exists. To satisfy the boundary conditions $y = 0$ when $x = 1$, we must pick λ so that

(41-7) $$J_m(\sqrt{\lambda}) = 0.$$

In Section 35, we stated that the Bessel function J_m has an infinite sequence $\{z_{mn}\}$ of positive zeros. In other words, $J_m(z_{mn}) = 0$ for $n = 1, 2, 3, \ldots$. Thus, we can solve the Characteristic Equation 41-7, and we see that the nth characteristic value of Bessel's Problem (of index m) is

$$\lambda_n = z_{mn}^2.$$

The corresponding characteristic function u_n can be chosen as the function that is defined by the equation

$$u_n(x) = J_m(z_{mn}x).$$

Example 41-3. Suppose that $m = 1$. Find the value of our first characteristic function u_1 at the midpoint of the basic interval.

Solution. The midpoint of the interval $[0, 1]$ is, of course, the point $x = .5$, and $u_1(x) = J_1(z_{11}x)$, so we are asking for the number $J_1(.5z_{11})$. The number z_{11} is the first positive zero of J_1; that is, it is the smallest positive solution of the equation $J_1(z) = 0$. Figure 35-1 suggests that this number is approximately 4. Thus, we are looking for the number $J_1(2)$, which (from Fig. 35-1 again) is approximately .6.

Example 41-4. Let u_n be the nth characteristic function of Bessel's Problem of index m, and let x be any point of the interval $(0, 1)$. Show that $\lim_{n \uparrow \infty} u_n(x) = 0$.

Solution. We are to show that $\lim_{n \uparrow \infty} J_m(z_{mn}x) = 0$. In Section 35, we pointed out that for n large, the members of the sequence $\{z_{mn}\}$ are about π units apart. Hence, $\lim_{n \uparrow \infty} z_{mn} = \infty$. Therefore, $\lim_{n \uparrow \infty} J_m(z_{mn}x) = \lim_{z \uparrow \infty} J_m(z)$. But from Equation 35-6, it is clear that $\lim_{z \uparrow \infty} J_m(z) = 0$, so the original statement is verified.

Values of arbitrary functions in the domain of L_B can be expressed as infinite combinations of values of its characteristic functions. We won't have time to discuss the details, which follow our earlier results almost exactly.

All our differential characteristic value problems fall into the same pattern, and it has no doubt occurred to you that it might be more efficient to study the general class of such problems all at once, rather than (as we did) look at specific examples. Of course, that is precisely what mathematicians do. The general class of problems of which our problems are examples is the class of **Sturm-Liouville** problems, and you will find a discussion of this class in many books (for example, [2], [5], and [10]). Our specific examples of Sturm-Liouville problems are perhaps the most common ones, but many others also arise in practice. For example, you may encounter the names of Hermite and Laguerre in this connection. As you can guess, one can spend any amount of time studying this interesting and important topic.

EXERCISE 41

1. If $|x| = \sum_{n=0}^{\infty} c_n P_n(x)$, what is c_{1861}?

2. If f is an odd function in $C''[-1, 1]$, and $f(x) = \sum_{n=0}^{\infty} c_n P_n(x)$, show that $c_{2k} = 0$ for $k = 0, 1, \ldots$. What is the formula for c_{2k+1}?

3. Show that $\int_0^\pi \sin tP_m(\cos t)P_n(\cos t)dt = 0$ if $m \neq n$. What if $m = n$?

4. (a) If $x|x| = \sum_{n=0}^{\infty} c_n P_n(x)$ for each $x \in [-1, 1]$, find c_0, c_1, c_2, and c_3.

(b) Compare $x|x|$ and $\sum_{n=0}^{3} c_n P_n(x)$ at the points of the set $\{0, .5, 1\}$.

5. Suppose that $x^5 = \sum_{n=0}^{5} c_n P_n(x)$.

(a) Set $x = 1$ to show that $\sum_{n=0}^{5} c_n = 1$.

(b) Apply the operator L_{Lx} to both sides of the equation, and then set $x = 1$, to show that $10 = \sum_{n=0}^{5} n(n+1)c_n$.

(c) Check the results of parts (a) and (b) with our explicit formulas of Example 41-2.

6. Use integration by parts to show that if u is a function in the domain of L_L, then $u \cdot L_L u > 0$, unless u is a constant function.

7. We have stated that x^m can be expressed as a linear combination of the members of the set $\{P_0(x), P_1(x), \ldots, P_m(x)\}$.

(a) Use this fact to show that if $n > m$, then $\int_{-1}^{1} x^m P_n(x)\,dx = 0$.

(b) Now show that if $r(x)$ is a polynomial of degree less than n, then $\int_{-1}^{1} r(x) P_n(x)\,dx = 0$.

8. If the equation $\int_0^1 J_5(z_{53}x) J_5(z_{54}x)\,dx = 0$ is not correct, what is?

9. If f is in the domain of L_B, and $f(x) = \sum_{n=1}^{\infty} c_n J_m(z_{mn}x)$, what is the formula for c_n?

10. It can be shown that $z_{03} = 8.653728$ (where z_{03} is the third positive solution of the equation $J_0(z) = 0$). Use the computer to make a table of values of the characteristic function u_3 of Bessel's Problem of index 0 at the points of the set $\{0, .2, .4, .6, .8, 1.0\}$. Sketch the graph of u_3 in the interval $[0, 1]$.

11. If u_n is the nth characteristic function of Bessel's Problem of index m, show that the equation $u_n(x) = 0$ has exactly $n - 1$ solutions in the interval $(0, 1)$.

12. It is an interesting fact that for each positive integer n the equation $P_n(x) = 0$ has exactly n distinct solutions in the interval $[-1, 1]$. You might verify this statement for $n = 1$, 2, and 3. Here is a way to prove it in general.

(a) If $\{r_1, r_2, \ldots, r_m\}$ is the set of solutions of the equation $P_n(x) = 0$ in the interval $[-1, 1]$, explain why $m \leq n$.

(b) Now let $r(x) = (x - r_1)(x - r_2) \cdots \cdots (x - r_m)$, and explain why $q(x) = P_n(x)/r(x)$ is a polynomial that has the same sign for each $x \in [-1, 1]$.

(c) Use the result of part (b) to show that $\int_{-1}^{1} r(x) P_n(x)\,dx = \int_{-1}^{1} r(x)^2 q(x)\,dx \neq 0$.

(d) Now use the inequality in part (c) and the result of Exercise 41-7(b) to show that the degree of $r(x)$ cannot be *less than n*.

(e) From parts (a) and (d), infer that $m = n$.

REVIEW EXERCISE, CHAPTER 6

Use the following exercises to test yourself on the material in this chapter.

1. Find an even function that takes only odd values and an odd function that takes only even values.

2. Theorem 30-2 says that it is all right to differentiate a power series term-by-term. By means of an example, show that it is *not* all right to differentiate an arbitrary Fourier series term-by-term.

3. Explain why the operator L_0 of Section 39 has an inverse, but the operator L_P of Section 40 does not.

4. Find a set of *normalized* characteristic functions for the operator L_0 of Section 39.

5. If $f(x) = a_0 + \sum_{n=1}^{\infty} (a_n \cos nx + b_n \sin nx)$ for each $x \in [-\pi, \pi]$, can you convince yourself that $\frac{1}{2}[f(x) - f(-x)] = \sum_{n=1}^{\infty} b_n \sin nx$? What is $\frac{1}{2}[f(x) + f(-x)]$?

6. (a) If $P_7(x) = a_0 + \sum_{n=1}^{\infty} (a_n \cos nx + b_n \sin nx)$, what is a_{17}?

   (b) If $J_8(x) = a_0 + \sum_{n=1}^{\infty} (a_n \cos nx + b_n \sin nx)$, what is b_{17}?

7. If $e^x = \sum_{n=0}^{\infty} c_n P_n(x)$, what is $\sum_{n=0}^{\infty} c_n$? $\sum_{n=0}^{\infty} (-1)^n c_n$?

8. (a) Show that our Bessel operator L_B is symmetric.
   (b) Show that the characteristic values of L_B are positive.

9. Let L_2 be the restriction of the operator $-D^2$ to those members of the class $C''[0, 1]$ that satisfy the boundary conditions $y = 0$ when $x = 0$ and $y = 0$ when $x = 1$. What are the characteristic values and corresponding characteristic functions for this operator?

10. Suppose that $\{u_i\}$ is a set of n orthogonal characteristic vectors of an n by n symmetric matrix A. Then we know that if $\mathbf{x}$ is an arbitrary element of R^n, there is a set $\{a_i\}$ of numbers such that $\mathbf{x} = \sum_{i=1}^{n} a_i \mathbf{u}_i$. Can you show that

$$|\mathbf{x}|^2 = \sum_{i=1}^{n} a_i^2 |\mathbf{u}_i|^2 = \sum_{i=1}^{n} (\mathbf{x} \cdot \mathbf{u}_i)^2 / |\mathbf{u}_i|^2?$$ What would be the corresponding

equation if we were talking about our operator L_0 of Section 39, instead of the matrix A?

11. (a) For each positive integer m, the equation $y = \sin m\pi x$ defines a function of class $C''[-1, 1]$; that is, a member of the domain of our Legendre operator L_L. Explain how our theory tells us that $\sin m\pi x =$

$$\sum_{k=0}^{\infty} c_{m,2k+1} P_{2k+1}(x), \text{ where } c_{m,2k+1} = (4k + 3) \int_0^1 \sin m\pi x P_{2k+1}(x)dx.$$

(b) On the other hand, in Section 40 we saw that for each non-negative integer k, $P_{2k+1}(x)$ can be written as an infinite linear combination of the members of the sequence $\{\sin m\pi x\}$ in the interval $(-1, 1)$. That is,

$$P_{2k+1}(x) = \sum_{m=1}^{\infty} b_{2k+1,m} \sin m\pi x. \text{ Show that } b_{2k+1,m} = \frac{2}{4k + 3} c_{m,2k+1}.$$

12. Show that $\int_0^1 P_{1492}(x)dx = 0$.

REFERENCES

1. Agnew, Ralph P. *Differential Equations*. Second Edition. McGraw-Hill, New York, 1960.

2. Birkhoff, Garrett, and Rota, Gian-Carlo. *Ordinary Differential Equations*. Second Edition. Blaisdell, Waltham, Mass., 1969.

3. Brauer, Fred, and Nohel, John A. *Ordinary Differential Equations*. Benjamin, New York, 1967.

4. ———. *Qualitative Theory of Ordinary Differential Equations*. Benjamin, New York, 1969.

5. Churchill, Ruel V. *Fourier Series and Boundary Value Problems*. Second Edition. McGraw-Hill, New York, 1963.

6. Coddington, Earl A., and Levinson, Norman. *Theory of Ordinary Differential Equations*. McGraw-Hill, New York, 1955.

7. Courant, Richard, and John, Fritz. *Introduction to Calculus and Analysis*. Volume I. Interscience, New York, 1965.

8. Fisher, Robert C., and Ziebur, Allen D. *Calculus and Analytic Geometry*. Second Edition. Prentice-Hall, Englewood Cliffs, N.J., 1965.

9. Moursund, David G., and Duris, Charles S. *Elementary Theory and Applications of Numerical Analysis*. McGraw-Hill, New York, 1967.

10. Ritger, Paul D., and Rose, Nicholas J. *Differential Equations with Applications*. McGraw-Hill, New York, 1968.

SELECTED ANSWERS

1. (a) no; (b) yes; (c) yes; (d) no. **2.** (a) $\{n\pi: n \text{ an integer}\}$; (c) e; (e) no solution; (g) $\bigcup\limits_{k=-\infty}^{\infty} [2k\pi, (2k+1)\pi]$; (i) 0. **3.** one real solution, four of the form $a + bi$, with $b \neq 0$. **6.** 3, 2. **7.** $f'(x) \neq 0$ for each $x \in (a, b)$. **8.** 1.68233. **10.** 4.27478.

EXERCISE 2. *Page 10*

1. (a) $x_1 = 1.0417$, $x_2 = x_6 = 1.4023$; (c) $x_1 = 2.7813$, $x_2 = x_6 = 2.7726$.
2. .5. **4.** (a) $x_{n+1} = x_n - (\sin x_n - p)/\cos x_n$. **5.** 3.14 feet.
7. $\{1.00000, 0.83333, 0.76438, 0.75502, 0.75488\}$. **8.** (a) 1.042336; (c) 2.772604.
9. 4.65878.

EXERCISE 3. *Page 16*

1. They are the same. **3.** $\exp^{-1} = \ln$. **5.** $f(x) = .5 - |x - \text{int}(x) - .5|$.
6. $y' = \cos x / |\cos x|$.

EXERCISE 4. *Page 20*

1. (a) domain $(0, \infty)$, range $(-\infty, \infty)$; (c) domain $(-\frac{1}{2}\pi, \frac{1}{2}\pi)$, range $[0, \infty)$.
2. $D_x f(2x) = 2f'(2x)$. **3.** $F(x) = |x|$. **4.** domain $[-3, 3]$, range $[0, \frac{9}{2}\pi]$.
5. $\frac{1}{4}(\pi - \ln 4)$. **7.** (a) $5^x + x^5$; (c) $2x \exp(x^4)$. **8.** local minimum when $x = 1$, local maximum when $x = 0$.

EXERCISE 5.   *Page 27*

7. integral = 3.1416.   **10.** *e.*

EXERCISE 6.   *Page 32*

9. Notice that $y = 2 \ln x$.

REVIEW EXERCISE, CHAPTER ONE.   *Page 33*

1. (c) domain $(-1, 1)$, range $(0, 1]$; (d) no.   **3.** $a^2 \leq 3b$.   **4.** $\int_0^5 \text{int } (x)\,dx$, $n = 5$.   **5.** (b) domain $[2, 6]$, range $[-1, 2]$; (c) no.   **7.** yes.

EXERCISE 7.   *Page 41*

1. (a) $y = \frac{1}{2}(\pi - \cos 2x)$; (c) $y = 5 + x|x|$; (e) $y = e - e^{1/x}$.
2. (a) $y = \frac{1}{2}(3 - \cos x^2)$; (c) $y = x \ln x - x + 3$.   **3.** $y = 4x^2 + 4$.   **5.** 4.7 meters per second, upward.   **6.** $v_{100} = 2000 \ln 3 - 980$ meters per second; that is, about 1217 meters per second.

EXERCISE 8.   *Page 48*

1. (a) $y = -\frac{1}{2}(e^{-2x} - 3)$; (c) $y = (1 - x)e^x$; (e) $y = -3 \sec x$; (g) $y = 6 \exp(x|x|)$.
2. 272.   **7.** (a) $y = 4/(3e^{-3x} - e^x)$.   **8.** account is empty after 14 years.
9. $A(t) = 10(1 - \exp(-t/10))$.

EXERCISE 9.   *Page 53*

1. (a) $(2 + x)/(1 - 2x)$; (c) $y = \sqrt{4 + x|x|}$; (e) $y = x + \frac{1}{2}\pi$;
(f) $y = \text{Tan}^{-1} x^2 + \pi$.   **2.** $f(x) = -\ln(5 - e^x)$.   **3.** $3x^2 - y^2 = -1$.
4. $y = -\text{Sin}^{-1} x^3 + \pi$.   **7.** $\sqrt{\frac{19}{2}}$.   **8.** $w(1) = 11 - \sqrt{3}$.

EXERCISE 10.   *Page 60*

1. (a) $y = 3 + 2x^2 - 2x - e^{-2x}$; (b) $y = (6 - 2e^{8x})/(3 + e^{8x})$;
(c) $y = 2 - \ln(-\cos x)$; (d) $y = 2 - \ln(1 + 3x)$.   **2.** (a) $y = -\ln(1 - 2x)$;
(b) $y = 2 \text{Tan}(2x + \frac{1}{4}\pi)$.   **5.** $y = 3e^x - 3x - 2$.   **6.** $y = \frac{5}{3} \sin 3x$.
8. (a) $y = e^x$; (b) $y = e^{-x}$.

REVIEW EXERCISE, CHAPTER TWO.   *Page 61*

1. $y' = [(e^x - \cos x)y + e^x(\cos x - \sin x)]/(e^x - \sin x)$.   **3.** $y = e^{x^2}$ and $y = e^{-x^2}$.   **4.** $y = 2 \exp(\frac{1}{2}x) - 2 - x$.   **6.** (a) $y = \sqrt{x^2 + 3x}$;
(b) $y = \frac{1}{2}\sqrt{4x^2 - 3x}$.   **7.** (a) $y = x$.   **8.** $y = (e^{|x|} - 1)x/|x|$.   **9.** We must solve the equation $\int_{x_0+y_0}^{x+y} \frac{du}{1 + f(u)} = x - x_0$ for y.   **10.** (b) $w''(0) = 2$.

EXERCISE 11. *Page 72*

1. $w(x) = -\frac{3}{4}x - \frac{3}{16}$, one.   **4.** (a) $y' = y/x$; (c) $y' = -2xy$.
5. $x^2 + y^2 = c$ represents the family of solution curves.   **6.** $y = ce^x - 1 - x$.
8. $y' = -G_1(x, y)/G_2(x, y)$.   **9.** $y = 6/x$.   **10.** $y = (x/|x|)(e^{|x|} - |x| - 1)$.
11. $y = cx^4$.

EXERCISE 12. *Page 81*

1. (a) $w(x) = (1 + x^3)/x$; (b) $w(x) = \sqrt[3]{1 + \sin x}$; (c) no solution;
(d) $w(x) = \text{Tan}^{-1}(e^x - 2) - \pi$.   **2.** (a) $\frac{1}{8}$.   **5.** $y = 10(\cosh .1x - 1)$.
8. (b) $f(x) = wx^2/2h$; (c) $25/\sqrt{3} + r$ meters high, where we are supposing that the
lowest part of the suspending cable is r meters above the roadway.

10. $w_n(x) = \sum\limits_{k=0}^{n} x^k/k!$.

EXERCISE 13. *Page 87*

7. no, no.   **8.** no.

EXERCISE 14. *Page 95*

1. (c) $y = 0$.   **3.** $b < \frac{1}{2}\pi$.   **4.** (a) no; $w_3'(x) > 0$ for each $x \geq 0$.
8. $y = 10$ also satisfies the initial value problem; maybe the poison doesn't kill any rats.
11. $y = 0$.

EXERCISE 15. *Page 103*

1. $y = \text{Tan}(x - 3)$, domain $(3 - \frac{1}{2}\pi, 3 + \frac{1}{2}\pi)$.   **4.** no; for example, $y = 1$
also satisfies the initial value problem.   **8.** $y = x$.

REVIEW EXERCISE, CHAPTER THREE. *Page 115*

1. (a) $9\pi - 25$; (b) $[9/\pi, 10/\pi)$.   **2.** $y' = 1 + y^2$.   **4.** (a) $y = 0$ satisfies the
differential equation, and solution curves do not intersect; (e) yes.   **6.** yes.
7. $y = 8x^3$ and $y = 0$.   **9.** (a) $u(x) = 5x + 5$; (b) $\frac{1}{5}$; (c) $v(x) = 4x + 5$; (d) $-\frac{1}{4}$;
(f) no.

EXERCISE 18. *Page 126*

1. (a) 5; (c) $5(\sqrt{5} - 5)$; (e) 1; (g) $\sqrt{2}$.   **4.** (b) $\begin{bmatrix} 3 & 0 \\ 0 & 5 \end{bmatrix}$.   **11.** (a) 1; (c) 0.

EXERCISE 19. *Page 132*

3. $(x, y) = (e^t + e^{-3t} + e^{2t}, e^t - 3e^{-3t} + 2e^{2t})$.   **4.** $(x, y) = (3e^{-4t} + e^{4t}, 2e^{4t} - 6e^{-4t})$.   **5.** $\mathbf{x} = e^{3t}(2, -1) + 2(e^{3t} - 1)(1, 0)$.   **6.** $t_0 + kh$.   **9.** (d) less
than 6 minutes.

EXERCISE 20.   *Page 138*

1. (a) $(-\frac{1}{2}\pi, \frac{1}{2}\pi)$.   4. (c) $(e^t, -e^t)$.   6. (a) $\begin{bmatrix} 1+t & t \\ -t & 1-t \end{bmatrix}$;

(b) $(t^2+1, 2t+2)$.   7. $\begin{bmatrix} \frac{3}{4}+\frac{1}{4}e^{4t} & \frac{1}{4}(e^{4t}-1) \\ \frac{3}{4}(e^{4t}-1) & \frac{1}{4}+\frac{3}{4}e^{4t} \end{bmatrix}$.

EXERCISE 21.   *Page 146*

1. (a) $-2, 3$; (b) $(2, 1), (1, 1)$; (e) $(4e^{-2t}-3e^{3t}, 2e^{-2t}-3e^{3t})$.   3. (a) $i, -i$; (c) $(1, i), (1, -i)$.   4. $(3e^t-e^{3t}+\sinh t, -e^{3t})$.   5. $(te^{-2t}+e^{-2t}+t, 1+e^{-2t})$.

EXERCISE 22.   *Page 152*

1. (b) $(3+\sin t, 3\sin t+1)$; (c) $(1+t+\sin t, 1+t\sin t+\sin t)$.
2. (b) (e^{-t}, t); (c) $(0, e^t)$.   4. $-2\exp(t^2+\sin t)$.   5. $\begin{bmatrix} 2e^{2(t-1)} & 3e^{2(t-1)} \\ 2e^{-3(t-1)} \cdot & 3e^{-3(t-1)} \end{bmatrix}$.
6. no such A.   8. (b) no.

EXERCISE 23.   *Page 159*

1. (a) $(0, \frac{1}{2}\pi)$; (c) $(\frac{9}{2}\pi, \frac{11}{2}\pi)$.   2. the second question is meaningless.
3. not if $u(t) = 0 \cdot v(t)$.   5. (a) 0; (c) $3\cos 4t - \sin 4t$.   6. (c) $-3t + 2e^t$.
8. (a) $3e^t - e^{-2t} + e^{3t}$; (c) $(3t-1)e^t + e^{-2t}$.   9. (b) $2\cos t - 2\sin t + t$.

EXERCISE 24.   *Page 165*

1. (a) $e^t\cos 2t, e^t\sin 2t$; (b) e^t, te^t; (c) e^{-t}, e^{3t}; (d) $1, e^{-3t}$.
2. (a) $2\cos 3t + \sin 3t$; (b) $e^{-t}(2\sin t - 3\cos t)$; (c) $2\cosh 3t + \sinh 3t - 2$;
(d) $e^{2t} - e^{-t}(t+2)$.   5. $a = 0, b > 0$.   6. $a > 0$.   9. (a) (t, t^{-3});
(b) (t^{-1}, t^{-2}); (c) $(t\sqrt{3}, t^{-\sqrt{3}})$; (d) $(1, t^{-3})$.

EXERCISE 25.   *Page 171*

1. (a) $\theta = .1e^{-.1t}\sin 2t$.   3. the earth.   5. (a) $\sqrt{\theta_0^2 + \theta_{1r}^2/g}$.
6. A is the maximum displacement only when $k = 0$, or when $\delta = 0$ or π.

EXERCISE 27.   *Page 185*

1. (a) $a < 0$; (b) $a^2 < 2$; (c) $a < 0$.   5. $K = 1, \alpha = 2$.   9. yes.   11. (c) no.

EXERCISE 28.   *Page 193*

4. after.   7. (d) yes.

REVIEW EXERCISE, CHAPTER FOUR. *Page 194*

1. (a) $P = \begin{bmatrix} 1 & 1 \\ 1 & -1 \end{bmatrix}$. **2.** $\begin{bmatrix} 9 & -8e^{4t} \\ 4e^{-4t} & -7 \end{bmatrix}$.

3. $W(u(t_0), v(t_0)) \exp\left(-\int_{t_0}^{t} p(u)\,du\right)$. **5.** $\begin{bmatrix} \cos t^2 & \sin t^2 \\ -\sin t^2 & \cos t^2 \end{bmatrix}$.

6. $w(t) = \sin(t + |t|) + \sinh(t - |t|)$ for $t \in (-\infty, \frac{1}{2}\pi)$. **10.** $\exp(e^{-2t} + t - 1)$.
11. $K = 1$, $\alpha = 2$.

EXERCISE 29. *Page 202*

1. (b) 0; (c) e^2, $e^2 - 1$. **3.** (a) converges; (b) converges; (c) converges;
(d) converges; (e) converges; (f) diverges.

EXERCISE 30. *Page 209*

1. (a) $\sum_{k=0}^{\infty} \frac{x^{2k}}{(2k)!}$; (c) $\frac{1}{2} \sum_{k=0}^{\infty} \left\{ \sum_{j=0}^{k} (-1)^{(j-1)/2}[1 - (-1)^j]/j!(k-j)! \right\} x^k$.

3. (a) $(-\infty, \infty)$; (b) $(-\infty, \infty)$. **4.** no. **7.** (a) $(-\infty, \infty)$; (b) 11.
10. (a) $(-1, 1)$; (d) $e^x/(1-x)$.

EXERCISE 31. *Page 218*

3. (a) $c_j = 4c_{j-2}/j(j-1)$. **4.** $y = 15x - 20x^3 + 4x^5$.

5. $y = \sum_{k=0}^{\infty} c_k(x-1)^k$, where $c_0 = 3$, $c_1 = -2$, and $c_j = -c_{j-2}/(j-1)$, $j = 2, 3, \ldots$

EXERCISE 32. *Page 224*

1. (a) $c_j = -(j^2 - 5j + 5)c_{j-2}/j(j-1)$; (b) $(-1, 1)$. **3.** $(-\infty, \infty)$.
4. (a) $c_1 = 1$, $c_2 = 0$, $c_3 = \frac{1}{3}$, $c_4 = 0$, $c_5 = \frac{2}{15}$; (c) $(-\frac{1}{2}\pi, \frac{1}{2}\pi)$.

5. $\sum_{k=0}^{\infty} c_{3k}x^{3k}$, $\sum_{k=0}^{\infty} c_{3k+1}x^{3k+1}$, where $c_j = c_{j-3}/j(j-1)$.

EXERCISE 33. *Page 232*

3. all numbers are 0. **6.** P_0, P_1, and P_2 are all solutions of *different* differential
equations. **8.** $\mu = -2n$. **9.** $d_0 = 1$, $d_k = \frac{1}{2}k^{-2}[n(n+1) - k(k-1)]d_{k-1}$.
10. $x^3 = \frac{3}{5}P_1(x) + \frac{2}{5}P_3(x)$.

EXERCISE 34. *Page 238*

2. $\frac{1}{2}$. **5.** 0. **6.** 0, no.

EXERCISE 35. *Page 243*

1. 0.   **2.** $z = 0$.   **3.** $u(x) = x^{-1/2} \cos x$, $v(x) = x^{-1/2} \sin x$.

REVIEW EXERCISE, CHAPTER FIVE. *Page 244*

3. $J_4(x) = (48x^{-3} - 8x^{-1})J_1(x) + (1 - 24x^{-2})J_0(x)$.   **6.** $e^{-x} \sin x$.
8. c_0 is arbitrary, $c_1 = c_2 = c_3 = 0$, $c_{j+4} = -c_j/(j+3)(j+4)$.

EXERCISE 36. *Page 253*

1. (a) $(0, 3)$; (b) $k(1, 1) + (3, 0)$; (c) no solution.
3. (c) $(1, 1) = \frac{7}{25}u_1 + \frac{1}{25}u_2$.   **4.** (a) $0, 2$; (b) $(1/\sqrt{2}, -1/\sqrt{2})$, $(1/\sqrt{2}, 1/\sqrt{2})$.
5. (a) $-2, 8$; (b) $(1/\sqrt{10}, -3/\sqrt{10})$, $(3/\sqrt{10}, 1/\sqrt{10})$.   **6.** yes, no, yes.

EXERCISE 37. *Page 258*

1. (a) $\int_0^x (x - t)r(t)dt$; (b) x^3.   **2.** (a) $\sin(x - t)$; (b) $x - \sin x$.
3. (a) $\sinh(x - t)$; (b) $\frac{1}{2}xe^x - \frac{1}{2} \sinh x$.   **4.** (a) $u(x) = x^3$, $v(x) = x^2$;
(b) $t^{-2}x^3 - t^{-1}x^2$; (c) $x^6 - 4x^3 + 3x^2$.   **7.** yes, L_0.
9. $L_0^{-1}r(x) = \int_{x_0}^x \exp\left(-\int_t^x p(u)du\right) r(t)dt$.

EXERCISE 38. *Page 264*

1. (a) $G(x, t) = \frac{1}{2}(xt + |x - t| - 1)$; (b) $\frac{1}{3}(x^3 - x)$.
2. $G(x, t) = (e^t - 1)(1 - e^{-x+1})/(e - 1)$ if $0 \le t \le x$,
$G(x, t) = (1 - e^{-x})(e^t - e)/(e + 1)$ if $x \le t \le 1$.
3. (c) $G(x, t) = -(\sin \pi t \cos \pi x)/\pi$ if $0 \le t \le x$, $G(x, t) = -(\sin \pi x \cos \pi t)/\pi$ if
$x \le t \le \frac{1}{2}$.   **4.** (b) $y = \frac{1}{3}x^3 - \frac{10}{3}x + 2$.   **6.** (b) yes.   **7.** (b) yes.

EXERCISE 39. *Page 274*

1. (a) 0; (c) $\exp(\pi^2) - 1$.   **2.** (a) $\frac{1}{2}\pi\sqrt{\pi/3}$.

5. $\left|\int_0^\pi f(x)g(x)dx\right| \le \left(\int_0^\pi f(x)^2 dx\right)^{1/2} \left(\int_0^\pi g(x)^2 dx\right)^{1/2}$.   **6.** (a) $\dfrac{8}{\pi} \displaystyle\sum_{k=0}^{\infty} \dfrac{\sin(2k+1)x}{2k+1}$;

(b) $\dfrac{2}{\pi} \displaystyle\sum_{n=1}^{\infty} \dfrac{1}{n}(\cos \frac{1}{2}n\pi - \cos n\pi) \sin nx$; (c) $2 \displaystyle\sum_{n=1}^{\infty} (-1)^{n+1} \dfrac{\sin nx}{n}$;

(e) $\dfrac{2}{\pi} \displaystyle\sum_{k=0}^{\infty} \dfrac{\sin(4k+1)x + \sin(4k+3)x}{2k+1}$; (f) see (b).   **7.** yes.

11. $(.8/\pi^2) \displaystyle\sum_{k=1}^{\infty} (-1)^{k-1} \dfrac{\sin(2k-1)x}{(2k-1)^2}$.

12. characteristic equation is $\tan \sqrt{\lambda}\,\pi = -\sqrt{\lambda}$.

EXERCISE 40. *Page 283*

3. (a) $\frac{1}{2}\pi - \frac{4}{\pi} \sum_{k=1}^{\infty} \frac{1}{(2k-1)^2} \cos(2k-1)x$; (b) add the results for part (a) and

Exercise 39-6(c); (c) $\frac{2}{\pi} \sum_{n=1}^{\infty} n^{-3}[(2 - n^2\pi^2)(-1)^n - 2] \sin nx$;

(e) $\frac{1}{2} + \frac{2}{\pi} \sum_{n=1}^{\infty} \frac{\sin \frac{1}{2}n\pi}{n} \cos nx$.   4. (a) $\frac{1}{2}\pi$; (b) 0; (c) 0.

5. $\{3a_n - 5A_n\}$ and $\{3b_n - 5B_n\}$.

EXERCISE 41. *Page 290*

1. 0.   2. $c_{2k+1} = (4k+3) \int_0^1 f(x)P_{2k+1}(x)dx$.   3. $2/(2n+1)$.

4. $c_0 = c_2 = 0$, $c_1 = \frac{3}{4}$, $c_3 = \frac{7}{24}$.   8. $\int_0^1 xJ_5(z_{53}x)J_5(z_{54}x)dx = 0$.

9. $c_n = \int_0^1 xf(x)J_m(z_{mn}x)dx \Big/ \int_0^1 xJ_m(z_{mn}x)^2dx$.

REVIEW EXERCISE, CHAPTER SIX. *Page 292*

1. $F(x) = 5$, $G(x) = 2x/|x|$.   4. $\{\sqrt{2/\pi} \sin nx\}$.   5. $a_0 + \sum_{n=1}^{\infty} a_n \cos nx$.

6. (a) 0; (b) 0.   7. e, $1/e$.   9. $\{n^2\pi^2\}$, $\{\sin n\pi x\}$.

10. $\int_0^\pi f(x)^2 dx = \frac{2}{\pi} \sum_{n=1}^{\infty} \left(\int_0^\pi f(x) \sin nx\, dx \right)^2$.

INDEX

305